TRANSFORMATIVE CARE

A TRAUMA-FOCUSED APPROACH TO CAREGIVING

ROBERT RHOTON, PSY.D., & THOMAS E. ROJO AUBREY, D.BH & J. ERIC GENTRY, PH.D

Originally developed and written by
Robert Rhoton, and Thomas E. Rojo Aubrey, and J. Eric Gentry

Printed by Buse Printing

Distributed by Arizona Trauma Institute

ISBN-13: 978-0-9997150-9-3

Printed in the United States of America

Names and identifying details have been changed to protect the confidentiality and privacy of individuals, except for those pertaining to the authors' family members. This book is not intended to substitute treatment from a trained mental health professional.

Transformative Care: A Trauma-Focused Approach to Caregiving is a comprehensive process to help non-clinical care professionals learn the essential information and skills to help trauma survivors recover fully from the events of their past. This book is tailored for teaching non-clinical trauma professionals, behavioral health paraprofessionals (BHPPs), behavioral health technicians (BHTs), nurses, emergency first responders, emergency medical responders, leaders, teachers, and other professionals how to utilize the principles of trauma-informed care and trauma recovery to assist the survivor in their process of recovery. We hope you enjoy your experience with us.

Contents

Preface

We would like to welcome you to what we hope will be a fascinating and highly relevant book on your journey to becoming a professional trauma-focused caregiver.

Transformative Care: A Trauma-Focused Approach to Caregiving was developed and written by Robert Rhoton PsyD, Thomas E. Rojo Aubrey DBH, and J. Eric Gentry PhD.

Ethical and legal consideration: The content covered in this book has been generalized for adaptability within the roles of various caregiving careers. Particular state laws and ethics are beyond the intent or capacity of this book. Therefore, it is the reader's responsibility to ensure you are practicing within your scope of competence and in compliance with local state laws.

This material is intended to help train mental health professionals and healthcare providers who function as caregivers (healers) for survivors of trauma and to become a source of healing to those who have suffered the aftermath of trauma. Our use of the term "healer" is not due to immodesty, but rather to the miraculous transformation observed in survivors who have healed from the wounds of traumatic stress using some of the skills you will learn in this book. In addition, it alludes to the seemingly infinite complexity, yet simplistic nature, of the fundamental principles used to heal a survivor's pain. The content will cover some of the major treatments for traumatic stress that have demonstrated effectiveness. It will consider ingredients that are vital and fundamental in all effective treatments of trauma, including elements that are integral to almost every evidence-based treatment modality for traumatic stress. The three primary ingredients that help survivors heal and upon which this book will focus are: (1) building and maintaining an excellent therapeutic relationship; (2) helping the survivor to regulate their own autonomic nervous system by teaching and coaching skills for acute relaxation; and (3) helping educate and restructure the way the survivor perceives themselves and their world.

There is an additional fourth "active ingredient" to healing trauma, and that is called exposure. After reviewing the work of Resick (1993), Resick et al. (1988), Marmar (1998), and Pennebaker (1997), we realized that exposure while in a relaxed state was a vital component to healing from the wounds of a traumatically stressful experience. If trauma professionals could help survivors construct complete narratives of their traumatic experiences while *in* that relaxed state, it would help them to accelerate the healing of their traumatic stress symptoms. By facilitating this important narrative process, not only are we assisting patients and clients with confronting the traumatic material, we're also helping them to structure the intrusive sensory trauma into language.

The use of exposure in confronting traumatic memories is a treatment reserved for licensed professionals, and thus will not be included in this book because it is beyond your scope of practice. This book will, however, teach you to help trauma survivors complete the important exposure process in confronting those day-to-day experiences they perceive as threatening *while in a relaxed body*. This method of trauma treatment will constitute much of the focus of this book, and will empower you to become an integral component of the treatment team with survivors of trauma.

Those previously mentioned researchers have been able to demonstrate that effectively constructing a narrative has a powerful ameliorative effect on the intrusive symptoms of trauma (i.e., flashbacks and nightmares). Virtually every treatment that has demonstrated effectiveness with traumatic stress has utilized some form of narrative (exposure) paired with some form of relaxation, which is why we're including it in our book.

Ethical warning: As professional trauma-focused caregivers and based on ethical scope-of-practice parameters, you will not be assisting survivors to construct narratives of traumatic memories or to process traumatic events (i.e., Stage #: Recovery/Resolution). Your caregiving role, nevertheless, will still play an important and vital role in helping your patients and clients to heal from traumatic stress. In fact, despite the ethical limitations inherent in the role of a nonclinical caregiver, research shows that the difference in outcomes between professionals, students, and paraprofessionals are little to none (Miller and Hubble, 2011). This means that with proper training and supervision, the outcomes of your care can be just as effective, if not more, than a master-level clinician.

As you gain a better understanding about the physiological functioning of the central nervous system and more firmly grasp the role of perceived threat and sympathetic dominance in the etiology of traumatic stress symptoms, you will begin to clearly see the importance of practicing body relaxation and self-regulation skills to build antibodies that combat the effects of traumatic stress. The model of treatment found in this book has the work of Dr. Robert Scaer integrated within it (2005), which will help you see that as a survivor is able to develop and maintain parasympathetic dominance (i.e., relaxation), their traumatic stress symptoms will abate.

You will learn techniques used by emergency medical technicians (EMTs) and neuromuscular therapists, as well as techniques used by psychiatrists and neurologists, to help activate parasympathetic dominance. These simple relaxation strategies fortify the individual with: (1) comfort in their body; (2) total access to memory, learning, language, and neocortical functioning; and (3) the capacity for intentional living (more about this in Chapter Two).

Based on the work of Hubble, Duncan, and Miller (1999) entitled *The Heart and Soul of Change*, you will learn crucial ingredients (besides narrative/exposure and relaxation—also known as "reciprocal inhibition") for the effective treatment of traumatic stress. In fact, one of the most important discoveries as a result of the meta-analytic study was about the predictors of positive outcomes in psychotherapy. They found that the *most* important predictor of positive outcomes in psychotherapy had nothing to do with the therapy itself. It was discovered that those occurrences *that happen outside of therapy* account for over forty percent of positive outcomes.

Of the sixty percent that we as caregivers can influence, about thirty percent is contingent on the development and maintenance of a good therapeutic relationship. The remaining thirty percent is split equally between positive expectancy, which has also been called either "hope" or "placebo" and techniques/models. In fact, it is instead the therapists who treat clients. With this in mind, we begin to see that what creates healing and change in those seeking our help is less the model of treatment utilized by, more importantly, the person delivering the treatment (Miller and Hubble, 2011; Miller, Hubble, and Duncan, 2007). Because of this, only one section in Chapter Six will provide an overview of effective models of trauma-focused treatment, while the rest of the book focuses on those therapeutic elements that are integral to almost every evidence-based treatment modality for traumatic stress.

There is a good argument that the process of developing expectancy/hope/placebo is also a relational function. If this is so, then that means the degree to which we can influence positive outcomes for our patients and clients—about seventy-five percent—is contingent upon relational factors, and twenty-five percent is contingent upon technical and/or philosophical factors. These data confirm what many marriage and family therapists, counselors, and social workers (those who view treatment systemically) have known for decades: people heal people. It is not EMDR or CBT or psychopharmacology that accounts for most of the magical transformation that happens in our offices. It is the quality of the relationships we build with our patients and clients.

All we have to do in order to confirm the gravity of this truth is to think back to a time in our own lives when we navigated through emotional difficulty, and we will see that it was the support, care, and presence of another that was the active ingredient in our own successful resolution of the problem.

This book will incorporate the work of Hubble, Duncan, and Miller to help you see that there are three "active ingredients" for the successful resolution of traumatic stress symptoms—relationship, relaxation, and narratives. Without a relationship that is developed and maintained, we will be unable to successfully teach self-regulation or co-construct narratives with trauma-survivor patients and clients. After treating thousands of people suffering the effects of traumatic stress, we have found that when we complete these three simple—but not easy—therapeutic tasks, then patients and clients no longer meet the diagnostic criteria for PTSD. And unless they have an additional organic condition, when they complete these tasks they no longer meet diagnostic criteria for *any* psychological disorder.

Helping survivors heal from traumatic stress will encompass three tasks: 1) building and maintaining a strong therapeutic relationship; 2) teaching survivors how to relax their bodies, especially in the context of a perceived threat; and 3) helping them construct and complete a chronological narrative of their traumatic experiences. It sounds simple, but simple is not always easy. Sometimes it takes years of work through countless sessions to complete these tasks, but as a professional caregiver with the right training, you can apply these methods to treatment for quantifiable, transformative results.

This book is chock-full of paradigm-shifting information that we hope will convince you of the value in this approach and why professional trauma-focused caregivers and licensed clinicians should expand beyond solely using cognitive work when providing therapy to the trauma survivor.

About the Book

The goal of this book is to train the professional caregiver, both in mental health and healthcare, to provide trauma-informed care and teach the skills required for trauma-focused caregiving. Our desire is to facilitate the creation of a trauma-informed therapeutic environment for survivors by helping professional caregivers learn new methods of treatment, so we decided to write this book based on our decades of clinical observation and supported by empirical research.

The approaches we have outlined in this book center on enhancing the professional caregiver's abilities to provide quality services that result in successful outcomes. One of the major challenges healers face in providing this level of care is an ongoing battle against the negative effects of helping trauma survivors. Caregivers such as counselors and psychotherapists, nurses, EMTs, police officers, and others are practicing in a field that is physically, mentally, emotionally, and even spiritually taxing. Because of this, they are at a higher risk for the symptoms of compassion fatigue and burnout (Sinclair et al., 2017; Sheppard, 2015; Leiter and Maslach, 2009; Lerias and Byrne, 2003). One cross-sectional study showed that approximately eighty-two percent of ER nurses "had moderate to high levels of burnout, and nearly eighty-six percent had moderate levels of compassion fatigue," while nurses in other inpatient and outpatient settings were at an increased risk for compassion fatigue, including burnout (Hooper et al., 2010).

Professional and volunteer caregivers who expose themselves to overtaxing and emotionally toxic environments in order to help the traumatized *must* learn skills to mitigate the effects of compassion fatigue, secondary trauma, and burnout. Contrary to other textbooks that start off by defining trauma and its treatments, we have intentionally decided to structure this book to address early on the resilient needs of the caregiver as a tool for ensuring quality care and career longevity.

Key Chapter-by-Chapter Content

Chapter One: **Introduction to the Trauma-Focused Caregiver** covers the skills, knowledge, and characteristics required to become an effective trauma-informed caregiver and provides an outline of assumptions for caregivers to follow.

Chapter Two: **Professional Resilience and Compassion Fatigue Prevention** provides a comprehensive understanding of compassion fatigue, including the history, etiology, and potential system and its effects. It defines compassion fatigue and its impact on the caregiver. It also provides help for the caregiver to build the resiliency skills needed to lessen and prevent the effects of secondary trauma and burnout by covering the basic understanding of self-regulation, intentionality, perceptual maturation, connection/support, and self-care/revitalization.

Chapter Three: **Foundations of Trauma-Informed Care** takes a historical look at the evolution of trauma-informed care and defines what it means to provide such care. It introduces the core principles as dictated by the Substance Abuse and Mental Health Service Administration (SAMHSA) and the National Center for Trauma-Informed Care (NCTIC).

Chapter Four: **Trauma and Traumagenesis** discusses the concerns with how professionals view and define trauma and provides a broader, more complex understanding of the various categories of trauma and its effects on our neurobiology. The chapter takes a comprehensive look at the neurobiological changes that occur when we face traumatic environmental activators and widens our viewing lens on the nature of traumagenesis.

Chapter Five: **The History of Traumatic Care and Current Trends** explores the roots of traumatic care in the field and how it has evolved over the years. We discuss the key historical events that influenced innovative improvements in trauma care, while going over the various effective trauma-focused treatments for adults and children.

Chapter Six: **Working with Trauma Survivors** provides a guide for the application of trauma-informed principles. It helps caregivers become strategic and intentional in their trauma-focused treatment.

Chapter Seven: **Empowerment and Resiliency Structure** outlines the stages of treatment in the Empowerment and Resiliency Structure model. It provides an overview of each stage and how they can improve and enrich the healer's quality of care.

Chapter Eight: **Safety and Stabilization in Crisis Work** provides you, as a care professional, with knowledge and skills to help create safety and stabilize a crisis situation, which is not uncommon when treating survivors of traumatic stress. You will learn to identify the negative effects chronic stress has in creating a volatile environment, as well as how to deescalate a crisis situation using the C-A-S-E-R Model.

Chapter Nine: **Integrated Care: Trauma-Specific Services in Primary Care Settings** introduces the caregiver to the treatment of comorbid medical conditions when working with survivors of trauma. It considers the prevalence of comorbid medical conditions for those who have suffered traumatic experiences and how these conditions influence the treatment outcome of one another. You will learn to understand the mechanisms of pain, its relation to traumatic stress, and tools to help survivors improve their quality of life.

Chapter Ten: **Ethical Considerations** uses the core principles, as defined by SAMHSA and the NCTIC, to ensure that the caregiver/trauma support specialist practices ethically.

Readers have the opportunity to read three case studies found in Chapters Two, Three, and Six, which highlight the applicability of principle-based, trauma-focused caregiving. The demographics of each case (i.e., name, age, and other identifying information) have been altered to protect confidentiality.

Focus questions are found at the beginning of each chapter and are based on the premise of the SQ3R reading system. First introduced by American educational psychologist Francis P. Robinson in 1946, this system is still used in many textbooks today to improve reading comprehension. The "Q," which represents developing questions, helps the reader to practice *deliberate* reading as opposed to the simple completion of a passage. By posing questions at the beginning of our chapters, we challenge you to read with intentionality and truly absorb the material we are presenting so that you can answer our questions with confidence and comprehension.

This book intends to empower and inspire the reader, many of whom are beginning their voyage of dedicating their lives to the service of others. Join us on this journey of trauma-informed care and trauma-focused caregiving, and we will change some lives together.

Chapter One

Introduction to the Trauma-Focused Caregiver

Focus Questions:

- What are the knowledge and skills needed to become an effective trauma-focused caregiver?
- What are the key characteristics of a trauma-focused caregiver?
- What are agencies that value trauma-focused care looking for in a staff member?
- What are the assumptions and philosophies of trauma-focused caregiving?

In this chapter you will learn more about:

- The role of the trauma-focused caregiver.
- The skills and knowledge required to become an effective trauma-focused caregiver.
- Some of the characteristics of a quality trauma-focused caregiver.
- Assumptions professional caregivers should abide by.

A healer is someone who seeks to be the light that she wishes she had
in her darkest moments.

– Vironika Tugaleva

Healing Trauma: Simple, Not Easy

As recognition of the effects of trauma has increased over the years, it seems like more and more well-intentioned professional caregivers are attempting to help survivors of trauma. Unfortunately, many professionals trying to treat a survivor have little to no trauma-informed care or evidence-based, trauma-focused treatment training, and as a result may be unethically practicing outside their scope of competency. Even though a professional caregiver may have the best of intentions, it is important they understand that without the proper training, more harm can result than good.

The exemplum of a Tanzanian folktale about how two monkeys saved a fish helps to illustrate how good intentions, without adequate knowledge, can result in harm to others. This folktale talks about a great flood that occurred during one of the rainiest seasons to date. As the waters started to rapidly grow higher, many of the animals ran for cover, but eventually drowned when they could not escape the rushing waters. The monkeys, however, were able to survive this great flood by using their agility to climb into the treetops. One day two monkeys were sitting on a treetop and noticed a pair of fish swimming and leaping out of the water as they hunted for food.

One of the monkeys turned to his companion in concern. "Those poor creatures are drowning! They'll die if we don't help them."

The other monkey nodded. "They're helpless without legs! We need to save them." The monkeys swung down from the branches and each grabbed a fish, taking them to a small, dry patch of land high in the mountains.

"Look how appreciative they are!" said the first monkey as the fish both frantically flapped on the ground, slowly getting less and less excited.

"Oh, they must be tired now," replied the second monkey when the fish had ceased to move, and with confidence and pride, the monkeys returned to their home in the treetops, unaware that they had just doomed the fish they had been trying to rescue.

In much the same way for trauma survivors, effective mitigation of symptoms requires a skilled caregiver who can provide trauma-sensitive treatment. Caring for a survivor of a traumatic event may appear simple, but it requires a level of understanding and sensitivity that is only available through adequate knowledge and training.

Many survivors of trauma exhibit anxiety- or fear-based symptoms, but it is the phenotype behaviors characterized clinically as anhedonic (i.e., without joy) and dysphoric (i.e., bad mood) symptoms, externalizing anger and aggressive symptoms, or dissociative symptoms that test the patience of many professionals struggling to show sensitivity and compassion (American Psychiatric Association, 2013, p. 265).

Without the intentional practice of regulation skills, many professionals will struggle to apply the principles of trauma-informed care when they are faced with naturally occurring adaptive and mitigating behaviors (i.e., socially disconnecting, shutting down, getting upset and yelling or cursing, etc.), which are the survivor's reactive ways to deal with the distress of trauma.

In other words, a trained trauma-sensitive caregiver understands that the natural galvanization of the threat-response survival system activates the sympathetic nervous system, which is a normal reactive response to alleviate pain. This is the same process that occurs if you place your hand on a hot stove—your threat-response system will activate your nervous system, which results in the reactive adaptation of swiftly jerking your hand away from the stove.

Someone who lacks training in trauma-sensitive care might interpret this harsh reaction poorly, and may judge the behavior as inappropriate when in fact it is a normal and congruent reactive physiological mitigation response to the threat. This impairment-based view or deficit model has not only contributed to the stigma in mental health, but it has also inhibited the survivors' abilities to recover and heal. Thus, the professional caregiver must always endeavor to avoid pathologizing, instead embracing a trauma-sensitive philosophy of healing.

Caregivers' Beliefs and Philosophy

All too often, untrained trauma-focused professionals including nurses, counselors, social workers, marriage and family therapists, psychologists, psychiatrists, and even educators will *themselves* become reactive to survivors' adaptive and mitigating behaviors. Many clinical or nonclinical professionals might then attempt to erroneously label survivors with a diagnosis from the *Diagnostic and Statistical Manual of Mental Disorders* (DSM), and may demand boundaries and limitations be enforced to stop the survivors' adaptive and mitigating behaviors. These are signs that the caregiver is struggling between the role of a helper and a judge, as their inner voice passes judgment on the survivor if they observe particular behaviors.

The inability for professionals to tolerate these overpowering behaviors is due largely to the lack of training in professional self-regulation and understanding that these patients' and clients' behaviors are a normal and *appropriate* behavioral response to a charged and overly activated neurobiological system. The expectations that these professionals have when treating trauma survivors is analogous to a primary care physician telling their patient to "simply stop producing cholesterol," instead of stabilizing the body and teaching ways to reduce low-density lipoprotein (LDL) intake. As a result, not only is this an ineffective form of treatment, but it also increases the likelihood that the individual will feel frustrated and incompetent.

Instead of deescalating the situation in a trauma-sensitive way, some professionals create a tense environment due to a lack of knowledge or proper attention given to how the human body and brain function. For some, the word "trauma" carries the fallacy that the experience was an isolated incident, but education on the long-term biological and physiological effects of post-traumatic stress decrease the shame and stigma surrounding it (Brown, Baker, and Wilcox, 2012).

By following the principles of trauma-informed care, a caregiver can prevent a harmful misunderstanding like that in the Tanzanian folktale by remembering that each of us are driven by our biology, including a central nervous system that has a powerful, driving capacity for intense emotions, distorted thinking, and unconscious egocentrism. Professional caregivers must recognize that these are not character flaws or psychiatric disorders, but the natural consequences of an evolved biological survival system. When this concept is grasped, we are able to provide trauma-sensitive care and help create a therapeutic environment conducive to change and healing.

An essential component to becoming an effective caregiver is practicing personal congruence. This means that we are also doing what we teach and avoiding the old adage, "Do as I say, not as I do." As caregivers we must strive to be congruent and genuine with those seeking our help, and this becomes difficult when we are not also applying the principles of self-regulation, exercise, healthy eating, etc. to our own lives. Although a trauma survivor may not know *every* detail of our personal lives, they can certainly tell when we are not living our message authentically. Those who have experienced adversity have a heightened sensitivity to insincerity, and once an injury to the therapeutic relationship occurs, survivors will consciously or unconsciously begin to minimize our message.

To provide congruent and genuine services, professional caregivers need to be intentionally active in their daily professional growth, becoming the change they wish to see by working on their own self-regulation, self-awareness, compassion toward others, and personal integrity. When this occurs, the healer is metaphorically extending their hand out to the survivor in an invitation for transformative growth and healing.

We encourage you to devise a plan to master the skills you'll glean from this textbook. If you are currently working in the field, take the time to reflect not on how you will "use these skills to help a patient or client," but how you will "intentionally practice these skills daily until mastery is achieved." This means that you will engage in what is known as *deliberative* practice, which is regularly practicing activities that directly improve your caregiving skills (Chow et al., 2015). Similar to the mastery of a musical instrument, art performance, or athletic pursuit, achieving mastery requires exponentially more hours of deliberate practice to improve caregiving skills. As a result, your delivery of services will come across with congruency and genuineness for improved outcomes.

Healers are not only endeavored to continuously hone and refine their caregiving skills, but to remember the importance of their role in illuminating the way for an individual's healing. Just as the lighthouse is a steering aid for ships coming to shore, the work of the professional trauma-informed caregiver represents a beacon of light leading survivors to a confluence of intentionality, awareness, and support. The trauma-focused caregiver provides solace and a guiding light for the right path during a turbulent storm, making it less daunting and easier to navigate.

The care provided during these tumultuous times is both a science and an art, and one that requires a skillful balance of both elements. The trauma-focused caregiver has training and a comprehensive knowledge of trauma survivors' behaviors and of how traumatic events influence human physiology. They continually practice intentionality, gentleness, honesty, patience, and possess the ability to tolerate with grace the bewildering range of emotions—from rage and depression to denial and a scrabbling determination to recover—rooted within the clients and their families.

It is important to understand that these responses are normal, and all of the skills and wisdom caregivers must develop will be employed while walking alongside clients as they negotiate a safe path through the furious winds and gigantic waves of the emotional storm trauma creates.

In this time of denial, anger, bargaining, depression, and acceptance (yes, those familiar stages of grief), the seeds of wisdom and a deeper humanity are sown. During the aftermath of trauma—and especially during the stage of bargaining—both the survivor and their family desire to heal from a sense of brokenness while yearning for stability and normalcy.

The aftermath of trauma can be subtle, insidious, or outright destructive. As a result, many individuals and their families may exhibit brief subclinical symptoms that can be misunderstood. It is during these times that professional caregivers need to understand that a wide range of emotions and behaviors are appropriate responses to abnormal circumstances in the grieving process. Survivors and their families are attempting to make sense of the traumatic event, tolerate their discomfort and sorrow, and find the goodness and mercy that, in time, will restore them once more to wholeness. These are critical times in which the survivor needs the caregiver's intentional compassion and tolerance, even when denial is expressed about the ongoing impact of the event, or the client exhibits an aggressive insistence on the restoration of "regular" everyday life.

In the weeks and months that follow a traumatic event in the life of clients and their families, professional caregivers will want to help them accept their experiences of grief and expressions of loss rather than to yearn for a previous normalcy that is gone forever. This phase in the aftermath of a traumatic event should be viewed as a "crosswalk" that can be named and even embraced. Those who have experienced a traumatically stressful event cannot go back down the previous path their life was once on, but other pathways are now open and new ones may continue to emerge. A trauma-focused caregiver can help a survivor to incorporate any loss and acknowledge the cost the event had in their life, rather than to simply let them cover up or deny the changes that now comprise their new reality.

Professional caregivers need to model a consistent willingness to tolerate, and even embrace, the difficult and confusing emotions the traumatic event has engendered in the lives of survivors. In turn, survivors will learn to trust and check in with their caregivers as they master the full range of coping strategies made available to them with courage, grace, and even gratitude.

The foundation of being a trauma-focused caregiver is that he or she functions in a variety of settings, including mental health agencies, primary care offices, hospital settings, and educational systems. Through the intentional application of compassion and the knowledge of what is normal for human beings to experience, these trained professionals provide healing within a context of cultural sensitivity.

Trauma-informed mental health agencies and primary care settings that employ the skilled support of specialists understand the effects of secondary trauma on staff, and work to ensure employees are practicing self-care and self-compassion. Trauma-informed leadership compassionately acknowledges that the longing of all human beings is to be understood, cared for without judgment and criticism, and to be encouraged and supported as they face individual challenges and hurts in their own personal lives. A leadership's intentional support of a trauma-informed organizational change can foster employees' professional resiliency against secondary trauma and burnout, and increases the probability of quality services provided to patients/clients and their families.

Although creating a trauma-informed culture within an organization sounds easily adoptable, it can be challenging to foster a new environment without the right building blocks for change. Even though the focus of this book is mainly to help professional caregivers build their skills and knowledge in working with survivors of trauma, these principles can also be applied within all organizational systems to encourage more efficient, effective, and humane treatment and services at every level.

The Role of the Healer

As humans, we are continually surrounded by the chaos of a constantly changing world with competing ideologies and demands. The forces of politics, social media, and sensationalized news stories present a vast array of competing and often incongruent demands for our time and attention. Add to these societal forces the normal risks of life, such as illness, injury, accident, loss of a loved one, the ending of relationships, and fluctuations in economy and employment, and it is no wonder our population is stressed out and physically ill. On top of these trials and demands of daily life, many individuals are suffering from prolonged and unjust abuse or maltreatment, or are attempting to glue back the shattered pieces of their lives after a traumatic incident.

Those who have experienced traumatic events or a life filled with adversity are often worn down by the journey they are making through life, and at times feel lost and in despair. This diminishing of hope begins to dim the brightness of the future, leaving the traveler in a tumultuous world of growing darkness. Many people who have experienced developmental trauma—the interference or interruption of normal relational, emotional, and cognitive milestones of a human being—feel unsafe in their daily lives. For them, the thought of letting go of this darkness becomes both fear-provoking and anxiety-inducing, and the changes they are required to make to brighten their future and heal from the wounds of traumatic stress often require the assistance of a trained caregiver.

The role of the caregiver is not to "heal," but rather to *facilitate* healing. These professionals must first and foremost become aware of the trauma in their own lives, and then through acts of love, encouragement, and kindness, can support others in doing the same. Caregivers are the catalyst for change by modeling self-regulation behaviors for their patients and clients. This requires a mastery of self-regulation skills and can only be accomplished through rigorous, deliberate practice.

In many ways, being a healer means redirecting travelers along the journey of life, while helping them to reclaim the desire to build a brighter future and appreciate even small, growing moments of satisfaction.

This evolving process for caregivers providing care to survivors generally involves the following:

1. Developing their desire to build a brighter future.
2. Fostering the belief that it is possible for them to act differently.
3. Enabling them to act on the growing belief of their capabilities with *intentionality*, by exercising choice and making decisions rather than simply responding.

As caregivers, we must abide by the following assumptions:

1. People are acting exactly as their history has wired them to act, perceive, and emote.
2. People are not broken; therefore, we avoid judging or diagnosing.
3. Survivors are still human beings who may have had some additional challenges, and they deserve respect and dignity.
4. Most poor or problematic behaviors are the consequence of reactive adaptations and mitigations (more about these behaviors in Chapter Four).
5. Growth and change require a sustained ability to stay in the parasympathetic system.
6. Growth and change require access to our neocortex for intentionality.

The healer's first action should always be to:

1. Build a relationship with the caregiving system and survivor.
2. Stabilize the survivor.
3. Utilize the caregiving system of one's choice in the process.

**Behavior should never be the starting point of treatment (except for immediate danger/injury to self or others).*

Professional caregivers, more than anyone else, understand the suffering that their clients are going through since they have worked on healing the wounds of their own traumas. They recognize that healing involves building the courage to tolerate change in one's behaviors and cognitions, which is a daunting task when someone does not know any other way to react to the traumatic memories of the past.

As caregivers, we realize that change requires believing in ourselves; therefore, we must empower our patients and clients to see a future of possibilities for a fulfilling and satisfying life. As professional caregivers we follow the Patient's Bill of Rights, which dictates that "the patient is entitled to relief from pain, anxiety, and depression…with the least intrusive interventions" (Cummings and Sayama, 1995, p. 1). In order to provide the survivor with this level of care, the caregiver needs to become competent in the specialty of trauma-focused treatment.

The action of the healer cannot be superficial, impulsive, or temporary—their determination to help a survivor build a brighter future needs to be heartfelt, unwavering, and permanent. The healer working with trauma survivors must in many ways embrace this concept expressed by American inventor Thomas Edison: "If we all did the things we are really capable of doing, we would literally astound ourselves." If we believe in the capacity of those who have been living their lives in pain due to trauma, we are likely to be astounded by what they are capable of doing. Conversely, we will astound ourselves with our own capacities as well.

> Man often becomes what he believes himself to be. If I keep on saying to myself that I cannot do a certain thing, it is possible that I may end by really becoming incapable of doing it. On the contrary, if I have the belief that I can do it, I shall surely acquire the capacity to do it even if I may not have it at the beginning.
>
> – Mahatma Gandhi

Chapter Summary

Caregivers operating in the role of a healer as well as a support, guide, coach, or encourager must clearly understand the impact of the history of adversity possessed by those they serve. Oftentimes survivors' thinking, emotions, and behaviors are frustrating or offensive, yet the trauma-focused caregiver realizes the heightened need to show patience and empathy for those with significant emotional, behavioral, and cognitive challenges related to the effects of trauma and a life filled with adversity.

In order to truly function as a trauma-focused caregiver, one must not get trapped in the belief that the symptoms are the problem; instead, they understand that the symptoms are *appropriate*, though often unpleasant, based on a person's history of adversity. If a caregiver lacks this basic understanding, it creates hurdles and roadblocks to successful service delivery. The primary reason for this is that it opens the door to judgment, criticism, and labeling that inhibits growth and recovery. When service delivery is inefficient, then the caregiver cannot provide support, encourage recovery, and sustain survivors' healing when they are at their most vulnerable.

Trauma-focused caregivers, on the other hand, have taken the time to understand how traumatic events change the body's natural response to threat. They are able to provide trauma-sensitive care and create a therapeutic environment that is conducive to change and healing. Trauma-focused caregivers also understand that their role is not to heal, but to facilitate healing for those seeking their help. As such, they abide by assumptions that allow them to provide trauma-sensitive services, while instigating self-compassion, self-regulation, and a renewal of hope within the lives of trauma survivors and their families.

Chapter Two

Professional Resilience and Compassion Fatigue Prevention

Focus Questions:

- How do caregivers develop personal and professional resilience?
- How do caregivers help others develop personal and professional resilience?

In this chapter you will learn more about:

- What constitutes compassion fatigue.
- The elements of an effective model to treat compassion fatigue.
- How to prevent compassion fatigue from happening to you.

Healing doesn't mean that danger never existed. It means the damage no longer controls your life.

– Akshay Dubey

This chapter explores the history, causes, treatments, and prevention of compassion fatigue, and examines the negative effects of helping survivors of traumatic stress. It is intended to be applied in the lives of professional caregivers who expose themselves to an emotionally toxic environment by helping survivors of trauma.

In this text we will draw from the limited studies to date that show promise regarding the effectiveness of the prophylactic treatment and prevention of burnout and compassion fatigue and post-traumatic stress disorder (PTSD) based on similar symptomatology with compassion fatigue (Hensel et al., 2015), which includes elements from the Accelerated Recovery Program for Compassion Fatigue (ARP), Certified Compassion Fatigue Specialist Training (CCFST), mindfulness-based stress reduction, physical activity, positive psychology, Cognitive Behavioral Therapy (CBT), as well as exposure therapy concepts and practices.

A model for understanding the multiple causes of compassion fatigue is presented, and the active ingredients for effective treatment and prevention are broken down. Symptoms of compassion fatigue are considered not only to be the disruptive and harmful effects of caring for the traumatized, but also the catalysts for positive change, transformation, and maturation in the lives of caregivers. Our model focuses on specific skills for resilience and optimization in the professional healthcare environment, including self-regulation, intentionality, perceptual maturation, connection, and self-care.

Disciplined use of these skills, principles, and practices will reward you with greater freedom from work-related stress, and continued practice of these skills can lead to increased well-being in your professional and personal lives. While these skills were developed to help professional caregivers navigate the difficult demands of the healthcare environment, they are equally useful across all spheres of life including family, marriage, community, and personal development.

What is Compassion Fatigue?

The notion that working with people in pain extracts a significant cost from the caregiver is nothing new. Anyone who has sat at the bedside of a seriously ill or recently bereaved loved one knows the toll involved in helping a suffering person. Only in the past century, however, has there been a substantial effort to study this impact on caregivers. The exploration and examination of these effects come to us from a wide variety of sources across several fields.

One of the earliest mentions of the cost of caring in scientific literature was made by Swiss psychiatrist Carl Jung (1907) in *The Psychology of Dementia Praecox*. Jung discussed the challenge of countertransference—the therapist's conscious and unconscious reactions to the patient—when working with psychotic patients. He suggested a treatment in which the therapist participated in the patient's delusional fantasies and hallucinations but warned that it could have significant negative effects for the therapist, especially if they had not resolved their own developmental and traumatic issues (Sedgewick, 1995). The study of countertransference produced the first writings in the field of psychotherapy that systematically explored effects on the therapist (Haley, 1974; Danieli, 1982; Karakashian, 1994).

The study of trauma also promoted a better understanding of the negative effects of helping. Psychological reactions to trauma were described with various labels such as "shell shock," "combat neurosis," "railroad spine," and "combat fatigue" (Shalev, Bonne, and Eth, 1996). It was not until 1980 that post-traumatic stress disorder (PTSD) was formally recognized as an anxiety disorder (American Psychiatric Association, 1980; Matsakis, 1994). Afterwards, research in post-traumatic stress grew at an exponential rate (Figley, 1995; Wilson and Lindy, 1994) and the field of traumatology was established with two of its own journals, several professional organizations, and a unique professional identity (Figley, 1988; Bloom, 1997; Gold and Faust, 2001). As therapists were increasingly called upon to assist survivors of violent crime, natural disasters, childhood abuse, torture, acts of genocide, political persecution, war, and terrorism (Sexton, 1999), their reactions were more frequently examined in the traumatology literature (Figley, 1983, 1995; McCann and Pearlman, 1990; Pearlman and Saakvitne, 1995; Stamm, 1995). Soon, therapists working with survivors of trauma reported experiencing symptoms similar to those of PTSD (Lindy, 1988; Wilson and Lindy, 1994; Pearlman and Saakvitne, 1995).

Psychologists Laurie Pearlman and Linda McCann first identified compassion fatigue in the late 1980s as "vicarious trauma." In 1995, three books were published that introduced the phenomenon of compassion fatigue to both the scientific literature and popular culture: *Compassion Fatigue: Coping with Secondary Traumatic Stress in Those Who Treat the Traumatized* by Charles Figley, PhD, *Secondary Traumatic Stress* by Beth Stamm, PhD, and *Trauma and the Therapist* by Karen Saakvitne, PhD, and Dr. McCann.

Dr. Figley originally defined compassion fatigue as the combined effects of secondary traumatic stress and burnout. In recent years, however, it has been broadened to include any of the negative effects that professional or volunteer caregivers experience as a result of their work with ill, suffering, or traumatized people, or the perceived stress and demands related to the work environment.

Secondary Traumatic Stress

Secondary traumatic stress (STS) refers to the development of PTSD-like symptoms in a care provider after witnessing the traumatic experience or suffering of another person. Several theories have been offered to explain it, including one that states mirror neurons are being triggered in the caregiver's brain. It has been suggested that the caregiver's level of empathy with the traumatized person plays a significant role in their susceptibility to secondary traumatic stress (Figley, 1995), and there is some budding empirical data to support this (Adams and Riggs, 2008; Salston, 2000).

The symptoms of STS include intrusion, avoidance, distorted perceptions, and arousal/reactivity (see Table 1). It can sometimes be difficult to tell the difference between the patient and the professional when looking at their symptoms.

Table 1. Secondary Traumatic Stress (STS) Symptoms

Intrusion	Avoidance	Distorted Perceptions	Arousal/Reactivity
· Frequently thinking about clients, patients, or sick loved ones · Nightmares · Taking work (and one's clients/patients) home with them · Developing a "heroic rescuer" identity	· Isolation · Withdrawal · Depression · Dread · Hopelessness · Social phobia · Diminished engagement with others or involvement in enjoyable activities	· Entitlement · Inadequacy · Perception of a dangerous world · Loss of humor · "Victim vs. perpetrator" perceptions · Blaming others · Blaming self · Loss of joy	· Anxiety/feeling stressed out · Alcohol/drug use (self-medicating) · Irritability/ aggression · violations of integrity

Burnout

Business and industry in the later twentieth century provided us with the concept of burnout (Freudenberger, 1974; Maslach, 1976) to describe the negative effects employees experience from the environmental demands of work over time. The term has also been used to describe "the syndrome of emotional exhaustion, depersonalization, and reduced personal accomplishment" (Maslach, 1976, p. 56) that psychotherapists suffer as a result of interactions with their patients/clients, or the demands of their workplace (Freudenberger, 1974; Cherniss, 1980; Farber, 1983; Sussman, 1992; Grosch and Olsen, 1994; Maslach and Goldberg, 1998).

Research has shown that therapists are particularly vulnerable to burnout because of personal isolation, ambiguous successes, and the emotional drain of remaining empathetic to those experiencing severe pain and suffering (McCann and Pearlman, 1990). Moreover, burnout makes the therapist less able to deliver competent mental health services (Farber, 1983). The literature on burnout, with its twenty-five-year history, thoroughly describes the phenomenon and prescribes preventative and treatment interventions for professional helpers.

Burnout refers to the draining effects of a care provider's interaction with the environment rather than direct patient care—things like the overwhelming demands of healthcare systems, scheduling, lack of funding, prejudicial evaluation by others, agency politics, or simply the anxious nature of the systems in which they work. Burnout symptoms seem to affect care providers in two primary ways: they can act anxious, with lots of energy, or might appear more like someone suffering from depression, with a flat, withdrawn, and hopeless presentation. Some caregivers go through cycles of these various behaviors, swinging like a pendulum between the two. Common burnout symptoms include:

1. Irritability.
2. Fatigue.
3. Hopelessness.
4. Anxiety.
5. Dread.
6. The desire to quit.
7. Frequently changing jobs.

The Gentry/Baranowsky Model of Compassion Fatigue

As a result of our work with hundreds of caregivers suffering the effects of compassion fatigue, we have added symptoms of primary post-traumatic stress to Figley's definition (1995). Many caregivers, especially those providing onsite services, have firsthand exposure to traumatic events (Pole et al., 2001; Marmar et al., 1999). For some of them, PTSD will not manifest until sometime later in life.

We have also found that some caregivers enter the profession with traumatic experiences in their own past (Gentry, 1999). As they begin to encounter the traumatic material presented by patients or clients, many of them will develop clinical PTSD associated with their past experiences. Thus, it is often necessary to address primary traumatic stress before addressing any issues of secondary traumatic stress or burnout.

Furthermore, we have found that primary traumatic stress, secondary traumatic stress, and burnout interact to produce a synergistic effect. Experiencing symptoms from one of these three sources makes the caregiver less resilient and more vulnerable to the other two. This can lead to a rapid onset of severe symptoms that are extremely debilitating to the caregiver.

Figure 1. The Gentry/Baranowsky (1997) Model of Compassion Fatigue

PRIMARY TRAUMATIC STRESS

+/**x** (synergistic effect)

SECONDARY TRAUMATIC STRESS

+/**x** (synergistic effect)

BURNOUT

COMPASSION FATIGUE

The bad news is that no one is completely immune to the negative effects of entering the world of the ill and suffering. Everyone who bears witness to pain, fear, and trauma is affected. Those who survive decades in caregiving professions need to develop their coping and resilience skills to avoid suffering significantly from their work. Many among us have lost jobs or marriages, suffered bouts of physical or mental illness, or found ourselves in so much pain from STS and burnout that we have considered leaving the field to which we have dedicated our lives. And when we seek help for this pain, it is often misdiagnosed as an anxiety disorder or depression.

Over the past several years, treatment programs have become available that specialize in the treatment of compassion fatigue. One program that has emerged and has shown notable effectiveness is the Accelerated Recovery Program for Compassion Fatigue (ARP).

The Accelerated Recovery Program for Compassion Fatigue

In 1997, two Green Cross Scholars and one doctoral student, under the supervision of Dr. Charles Figley at Florida State University, developed the Accelerated Recovery Program for Compassion Fatigue (ARP) (Gentry, Baranowsky, and Dunning, 1997, in press; Gentry and Baranowsky, 1998, 1999a, 1999b, 1999c). This five-session protocol is designed to address the symptoms of compassion fatigue in caregivers.

The ARP was presented in the fall of 1997 at the International Society for Traumatic Stress Studies in Montreal, Canada. One of the attendees at this presentation was an official with the Federal Bureau of Investigation, and the FBI later adopted the program (McNally, 1998, personal communication). Twelve professionals who worked with the survivors of the Oklahoma City bombing also requested treatment, and the program was significantly successful for each of them (Gentry, 2000).

In late 1998, Dr. Gentry and Dr. Anna Baranowsky (two of the developers of the ARP) were approached by Florida State University's Traumatology Institute to create a training program for professionals interested in treating compassion fatigue. It was decided that the program would be designed around implementing the five sessions of the ARP, with firsthand experiential training in each of the ARP interventions. In addition, the training would provide an in-depth understanding of the causes, development, and treatment/prevention of compassion fatigue, including secondary traumatic stress and burnout. Those who completed this training program were certified by the Traumatology Institute as Compassion Fatigue Specialists.

The Certified Compassion Fatigue Specialist Training (CCFST) was the first conceptualization of the "training-as-treatment" model (Gentry, 2000) for addressing the participants' own compassion fatigue symptoms. The rationale was that since the interventions were effective with the people they treated, they would also be effective for the participants in the training.

Beginning with the first training in January of 1999, data were collected and analyzed for 166 participants who completed the CCFST (Gentry, 2000). The protocol had clinically and statistically significant results ($p < .001$) in improving scores on the compassion fatigue, compassion satisfaction, and burnout subscales of the Compassion Satisfaction/Fatigue Self-Test (Figley and Stamm, 1996). Since then, ten published studies have demonstrated these positive effects for the one-day Professional Resilience and Optimization workshop (Baranowsky, Gentry, and Baggerly, 2005; Cragie et al., 2016; Rank, Zaparanick, and Gentry, 2009; Gentry,

2002; Potter, DeShields, and Rodriguez, 2013; Potter, Pion, and Gentry, 2015; Gentry, Baggerly, and Baranowsky, 2004; Flarity, Gentry, and Mesnikoff, 2013; Flarity et al., 2016).

Developing Skills for Resilience

When professional caregivers and volunteer care providers learn to manage their physiology, evolve their perceptions, and become intentional in their behaviors, they can significantly diminish—if not dispel—the negative effects of their work. The skills for resilience and optimization offered here are born from the principles that made the ARP the first and only evidence-based treatment for the symptoms of compassion fatigue.

Today, the tools of this training are being utilized in many different healthcare contexts all over the United States with clear results: professionals who practice its simple disciplines and principles find themselves happier, healthier, more productive, and less stressed. Empowered with the knowledge and skills for regulating themselves, they develop increased resilience to their work environments and a capacity for optimizing their quality of life.

Perceived Threat and the Autonomic Nervous System

The first step in building resilience with compassion fatigue is educating you about the principles involved, and starts with a question: "Would you be interested in learning over the next thirty minutes how to be stress-free for the rest of your life?"

This provocative question is intended to pique your interest and participation, and most people, even skeptics, are willing to hear more at this point.

Next, we want to ask you to identify causes of stress in your life. Many of you may write things like finances, relationships, work, traffic, the economy, etc. Once you have completed this list, ask yourself: "What effects are these stressors having in my life?"

Most individuals will list symptoms that include somatic problems (i.e., headaches, GI disturbances, or chronic pain), anger/irritability, sleep problems, overeating/undereating, substance abuse, relational problems, or anxiety (see Figure 2).

It is important that you as a professional caregiver understand that the list you just wrote and those items found in Figure 2 are *not* the causes of your stress. As long as you believe they are, there is a good chance you will keep experiencing symptoms. Thus, the first step to building resiliency against the effects of stress is understanding the true nature of their cause.

Figure 2. Causes and Effects of Stress

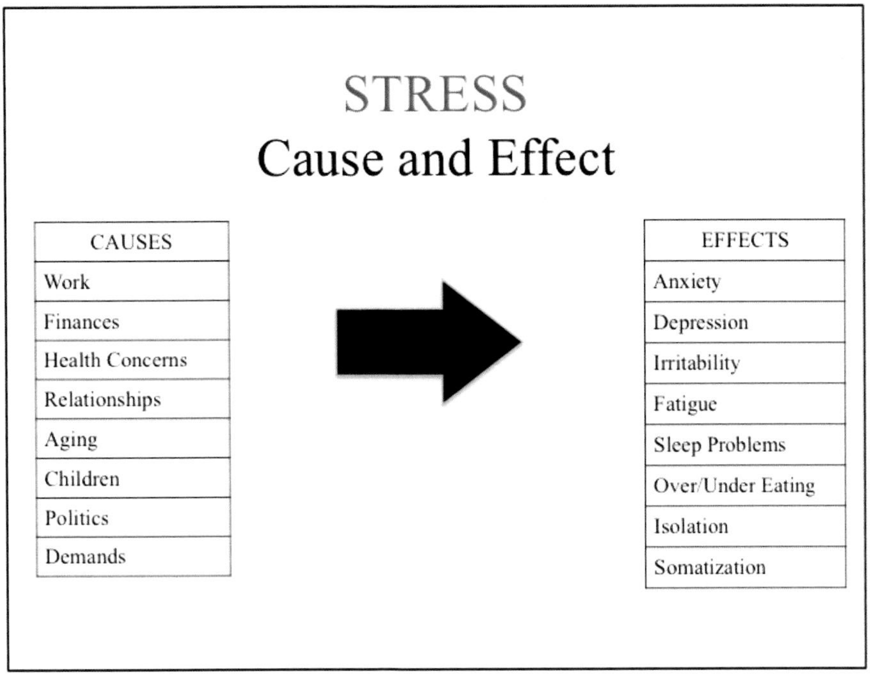

STRESS
Cause and Effect

CAUSES
Work
Finances
Health Concerns
Relationships
Aging
Children
Politics
Demands

EFFECTS
Anxiety
Depression
Irritability
Fatigue
Sleep Problems
Over/Under Eating
Isolation
Somatization

The true cause of all types of stress is *perceived threat*. We feel stress at work or in traffic because painful past experiences have *taught* us to perceive a threat in these situations or environments. Stress is the body and mind's reaction to the danger, whether it is real or not (Cox, 1992; Hamarat et al., 2001).

When we do not perceive threat or when we intentionally relax our bodies, the parasympathetic nervous system dominates (De Champlain et al., 1999). Parasympathetic nervous system dominance can be described as feeling "comfortable in our own skin."

When we *do* perceive a threat, our sympathetic nervous system activates. The signs of sympathetic nervous system dominance include increased heart rate and breathing rate, decreased peripheral circulation, muscle tension, and increased energy (Sapolsky, 1996). Brain activity also changes (Critchley et al., 2001; Porges, 2001; Scaer, 2005). The thalamus, brain stem, and basal ganglia—together sometimes called the "reptile brain"—become more active, and the neocortex, or "thinking" part of the brain, is less active. The neocortex houses our "higher executive" functions (Goldberg, 2001) such as judgment, reasoning, discernment, fine motor control, identity, time management/conceptualization, language, speech, and the ability to discriminate between real and perceived threats. The longer we spend perceiving a threat without intentionally relaxing, the more we compromise those areas of our brain. We become less clear and rational, less agile, worse at solving problems, and less capable of "being ourselves."

Figure 3. Sympathetic Nervous System

Perceived Threat

Physiological	Brain Mechanics	Other Effects
▲Heart Rate	▲ Basal Ganglia & Thalamic Fx	▲Obsession
▲ Breathing Rate	▼ Neo-cortical Fx	▲Compulsion
▼ Breathing Volume Centralized Circulation	▼Frontal Lobe activity ▼Executive Fx ▼Fine motor control ▼Emotional regulation	▼ Speed & Agility
▲ Muscle Tension	▼Temporal Lobe Activity ▼Language ▼Speech	▼ Strength
▲ Energy	▼ Anterior Cingulate	Constricted thoughts & behaviors
▲ DIS-EASE		Fatigue

Fight OR Flight

Of course, activating the sympathetic nervous system does have benefits. It helps us focus and gives us energy, strength, excitement, and joy. It is only when it dominates that it causes problems (Sapolsky, 1996; Scaer, 2005). Chronically perceiving threat without relaxing your body is like flooring the accelerator of a car while keeping your other foot on the brake: you burn out your engine and get nowhere. Research points to this phenomenon as a cause of many diseases (Scaer, 2005; Rothschild, 2000; van der Kolk and McFarland, 1996).

In 1908, psychologists Robert Mearns Yerkes and John Dillingham Dodson demonstrated the relationship between arousal (or sympathetic nervous system activity) and performance. This research later produced the Yerkes-Dodson Law (Yerkes and Dodson, 1908; Diamond et al., 2007) to help improve performance in various fields.

Figure 4 shows the relationship between performance and arousal. A certain level of arousal is required for better performance, or "flow"—no one performs complex tasks while napping (Csikszentmihalyi, 1997). But when the energy in our bodies climbs higher, performance drops sharply and we become fatigued and overwhelmed. Recent research (Dovan, 2013; Taylor, 2012) suggests that the more difficult the task, the more we need to reduce our level of arousal.

Figure 4. Yerkes-Dodson Curve

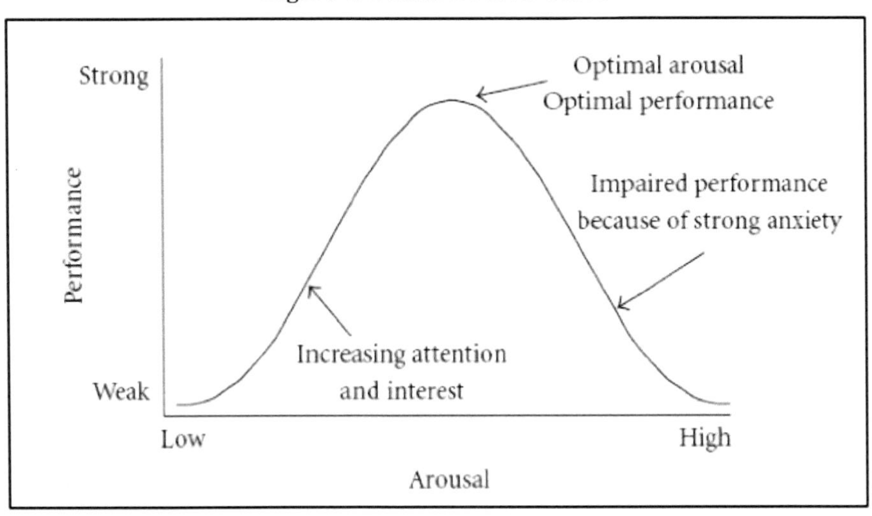

While understanding how to regulate and control our sympathetic nervous system activity is a key facet of treating compassion fatigue, another piece is understanding *why* we perceive threats so often. A 2007 article by the World Health Organization (WHO) stated that in high-income countries (North America, Europe, some of Asia, and some of South America), our circumstances are the safest they have *ever* been in the history of time. We are less likely to experience war, starvation, disease, disaster, or crime than past generations—yet we also seem to be more afraid. What is different for us?

In 1990, Drs. Pearlman and McCann demonstrated that we do not need to directly experience a traumatic event to become traumatized—we only need to witness it. Today, through television and other media, we see traumatic events across the world in a way that was impossible for our ancestors, and that leads to more perceived threats.

Here is an example of this occurrence. If people are asked, "Have you ever been attacked in a parking garage?" they are likely to say no. But when you ask, "Do you find yourself on guard and anxious in a parking garage?" many will answer yes. To explain this anxiety, they might mention the evening news, *CSI*, or the newspaper.

When we experience something painful or frightening, we will start to perceive similar situations as threatening. When we witness a traumatic event through the media, listen to someone's harrowing story, or care for a traumatized person, we are *also* likely to perceive a threat in situations that are similar to those seen or heard about. These past learning experiences often cause us to perceive a threat where there is no actual danger.

The sympathetic nervous system does not care whether the threat is real or imagined—it will activate either way. If we stay in the threatening situation (i.e., the parking garage) without intentionally relaxing our bodies, we will begin to experience the symptoms generated by the sympathetic nervous system (such as anxiety, panic, difficulty concentrating, and irritability).

The original purpose of the sympathetic nervous system response was survival—to recognize and rapidly respond to threats. Over time, however, humans have developed a frontal lobe that gives us the capacity for reasoning and discernment. It is no longer necessary or even useful to respond to a perceived threat by allowing the sympathetic nervous system to dominate. Any athlete or performer will tell you that they do their best when they are relaxed and in a state of parasympathetic nervous system dominance. Any martial artist will confirm that they can protect themselves more effectively when they are relaxed.

So what is the right thing to do when we perceive a threat? The answer will always be to *relax our bodies*.

Figure 5. *True* Cause of Stress

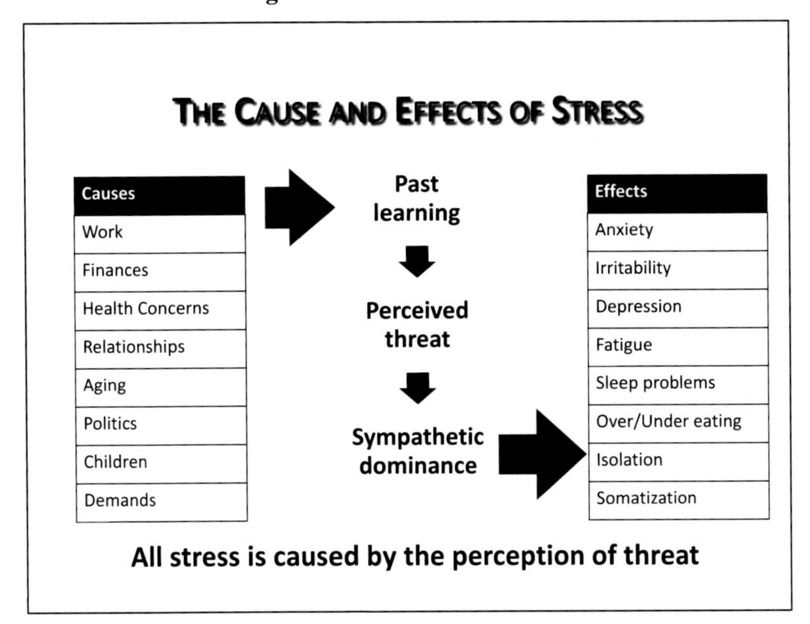

Anxiety Management/Self-Regulation

The next step, after discovering that perceived threat is the cause of our stress, is learning skills for self-regulation of the autonomic nervous system (Gentry, 2002; Perry and Szalavitz, 2007). This is different from relaxation, even though relaxation is a crucial part of it. Self-regulation here is defined as the intentional and conscious process of monitoring and relaxing one's body while in the context of a perceived threat, preventing the sympathetic nervous system from achieving dominance.

Essentially, self-regulation is the ability to consciously move away from overstimulation and toward relaxed comfort while engaging in the everyday demands of work and life. With practice, we can bring just the right amount of energy to each task, perform better, and make our work less fatiguing. We only need to be aware of sympathetic nervous system activation, and then use relaxation skills to prevent it from achieving dominance. Said even more simply: we need to stop clenching our muscles!

The state of sympathetic nervous system dominance is what generates the negative effects associated with caregiving work. This buildup of energy is typically called "stress." The concept of stress is not a helpful one—it attributes the symptoms to outside factors, creating an external locus of control for its existence. For example, when a caregiver says, "I have a stressful job," they are stating that factors associated with their work, over which they have no power, are preventing them from being happy and comfortable. If they can say instead, "I perceive threats at work, but there is no danger. Let me relax," they are moving away from sympathetic nervous system dominance and toward an internal locus of control. They become less agitated, more comfortable, and happier.

If we fail to develop the capacity for self-regulation and are unable to reduce our own levels of arousal, we will perceive more and more threats and respond with anxiety, believing that benign people, objects, and situations are dangerous. Providing caregiving services while experiencing intense anxiety is thought to be one of the primary causes of compassion fatigue symptoms (Escribà-Agüir and Pérez-Hoyos, 2007; Sorenson et al., 2016).

As one insightful workshop participant stated, "Maybe the symptoms of compassion fatigue are a good thing. They force us to become stronger [if treated]." It does seem to be true that those caregivers with well-developed self-regulation skills who do not resort to self-destructive, comfort-seeking behaviors are less likely to suffer compassion fatigue.

Both the ARP and the CCFST teach caregivers to develop self-management plans that will assist them in achieving and maintaining a non-anxious presence—a level of relaxed mindfulness and comfort in their bodies. We believe that to the degree that a caregiver is able to remain non-anxious, the caregiver will resist compassion fatigue. This ability to remain non-anxious when facing the pain, horror, loss, and powerlessness associated with patients' or clients' traumatic experiences, or to calmly "bear witness," is an essential part of treating and preventing compassion fatigue symptoms.

Just relax when witnessing traumatic situations or encountering perceived threats. Sounds simple, right? Yes, the idea is simple but the discipline to practice it is not. The ability to self-regulate and soothe anxiety is thought to be a hallmark of maturity, and mastery of these skills comes only with years of practice. Many care providers who have succeeded report that they could only do so after their work-related distress was severe enough to motivate them.

The traditional relaxation approaches used in mental health treatment require attention and dedication, and are not effective with everyone. Most of these techniques help people to achieve relaxation, but not to maintain it. In addition, methods like progressive relaxation, paradoxical relaxation, meditation, and autogenesis require clients to disengage from their current activities to some degree. These methods work when a person has time and space for them (Sadigh and

Montero, 2013; Mandl et al., 1998; Jacobson, 1938). However, practicing them while engaged in caregiving work—especially in an environment full of perceived threats—is very difficult.

The self-regulation method taught in the ARP is simple enough to practice during the workday, although it is not easy. It involves a commitment to discovering and relaxing tense muscles in a disciplined and consistent way. Many people who practice it find that they need to attend to their bodies approximately every five minutes to maintain a non-anxious state. This is especially true during demanding activities; the more demands placed on us, the more we need to pay attention to regulating the energy in our bodies.

Dr. Gentry has called this ongoing identification and regulation of muscle tension "bodyfulness." While mindfulness asks us to be aware of our thoughts without controlling them, the "bodyfulness" of self-regulation asks us to be aware of our muscles in order to relax them (Jamison, 1999; Kabat-Zinn and Hahn, 2009).

Take a moment to do a body scan and become a "wet noodle," relaxing all of the muscles in your body. Start to scan your body, either head to toe or toe to head, whatever feels more comfortable. As you do this, notice any tense or tight muscles and intentionally relax or stop squeezing them while you continue your body scan. Congratulations, you are capable of self-regulation! Whenever a person discovers constricted muscles and then intentionally releases and relaxes them, they are practicing self-regulation. If you feel tightness in your neck while sitting in a meeting and then relax it, you are practicing self-regulation. If you are driving and notice the muscles in your lower back have been tense for a period of time and you then release this tension, you are practicing self-regulation. Developing this skill is a lifelong process that produces immediate results in lessening stress.

The challenge is that we may lack conscious awareness of tight muscles in our body unless the tension is causing discomfort, so developing the ability of muscular interoception is crucial. Interoception is the awareness of the internal state of our body, thus muscular interoception refers to the awareness of the muscles in our body (or *bodyfulness*). This requires intentional and deliberate body scans and acute relaxation being frequently conducted throughout the day.

Contrary to those traditional relaxation approaches that may disrupt daily activity, body scans can be conducted during your everyday activities at work and in your personal life. For example, if a husband is having an unpleasant conversation with his wife, he can shift his awareness from the conversation to muscular interoception for acute relaxation of his muscles, then back again, all within seconds. The same can be done by a caregiver who is attending to the traumatic story of a survivor during therapy.

It is our belief that this professional resiliency skill provides the caregiver with an inoculation against stress and the harmful effects of treating someone who is suffering. Without developing this skill, caregivers become vulnerable to compassion fatigue and burnout, which results in poor quality of care to their patients and clients.

Another challenge is learning to maintain this state in high-demand and perceived threatening contexts. Reciprocal inhibition—pairing exposure (to perceived threats) with relaxation—is the engine of all effective treatments of trauma. If a caregiver embraces this discipline, they begin to find that not only have their symptoms lessened, but they have also begun to optimize their life.

Anytime you discover constricted muscles in your body and then release the tightness of these muscles, you are practicing self-regulation. Again, it is that simple. This two-step process of monitoring our bodies for tightness and then engaging in acute relaxation—in one or two seconds—is a powerful method for regulating the autonomic nervous system.

Many clients and professionals we have taught self-regulation to have found it particularly helpful to focus upon the pelvic muscles as the primary group of muscles for interoception and acute relaxation. There is some research (Berceli, 2007; Heim et al., 1998; Krost, 2007) that indicates that the constriction—and conversely, the relaxation—of these muscles have a powerful effect upon autonomic nervous system arousal and regulation. Relaxing these muscles can cause profound relaxation in the entire body, often within a few seconds; the effects include slower and deeper breathing, a slower heart rate, relaxed core and peripheral muscles, and reactivated neocortical function (Staugaard-Jones, 2012). Thus, developing awareness of these muscles' constriction followed by the conscious and acute relaxing of them throughout your day is a good way to practice self-regulation.

As you become increasingly successful at bringing relaxation to constricted muscles, take heart that you have acquired the skills to achieve immediate comfort, improve performance in your work, and stay faithful to their principles and morality. When you put these skills into practice, you will likely discover a growing sense of hope and optimism in your work and life.

With your newfound capacity for self-regulation and growing competence, we are ready to explore the next resilience skill: intentionality.

Intentionality

Intentionality is another key part of resilience, and is split into two related concepts: deliberateness and integrity. Think about a coworker, fellow student, or a family member who might be experiencing stress and burnout. How much do they complain? How snarky are they? How often do you see them act in impulsive, self-defeating, and destructive ways?

One of the consequences of stress is reactivity—compulsive or impulsive behavior. When we continue to perceive threat without relaxing our bodies, the sympathetic nervous system floods us with energy and chemicals and overwhelms the neocortex's ability to manage our behavior (Katz and Yehuda, 2006; Cox, 1992; Sapolsky, 1996; Critchley et al., 2001; McNaughton, 1997; Shusterman and Barnea, 2005). We soon find ourselves "acting out" in ways we do not want to act (Takahashi et al., 2005; Yartz and Hawk, 2001). This is the opposite of intentionality.

For example, imagine someone criticizes you during a work meeting and you perceive their remark as a threat. Your sympathetic nervous system response is triggered: your face flushes, fists clench, and jaw tightens, but you say nothing, not wanting to disrupt the meeting or trouble your coworkers. If you do not relax, you will soon notice yourself becoming more and more irritated by the remark. As you continue thinking about it and keeping yourself in the context of the perceived threat, your sympathetic nervous system ratchets upward and your judgment gets worse. You find yourself giving the offender resentful looks and making unkind comments to them (fight). After the meeting you avoid contact with them (flight).

In this scenario, your intention was to stay true to your values of compassion, tolerance, and focusing on your work. You did not want to start a conflict or begin resenting your coworker, but you felt unable to resist, even with your best efforts. A threshold was crossed and you were compelled, against your will, to choose either fight or flight.

When the rising energy in our bodies overwhelms our neocortex, we can no longer hold on to our intention. Instead, we find ourselves involuntarily responding to danger that is only perceived. We act out, saying things we do not mean, hurting others, isolating ourselves, overeating, overspending, drinking or using drugs, and engaging in other self-destructive behaviors to soothe the discomfort of sympathetic nervous system dominance. Whenever someone acts against their principles, breaches their integrity, or does anything of which they are ashamed, chances are they did so while their sympathetic nervous system was dominant (Takahashi et al., 2005). All such behavior directed by the sympathetic nervous system is an attempt to escape or fight off a perceived threat.

Professional caregivers suffering from compassion fatigue find themselves frequently acting in ways they do not want to act. They are fighting with their spouses, yelling at their children, and dreading the work they chose as their mission. Based on the model described in this chapter, it is clear that these symptoms are the result of chronic sympathetic nervous system dominance. The more "stressed out" they feel, the more often they engage in this thinking and behavior. They may try to manipulate the environment, which is often beyond their control, or they may compulsively avoid activities, people, or objects they perceive as threatening.

Figure 6. Threshold

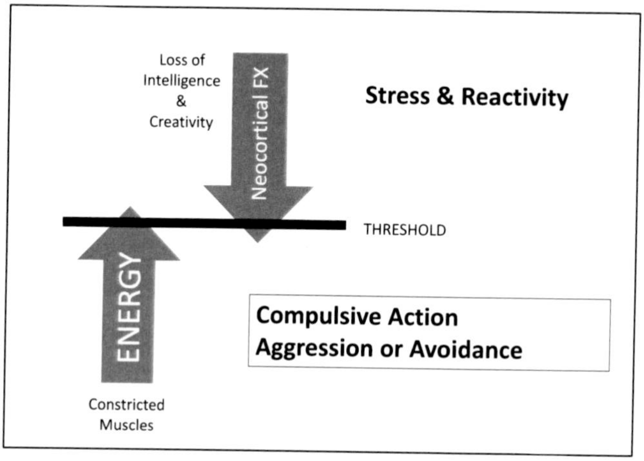

Versus:

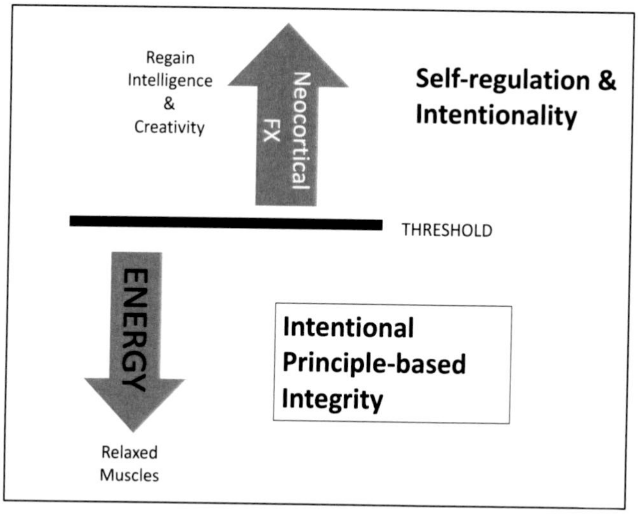

People cannot live in a state of constantly breached integrity without suffering from it. We break our principles and fail to maintain intentional behavior because we have failed to relax our bodies and self-regulate when we perceive threats. As professional caregivers learn to maintain relaxed bodies despite perceived threats during work and personal activities, they find it easier to behave according to their principles; they become the people they intend to be and act the way they choose. They enjoy the relaxed comfort of parasympathetic nervous system dominance no matter what is happening around them.

The opposite of reactivity is intentionality. Treatment for compassion fatigue teaches professional caregivers to be deliberate instead of being compulsive or impulsive. Intentionality is associated with resilience and maturation, and the path to intentional living is not through brute force, but elegance and relaxation.

We engage in reactionary behavior to vent the anxious energy produced by the sympathetic nervous system. Practicing self-regulation when we experience "triggers" or perceived threats allows the parasympathetic nervous system to dominate. In this state, we are comfortable in our bodies and can decide how we want to handle any situation. This is the deliberate part of intentionality.

The integrity part of learning this skill involves first becoming aware of intention. You cannot be intentional unless you know what you intend, and that means turning your intention from a vague notion into a clear, explicit statement. Thus, to express their intention in words, caregivers must write a "covenant" or personal mission statement. This statement expresses their overarching mission in life, as well as their intention while at work each day. The caregivers also identify the personal principles that guide their behavior, writing them out as a "code of honor." In this way, they begin to see themselves as people who are going to work with a purpose. They come to define success and worth not by the opinions of others, but by their ability to live out this purpose.

Through this process, even the most jaded veteran caregivers have found a new passion for their professions and reconnected with their original reasons for working in healthcare. They become able to focus on what they can control—themselves and their own behavior—and let go of the external pressure and demands of others.

Many caregivers who experience symptoms of compassion fatigue will try to ignore their distress until a threshold of discomfort is reached. This may mean that they are unable to perform their jobs as well as they once did, or as well as they would like. It may involve physical deterioration associated with somatic symptoms, or embarrassment and emotional pain associated with self-destructive behaviors. Whatever the motivation, we have found that successfully treating compassion fatigue symptoms requires the caregiver to intentionally acknowledge and address, rather than avoid, the symptoms and their causes.

Additionally, setting goals and creating a personal/professional mission statement are invaluable in moving away from the reactivity associated with compassion fatigue and toward the resilience and intentionality of mature caregiving.

Narrative

Many researchers have identified the creation of a chronological verbal or graphic narrative as an important ingredient in the healing of traumatic stress, especially intrusive symptoms (Tinnin, 1994; van der Kolk and McFarland, 1996; Foa et al., 1999). We have found that creating a timeline of one's caregiving career that identifies the clients and experiences that produced traumatic stress is invaluable in the resolution of compassion fatigue symptoms, especially those associated with secondary traumatic stress.

In the ARP, we instruct each participant/caregiver to "tell your story from the beginning, starting with the first experiences in your life that led you toward caregiving and ending with the present." We use a video camera to record this narrative and ask the caregiver to watch it later that day while drawing a graphic timeline, taking care to identify the experiences that have led to any primary and/or secondary traumatic stress (intrusive symptoms).

In the CCFST, two participants each take a one-hour block of time to tell their narratives to each other and practice non-anxious "bearing witness."

Desensitization and Reprocessing

After completing the narrative and identifying the past experiences that are encroaching upon present-day consciousness in the form of primary and secondary traumatic stress, the caregiver is now ready to resolve these memories. In the ARP, Eye Movement Dissociation and Reprocessing (EMDR) is the method of choice for this work (Shapiro, 1989, 1995). In the CCFST, we use a hybridized version of a Neuro-Linguistic Programming (NLP) anchoring technique (Baranowsky and Gentry, 1998). Any method that employs simultaneous exposure and relaxation (i.e., reciprocal inhibition) is appropriate for this important cornerstone of treatment. We have also had success with Traumatic Incident Reduction (TIR) (French and Harris, 1998), the anamnesis procedure from the Trauma Recovery Institute Method (TRI) (Tinnin, 1994), and many techniques from Cognitive Behavioral Therapy (CBT) (Foa and Meadows, 1997; Follette, Ruzek, and Abueg, 1998; Rothbaum et al., 2000).

With the successful desensitization and reprocessing of the caregiver's primary and secondary traumatic stress comes relief from intrusive symptoms, and also a sense of rebirth, joy, and transformation. This important step in the treatment of compassion fatigue should not be minimized or overlooked.

In our work with the responders to the Oklahoma City bombing, none reported experiencing intrusive symptoms of traumatic stress until days, weeks, months, or even years after their work at the site. An incident commander for a team of mental health responders who worked with over 2,700 victims in New York City after the 9/11 attacks (Norman, 2001) indicated that at least one Certified Compassion Fatigue Specialist for every ten responders was available to provide daily debriefing services. He further indicated that if a responder began to report symptoms or show signs of significant traumatic stress, they were stabilized by the team and then transported back home with a referral to a mental health practitioner in the worker's hometown.

With the intense demands of critical incident work and the paramount importance of worker safety, trying to treat care providers' primary and secondary traumatic stress onsite seems counterproductive, as it draws from the already depleted resources of the intervention team. For this reason, it is recommended that they address the effects of accumulated traumatic memories only after safely returning to the support of their family, friends, churches/synagogues, and healthcare professionals in their hometown.

For professional caregivers, it is important to work through (i.e., desensitize and reprocess) secondary traumatic stress memories if they are contributing to the symptoms of compassion fatigue and diminishing professional quality of life. This can be done by engaging in an ongoing therapeutic relationship with a mental health professional who is skilled in one of the methods above.

We have worked with many caregivers who have worked with this mental health professional periodically when they found they were becoming symptomatic from their work. However, this desensitization of secondary traumatic stress, in most cases, will not need intervention by a mental health professional. Instead, care providers experiencing the negative effects of secondary traumatic stress can usually resolve these effects through peer support. Using this method requires developing a support network of caring peers who can listen, without interruption, while you narrate your painful work experiences. As you tell the stories of your painful work experiences (ones contributing to secondary traumatic stress symptoms) while *simultaneously relaxing your body*, you are engaging in the reciprocal inhibition process and desensitizing the negative effects of these past painful experiences upon present-day functioning. This simple process of "telling the story" while remaining in a relaxed body is at the core of all effective trauma treatment.

Self-Supervision

This aspect of treatment is focused on correcting distorted and coercive thinking. Distorted thinking may develop during childhood experiences of adversity, or in response to traumatic stress later in life. Whatever the cause, we have found that once a caregiver contracts the negative symptoms of compassion fatigue, they will not fully resolve until distorted beliefs about self and the world are addressed. This is especially true for the ways in which we supervise and motivate ourselves.

Caregivers recovering from compassion fatigue will need to soften their critical and coercive self-talk and shift toward a more self-accepting and affirming language and tone. For many, this is a difficult, tedious, and painstaking breaking-of-bad-habits process that can take years to complete.

In the ARP and the CCFST, we have employed an elegant and powerful technique called "video-dialogue" (Holmes and Tinnin, 1995) that accelerates this process significantly. This technique, adapted for use with the ARP, challenges the participant to write a letter to themselves from the perspective of the "Great Supervisor," lavishing upon themselves all the praise, support, and validation that they wish to hear from others. They are then requested to read this letter into the eye of the camera for later viewing.

While watching the video, the caregiver is asked to "pay attention to any negative or critical thought that thwarts your acceptance of this praise." They are instructed to give these critical and negative thoughts a "voice" and express them to the video camera currently playing their recording of positivity. This back-and-forth argument between the "self" and the "critical voice" of the caregiver continues until both "sides" begin to see the utility in both perspectives. When this is completed, polarities relax, self-criticism softens, and integration is facilitated. This technique is powerfully evocative and can rapidly transform self-critical thinking styles.

Another useful tool is the cognitive therapy "triple column technique" (Burns, 1980) that helps identify particular cognitive distortions, challenging the caregiver to rewrite them into thoughts that are more adaptive and satisfying.

As caregivers suffering from compassion fatigue symptoms become more skilled in resolving their internal divisions and conflicts, they are challenged to identify and rectify conflicts with significant others. Traumatized individuals who are able to "unfreeze" themselves from their polarities, resentments, and cut-offs will be rewarded with less anxiety, more comfort in their own skin, and a greater sense of freedom from the past to pursue their mission for the future.

Perceptual Maturation in the Workplace

Dr. Wayne Dyer (2004) said, "Change the way you look at things and the things you look at change" (p. 183). If we are willing to change the way we look at our work through a disciplined and intentional process, we can transform our work experience. We can become excited, challenged, and stimulated instead of overwhelmed and stressed. We can find comfort, mastery, and confidence where previously we felt diminished and damaged by our work. *Nothing has to change in the workplace for the workplace to change.* We can focus on regulating our physical responses and managing our thoughts, stop trying to manage what is beyond our immediate control, and become more resilient, competent, and satisfied with our work.

Caregiving work is stressful, right? The answer for most is an automatic "obviously, yes." However, the more automatic our "yes," the more likely it is that we are experiencing the negative effects of stress from our work in healthcare.

The constant and changing demands on a caregiver's time and resources are often too numerous for us to meet. When we allow ourselves to react to this overwhelmed feeling by perceiving it as a threat and letting unexamined stress build in our bodies, we come to dread the work environment, possibly labeling it as "toxic." Until we recognize that the cause is inside *us* rather than outside and learn to self-regulate better, the stress we experience at work and at home will get worse.

As we begin to understand that our stress is a response to our internal state, we can start to change that response when we are facing the demands of caregiving work. When we make this shift to an internal locus of control and build resilience skills, we can learn to find satisfaction in our work again. What is more, because our brains and bodies will no longer be suffering from stress, we can perform better and work smarter.

We must evolve and mature in the way we see our work, our workplaces, and ourselves. The way to do this is to replace those automatic, reflexive responses with conscious, intentional ones. Practicing this discipline of perceptual maturation takes power away from the "toxic" environment and returns it to us, giving us control over how we experience the situations we encounter in our work. Table 2 lists four important aspects of perceptual maturation in caregiving.

Table 2. Perceptual Maturation in the Workplace

Demand vs. Choice	· There are no demands on you. · You choose the work-related tasks you perform, even the less desirable ones. · You always have a choice.
Outcome-Driven vs. Principle-Based	· The outcome of your work is beyond your control. · Focus on your present behavior, not the outcome. · Your best work is good enough, as long as you maintain your integrity.
Relinquishing Entitlement and Secondary Gains	· You worked hard to earn your position; it is not victimizing you. · You are not entitled to more than others are. · You derive certain "gains" from seeing yourself as victimized; recognize them and decide whether they are worth it. · Your workplace gives you the chance to live out your values and evolve as a person.
System Demands	· All caregiving systems ask for more than we can give them. · While patients/clients may want more than you can give, this is not threatening. · Acknowledgement and appreciation are not guaranteed. · Work situations do not cause stress—your internal response to them does.

1. Demand vs. Choice: When you hear the statement "nothing is demanded of you," how do you react? Do you instantly want to laugh, contradict it, or dismiss it? If you do, it may be because you have been trained to see your workplace as a demanding and stressful environment. Throughout our lives, experiences with parents, school, work, and the media can hammer home the idea that requests from others are demands we're *required* to meet.

When we see a request from a boss, a patient/client, or a family member as a demand, then it is likely we will: 1) perceive it as a threat or something outside of ourselves that is placing a burden or requirement on us that is undesirable or unpleasant; 2) have feelings of dread and avoidant behaviors associated with this "demand"; 3) utilize brute force, sometimes referred to as "white-knuckling" our way through a situation, to make ourselves comply with the dreaded demand.

The more people request from us on a given day, the more we are likely to feel overwhelmed, start perceiving the requests as demands and threats, and fall into a state of sympathetic nervous system dominance. This is a common pattern in "toxic" work environments. Instead of giving in and allowing our brain and body to react with overstimulation that leads to stress and compassion fatigue, we need to change our perception of these requests. When someone asks for something, we must see it as a choice: we can choose to do or not do this task. We can consider the consequences of each option, and do what is in our best interest. "Choosing" to engage in and complete work tasks—even the ones you do not want to do—can significantly lessen the stress you experience from your work.

2. Outcome-Driven vs. Principle-Based: If you do caregiving work, whether professionally or in your personal life, you are likely very concerned about the outcomes of that work. You feel responsible for the well-being of the people in your care. You may even attach your self-worth to succeeding with your patients and beat yourself up when they do not succeed.

Supervisors and others you work with may encourage you to take on this responsibility, but there are *many* factors that determine a patient's outcome beyond your input or treatment. It is impossible for you to control all these factors, and if you demand impossible things of yourself, you are highly likely to feel stressed and fall into sympathetic nervous system dominance.

A healthier approach is to focus on doing the best you can with what is in your control, not on the outcomes. This does not mean abandoning treatment goals; you can still check in with your goals and reorient yourself toward working on them every so often. However, at work or on an everyday basis, just do your best and stay faithful to your principles. We can apply learning to future situations, but in the present we can only do what we can do. Surprisingly, many caregivers report that their patients experience better outcomes when more focus is placed on the journey rather than on the end result.

3. Relinquishing Entitlement and Secondary Gains: Frequently, caregivers or healthcare professionals suffering from burnout end up cultivating a strong sense of entitlement related to their work. Because they feel like they have made significant sacrifices, they believe they deserve something in return.

The distress they feel from constantly perceiving threats around them at work has made them feel like victims. When this goes on for too long, they become accustomed to this state and the way others may cater to their suffering and feel sorry for them. These are the secondary gains you will have to relinquish when you give up victimhood and stress. When you come to recognize this entitlement in yourself for what it is, you can release it, and let go of feeling like a victim.

Many professional caregivers tend to forget that they chose their field, persevered through academic endeavors, and worked hard to achieve their positions. We are not victims of our work! What we do and where we work are *choices* we have made. Releasing a victim status enables us to rediscover our mission, our integrity, and the enthusiasm for helping people that led us to train for this work.

When you give up entitlement, it frees you to act with intention and integrity in your work, whether you are dealing with clients, patients, supervisors, coworkers, family members, or yourself. When you change your perception of your work, it becomes a way to grow and evolve and is no longer a toxic or harmful burden. Through your work you can mature and make yourself a stronger, more resilient, and more caring person.

4. Systems Demand: The organizations we work for and the people we care for are always going to need more than we alone are capable of giving. Part of maturing and changing our perception is realizing this, and learning to set boundaries for ourselves to maintain our integrity and well-being. We must develop the skills to be resilient, advocate for ourselves, and self-regulate in order to keep doing our work and sticking to our principles, especially when we feel like the system is pressuring us to give more than we are capable of.

An important sign of professional maturity is the ability to work with personal integrity in a setting that has the potential to breach that integrity.

Self-Optimization

The resilience skill of self-optimization is about changing our perception of ourselves rather than our workplace. The field of positive psychology has a lot to say about this, as do those who practice and study mindfulness. Self-optimization as discussed in this program has four major elements (see Table 3).

Table 3. Self-Optimization

Mindfulness	· You keep your body calm. · You maintain an observing mind. · You accept the current situation and do not judge. · You cultivate curiosity and stay teachable. · You improve your capacity to focus.
Science of Happiness	· You understand that you can create positive emotions through intention. · When you are more positive, you are more effective and more resilient. · You engage in disciplined activities to develop a more positive-focused brain. · You practice gratitude, service, and goodwill.
Self-Validation	· You rely on yourself rather than patients, supervisors, or colleagues for your self-worth. · You understand that needing outside validation turns all human interactions into perceived threats. · You become less invested in others' opinions of you.
Personal Development	· You strive for intentionality. · You work to bring yourself into alignment with your own principles. · You use grace and elegance instead of "brute force." · You work smart instead of hard.

1. Mindfulness: Mindfulness meditation is a centuries-old practice rooted in the Buddhist and Taoist traditions. It involves becoming aware, or mindful, of your thoughts, feelings, and mental processes, and observing them in a disciplined way without engaging with them.

Over the past few decades, the field of psychology, especially positive psychology, has embraced the principles of mindfulness. They can be used in therapy to help people manage anxiety, change habits of negative thinking, and treat a wide variety of other mental health problems. Today, mindfulness is a central technique in many treatment approaches and psychotherapies. It is also been adopted by the business community as a way to promote inspiration, creativity, and satisfaction (in other words, resilience) at work. Thus, practicing mindfulness is a valuable step in addressing compassion fatigue.

In the words of Jon Kabat-Zinn, PhD:

> Mindfulness practice means that we commit fully in each moment to be present, inviting ourselves to interface with this moment in full awareness, with the intention to embody as best we can an orientation of calmness, mindfulness, and equanimity right here and right now. (p. 22)

Most mindfulness practices require a collection of skills, often used simultaneously. These skills are briefly described below:

1. Calming the body. This is often achieved through breathing in a certain disciplined fashion. It can involve breathing into the belly, regulated breathing, or counting breaths. Being intentional about your breathing in any of these ways will reduce anxiety and calm you. As we have already discussed, relaxing your body improves brain function, and when you are calm, you have more control over your thoughts.

2. Awareness. This includes being aware of and recognizing all the things that are going on around you (i.e., sights and sounds), as well as those inside you (i.e., thoughts and physiological states). Another aspect of awareness is being able to focus your attention on only one of these things at a time. Research has shown that multitasking is not an efficient way of working and can contribute to making you feel stressed (Carrier et al., 2015; Dindar and Akbulut, 2016; Rubenking, 2017).

3. Nonjudgmental/nonevaluative observation. This means looking at your experiences objectively without labeling them as either "good" or "bad." You refuse to judge yourself and others because you have compassion for yourself and for them.

4. Being in the present moment. This means consciously focusing on what is going on and how you feel in the present instead of losing yourself in memories of the past or worries about the future. When you are in the present moment, you actively participate in your experiences and your work instead of just "going through the motions" or "being stuck on autopilot."

5. Beginner's mind. This means going into situations without a preconceived idea of what they are so that you remain open to new possibilities. When you already have a belief about how something will go before you start, it affects your experience and prevents you from getting in touch with the reality of it. These skills must be practiced to become effective. You can designate a special time for mindfulness meditation, or you can practice mindful awareness during your everyday life. It is possible to work toward being mindful and in the present during daily activities we tend to do "on autopilot," such as household chores, cooking, eating, driving, bathing, or exercise.

2. Science of Happiness: Happiness is a "state of well-being and contentment," according to Merriam-Webster. Psychological research into happiness and how it is achieved has produced some interesting findings.

In *The Happiness Advantage*, Shawn Achor, MA, (2010) noted that people often think of happiness as the result of reaching some distant goal: "I'll be happy when I find a job"; "I'll be happy when I get a promotion"; or "I'll be happy when my dissertation is finished." Dr. Kirk Schneider (2010), another happiness researcher, indicated that a focus on a life *well-lived* would reap far more contentment than a centered goal on "achieving happiness."

Other happiness research tells us that humans have a negativity bias: we notice, react to, and remember negative information before positive information. This may be a strategy for survival, much like the sympathetic nervous system response, but it tends to work against our contentment. Because of this bias, we fail to notice many of the positive things that happen to us every day. For example, if someone compliments you, you may reflexively dismiss it because you have heard too many negative things in the past and you believe it cannot be true. Psychologist John Gottman (1999) writes that it takes five positive interactions to make up for one negative one.

According to *Hardwiring Happiness* by Dr. Rick Hanson (2013), it *is* possible to conquer this negativity bias. We can work to internalize positive experiences more deeply while minimizing the harm of dwelling on negative ones. If you make an effort to notice positive things first, you can make yourself happier. Furthermore, happiness helps you succeed. Positivity improves outcomes in relationships, in education, and at work. Cultivating happiness makes you more likely to reach all your other goals in life.

Achor (2011) recommends five habits that can help us change our "hardwiring" in this way, and suggests trying to maintain one of them for twenty-one days in a row to help reinforce happiness. The five habits are as follows:

1. Think of three things you are grateful for each day and write them down.
2. Spend two minutes daily describing something good that has happened to you in the past day.
3. Spend ten minutes a day exercising.
4. Spend two minutes a day in meditation, focusing on your breath.
5. Send a message praising or thanking a coworker as your first task each day.

According to Achor, these simple habits can improve optimism, make you a more meaning-based thinker, teach your brain to believe that your actions matter, decrease stress and the harmful effects of multitasking, and build social support.

These are only a few of the many recommendations based on positive psychology research that are geared toward promoting happiness. When we allow ourselves time to focus on positive experiences, our brains become more accustomed to happiness and then learn to embrace it.

Furthermore, happiness is closely connected to resilience and is an important tool for fending off compassion fatigue. Close relationships bring people joy and satisfaction, while also providing social support for them during difficult times. People derive feelings of pleasure and meaning from doing their best at work, maintaining their integrity, and overcoming adversity.

Happiness means having positive feelings and experiences, but it also means being satisfied with your life and finding a way to see meaning in it. People who call themselves happy experience adversity and negative emotions as well, and some may achieve happiness by overcoming challenges and growing *despite* that adversity.

Positive emotions can be directly linked to negative emotions or difficult experiences as well. For instance, the Buddhist teacher Pema Chödrön (2016) suggests that forgiveness and compassion can become responses to being wronged. Creativity and flow involve taking risks, sometimes failing, and trying again. Awe, inspiration, serenity, and gratitude mean recognizing that you are smaller than something else or indebted to someone else. And generosity requires acknowledging other people's needs and wants and sometimes putting aside your own desires.

Psychologists Jack Bauer and George Bonanno (2001) studied the connection between negative and positive emotions by interviewing people who had lost spouses and tracking their positive and negative statements. Two years after the initial interviews, the people who had made five positive comments to each negative one were the most successful in adjusting—better than those with all negative or all positive comments. Their success may have come from being aware of their sadness but refusing to let it dominate their lives.

Another psychologist who studied positive emotions, Barbara Fredrickson (2000), called them the "fuel for resilience." Positive emotions are important because they help people find meaning in their lives and the adversity they face. Finding meaning in turn creates more positive feelings, and this becomes a cycle of beneficial feedback that improves well-being. Fredrickson and her colleagues found that resilient and happy people still had the same amount of negative feelings as others, but their positive feelings helped them bounce back and return to happiness instead of falling into depression. They were happy because they felt good, not because they escaped feeling bad.

Positive feelings make us more resilient as people and as caregivers because they help us build skills and resources to respond to the world, like the resilience skills discussed in this chapter. Kindness, amusement, creativity, and gratitude enable us to navigate our lives and our work better, and create a well of support we can draw on when times are more difficult. In other words, "Happy people become more satisfied not simply because they feel better, but because they develop resources for living well" (Cohn et al., 2009, p. 362).

3. Self-Validation: Another aspect of self-optimization is learning to find validation in oneself rather than seeking it in the opinions of others. This can be an extremely challenging and even lifelong effort.

As professional caregivers, we often look to supervisors, coworkers, and patients as sources of validation. When we allow their approval to determine our sense of worth, criticism feels like a dangerous threat. The need for validation from other people creates perceived threat, a.k.a. stress, in social situations. We become hypersensitive to what others think of us and respond with unhealthy, reactive behaviors, including competing for attention, sabotaging others, being contemptuous, self-aggrandizing, or completely isolating ourselves.

When we understand how the brain and body react to perceived threats, these behaviors make more sense. They are all driven by the sympathetic nervous system and have one of two goals: fight or flight.

When we "fight," we are attempting to neutralize the threat, for instance, by acting rigid, controlling, and aggressive in social situations. Conversely, "flight" behaviors—attempting to get away from the perceived threat—include trying to ingratiate ourselves with others, failing to speak up for what we believe is right, or avoiding other people entirely.

When we learn to relax and avoid the automatic sympathetic nervous system response in these situations, self-validation becomes an easier thing to achieve.

4. Personal Development: This resilience skill is an especially useful one for all aspects of life in the workplace and beyond. When you are able to identify your personal principles, morals, and values and can remain in alignment with them, you build an unshakeable foundation that will not be swayed by criticism, negativity, or obstacle.

You are intentional in your decisions and behaviors, demonstrating full autonomy over them, so that you never feel out of control or at the mercy of others' actions or choices. Instead of deigning to answer a demand when the stress grows too great (the "brute force" we inflict upon ourselves to get things accomplished), you are proactive, graceful, and elegant in responding to the expectations placed upon you, giving your best and recognizing that you have done so regardless of the outcome. You work strategically, showing initiative and resourcefulness that allow you to complete things in a smarter—not harder—manner.

Connection and Support

> For years mental health professionals taught people they could be psychologically healthy without social support, that 'unless you love yourself, no one else will love you.' … The truth is, you cannot love yourself unless you have been loved and are loved. The capacity to love cannot be built in isolation.
>
> – Bruce D. Perry (2006)

One of the ways trauma seems to affect us all, caregivers included, is to leave us with a sense of disconnected isolation. A common thread we have found with sufferers of compassion fatigue symptoms is that they progressively lose their sense of connection and community, with many of them isolating as their symptoms intensify. They cite fear of being perceived as weak, impaired, or incompetent by peers and patients/clients, along with time constraints and loss of interest, as reasons for this lack of connection. Developing and maintaining healthy relationships is a powerful factor in resolving and preventing compassion fatigue, as they provide support and give care professionals a way to share and dilute the impact of the images and stories associated with secondary traumatic stress.

The ARP includes a peer-to-peer element that can help caregivers build supportive relationships with each other, and the CCFST incorporates exercises specifically designed to dismantle interpersonal barriers and enhance self-disclosure. Through these connections, caregivers suffering compassion fatigue come to understand that their symptoms are not an indication of some pathological weakness or disease, but natural consequences of providing care for traumatized people.

In addition, sharing experiences with empathetic, understanding peers can help caregivers see their symptoms as signs of the need to make changes in their self-care and caregiving practices. A warm and supportive environment in which caregivers can discuss the intrusive traumatic material, challenging cases, symptoms, fears, shame, and secrets is one of the most critical ingredients in the resolution and continued prevention of compassion fatigue.

We also feel it is essential to work within our communities, drawing support from them while reinforcing the positive aspects of the community for others. Good therapists go to colleagues regularly for their own therapy—no one can provide exceptional caregiving work in isolation and without support. For our own health, we need to build an intentional support network of trusted people whom we can talk with regularly (weekly or monthly, for example) to share and ease the emotional burden of our work. This support network can serve four very important purposes for a caregiving professional.

1. Sharing trauma narratives (both primary and secondary trauma). This chapter previously mentioned the value of narratives in treating traumatic stress. Telling the story of a traumatic experience helps us to time-stamp it to the past and stop it from intruding into the present. When primary or secondary traumas appear in our present thoughts and dreams and cause distress, sharing them with supportive people is one way to process them and work through that distress. This can be helpful whether the trauma is from a direct personal experience or the story of a patient.

2. Empowering our support network to confront us. On our own, it is very difficult to recognize the symptoms of traumatic stress and how our body perceives threat internally and externally. If we do notice these symptoms, we tend to push them aside until some point of crisis is reached. If not stopped, this process inevitably leads to compassion fatigue. When people in our support network notice us falling into this pattern, they can confront us to get us back on track. Choose someone you trust and ask them to "get in your face," push back, and remind you of your principles if they see signs of infidelity to your purpose and mission in life.

3. Telling on ourselves. When we do realize we are falling into harmful patterns and breaching our integrity, sharing that with our support network is a valuable form of self-care. Avoidance, denial, suppression, and procrastination are not good coping strategies for managing stress; they exacerbate the situation and make us less resilient. Secrecy about these matters is unhealthy and unproductive, while discussing them not only makes us feel better, but is a sign that we are maturing as professionals.

4. Accountability. The people who support us can witness our commitment to act according to our principles and code of honor, and keep us accountable by gently checking in with us about them on a regular basis. Commitments made in front of other people are more likely to be kept because of this sense of accountability.

When you choose people for your support network, they may genuinely want to help but might not know what you need from them. If they are anxious about how to play this role appropriately, their anxiety can be counterproductive and create a perceived threat for them and you. Thus, you should carefully choose people you believe are able to handle the demands of supporting you as a caregiver. When you first meet with them in a relaxed context, explain what you need and how they can help most effectively. This is a script you may want to use or adapt for contacting potential support people:

> "Hey, I just learned that I might be at high risk for compassion fatigue and that sharing stories and feelings about my work with other people can help prevent it. I'd like for you to be one of those people. If you're willing, I'd also like to show you this technique I learned about how to keep your body relaxed while you're listening to me so that you don't feel stress from it [teach pelvic floor relaxation].
>
> I promise I will always ask permission and give you time to prepare yourself before I start talking about these issues—I won't surprise you. I just ask that you be available to talk sometime within seventy-two hours, either in person or by telephone. When we meet, I'll have everything I need to share organized into a twenty-minute narrative. I ask that you just listen during that time, but I'd love to hear your comments or suggestions afterwards.
>
> If you're willing to do this for me, of course I'll do the same for you in return. Just ask me first and I'll make myself available to you within seventy-two hours."

Now you just need to schedule your first meeting.

Self-Care and Revitalization

Psychiatrist and Holocaust survivor Viktor Frankl wrote, "That which is to give light must endure burning" (1963, p. 56). This quote is at the core of our work with resilience. As caregivers, we must endure burning, meaning that our work will inevitably cause us pain—being an empathetic person while working with the sick, troubled, and dying means witnessing and sharing their pain. To endure it, we must become resilient enough to keep it from doing lasting damage.

We also need to refuel and restore ourselves. If we use up all of our emotional resources and have nothing left to replenish them, we will eventually burn out. We must develop a systematic discipline of refueling ourselves physically, emotionally, psychologically, spiritually, relationally, and professionally.

Closely associated with self-management is the concept of self-care, or the ability to refill and refuel oneself in healthy ways. It is very common for caregivers to find themselves anxious during and after working with severely traumatized individuals. Instead of resolving the anxiety through healthy self-care practices, such as peer support or sharing with colleagues, physical exercise, meditation, nutrition, and spirituality, many caregivers find themselves redoubling their work efforts.

This constricting cycle of working harder in an attempt to feel better creates a distorted sense of entitlement that can lead to overstepping personal and professional boundaries. We have worked with many caregivers who have reported falling prey to compulsive behaviors such as overeating, overspending, or alcohol/drug abuse in an effort to soothe the anxiety they feel from the perceived demands of their work. Others have candidly admitted to breaching professional boundaries and ethics at the low point in this cycle, believing that they "deserve" this "special" treatment or reward.

Meta-analyses of psychotherapy outcomes consistently point to the quality of the relationship between therapist and client as the single most important ingredient in positive outcomes (Bergin and Garfield, 1994). The integrity and quality of this relationship both depend on the therapist maintaining their own mental health and sense of meaning.

When caregivers fail to enrich their lives with meaning and gratification outside of the professional arena, they look to work to provide those things. Caregivers who do this are interacting with their patients and clients from a position of depletion and need, and it is completely understandable that this behavior would lead to compassion fatigue symptoms.

On the other hand, professionals who responsibly pursue meaning and this sense of aliveness outside the closed system of their jobs are able to work with traumatized people while sharing their own fullness, meaning, and joy. The cycle of allowing work to deplete us and then intentionally refueling ourselves in healthy ways outside of work, often on a daily basis, may have been what Frankl meant when he challenged us to "endure burning."

We have seen a few caregivers suffering from compassion fatigue symptoms that seem to have been caused by working beyond their level of skill or training. Working with traumatized individuals, families, and communities is a highly skilled activity that requires many years of training in different areas. Trying to shortcut this process and prematurely work with trauma survivors can very easily overwhelm even the most seasoned of clinicians.

While there is no research into the effects of working beyond the levels of professional competency or providing services while suffering symptoms of stress, we believe that these factors contribute significantly to the frequency, duration, and intensity of compassion fatigue symptoms.

Sometimes practical trainings such as EMDR (Shapiro, 1989, 1995) or TIR (French and Harris, 1998) can have a powerful effect on the symptoms of compassion fatigue while bringing a sense of empowerment to master-level caregivers who were previously overwhelmed. However, they may also emerge from these trainings with an inflated sense of skill and potency and be tempted to practice even further beyond their level of competence. This scenario highlights the importance of good professional supervision during the developmental phases of one's career.

These professional and peer supervisory relationships can serve as excellent opportunities to share, and therefore dilute, the effects of secondary traumatic stress. Professional supervision is also reported to have an overall beneficial effect on compassion fatigue symptoms (Pearlman, 1995; Catherall, 1995), and seeking it out can be a form of self-care.

Every caregiver's self-care needs are different. Some will need to remain vigilant in the monitoring and execution of their self-care plans, while others may be able to maintain resilience with less effort. However, we strongly urge caregivers at any education level who specialize in working with trauma and trauma survivors to develop a comprehensive self-care plan. This plan should address and meet their individual needs for each of the areas discussed in this chapter. This self-care plan is like wearing a seatbelt while driving; it helps protect and buffer you from the symptoms of compassion fatigue in advance.

Because everyone is different, there are many different ways to achieve this refueling and revitalization. Some are more physical, some intellectual, and others involve artistic expression or spirituality. We must discover what works for us to sustain energy, optimism, and hope and practice it on a regular basis. Despite the wide variety of possible self-care activities that exist, we have found a number of things that consistently work for a majority of people. Listed below are the essential components of good self-care:

1. Regular (three times per week) exercise.
2. Good nutrition.
3. Good sleep hygiene.
4. Regular social activities.
5. Creative activities or hobbies.
6. Spiritual practices.

7. Professional enrichment.

One of the most important types of self-care we have noticed in our work with caregivers is a regular exercise regimen—no other single behavior seems to be as important as regular aerobic and anaerobic exercise. We encourage you to find time to gradually add each of these components to your life, not as a chore, but as something you enjoy that revives you.

It should be noted that care providers responding onsite to crisis situations, such as those caused by the events of September 11th, may have limited ability to do self-care. They may not have access to gymnasiums or exercise facilities, nutritious food and water may be scarce for a period of time, and it is doubtful that care providers deployed in situations of mass destruction will have access to their traditional support network.

While most trauma responders are a hardy and resilient breed, we simply cannot sustain the rigors of this depleting and intensive work without intentional concern for our own health and welfare. Finding ways to establish respite and sanctuary for ourselves, even in the most abject of circumstances, can have an enormous effect in minimizing our symptoms and maximizing our sustained effectiveness. Many responders have reported acts of kindness as simple as the gift of a bottle of water, a pat on the back, or an opportunity to share a meal with another responder as having a powerfully positive impact on their morale and energy during these difficult times.

Self-care is essential to ward off compassion fatigue. No matter the circumstances, each and every caregiving professional should find ways to engage in self-care and revitalization, or risk burning out and exhausting their ability to give light.

Case Study with Dr. Gentry: Myra

Myra was a thirty-six-year-old woman in early recovery from chemical dependency working as a residential counselor at a halfway house for women called A New Hope. She also resided at the house, which was located near downtown Portland.

Myra had been clean for the past five years and had a thirteen-year-old daughter named Sierra who lived with Myra's parents nearby. Since getting clean and divorcing her husband three years earlier (a heroin addict who was homeless in Los Angeles, last she'd heard), Myra had significantly repaired the relationships with both her parents and daughter. Myra had lost all visitation rights while she'd been using, but since getting clean she'd begun to spend several evenings a week having dinner with her parents and Sierra.

When she began meeting with me, Myra reported feeling positive about how far her relationships had come, and her plans to move into an apartment within the next year so Sierra could come and see her on the weekends. Myra had completed several years of college in her late teens and early twenties, but drug use had derailed her from graduating. She'd returned to school two years prior and only had one semester left before she'd receive her bachelor's degree in social work. Myra had also just found out she'd been accepted to a master's program through the same university, and would begin in the fall.

By Myra's account her life was going well, but when she looked at me during our first counseling session, her eyes were filled with tears. "I know the fact I'm alive is a miracle and that things are going amazing for me…so why do I feel so bad?"

Myra had contacted me after taking one of my Professional Resilience and Optimization courses through the treatment center, which was offered to all staff members at New Hope as a professional development resource for continuing education. She emailed me afterwards, asking if she could take advantage of the free thirty-minute consultation I offered to anyone who took one of my courses.

As we spoke during our initial telephone conversation, Myra described a steady decline in her mental health and quality of life over the past few years—shortly after she'd begun working at the halfway house and returned to school to finish her degree.

"I think I'm going crazy," Myra said to me over the phone. "I've even had thoughts about killing myself. But I don't want to die! I love my life. I'm on my way to getting everything I've ever wanted—I have my family back, I'm sober, I have a job, I'm doing well in school…" Myra then described the symptoms of fatigue, overeating, stress, irritability, and poor sleep she'd been experiencing, as well as generalized fear and a pervasive feeling of doom and hopelessness that never went away. "Should I see a psychiatrist? Do I need meds?"

"Possibly," I replied. "But there might be another option."

Myra was very reticent about taking psychotropic medication after her addiction, and avoided any drugs, even aspirin. "What's the other option?"

"I offer a two-day intensive treatment for the symptoms of compassion fatigue, which is what I think you might be experiencing. You can see if the treatment's helpful, and if not, then maybe it's time to consult a psychiatrist or medical professional for an evaluation."

"Okay…I'm definitely interested, but I don't want to rehash the past. I do enough of that with my sponsor," Myra said, continuing that she'd speak to her parents about whether they could help with the cost.

The next day she called to inform me that her parents had enthusiastically agreed to pay the fees and her travel expenses to come for the two-day intensive treatment. We scheduled it for a weekend later that month, and soon Myra was sitting across from me in our first session.

We began our work with an articulation and clarification of goals for our time together.

"I just want my fear to go away," Myra said, brown eyes wide and desperate. She believed her heightened fear and anxiety over the past eighteen or so months were at the root of all her other symptoms, and I agreed.

After having her complete the Pro-QOL, Adverse Childhood Experiences (ACE) Scale, and Trauma Recovery Scale, I learned from the assessment instruments that Myra had experienced some significant childhood trauma and had an ACE score of 4.

Her birth father was an alcoholic and had been prone to fits of rage. He'd hit Myra and her mother multiple times during her early childhood, and had ultimately been arrested for domestic violence. Myra's parents had divorced by the time she was seven, and her mother remarried when she was nine.

"I have a great relationship with my stepdad; he's always believed in me, even when everyone else gave up," Myra said, detailing the significantly stabilizing effect her stepfather had had on their family.

On the Pro-QOL, Myra had high scores for secondary traumatic stress, medium-high scores for burnout, and high scores for compassion satisfaction. Those numbers represented a very positive prognosis for compassion fatigue treatment, and I discussed the possibility that much of Myra's distress was work-related.

Finally, her Trauma Recovery Scale mean score was 65, which indicated that she had some moderate distress and impairment, but was still remaining functional. The scale also revealed that her most significant distress was focused around intrusion and arousal symptoms.

As I explained this to Myra, she became visibly more animated and relieved as she began to see that perhaps her symptoms were adaptations to her childhood and work trauma, rather than a confirmation that she was "crazy."

After completing the narrative process where I had Myra tell me her life story, we began working on understanding and then regulating her overcharged autonomic nervous system. As she practiced intentionally getting the muscles in her body relaxed, Myra tearfully looked at me and said, "*This* is what I was looking for every time I got high."

We soon concluded for the day, agreeing to adjourn until the next morning. On day two, we decided to do EMDR to help Myra desensitize and integrate some of the secondary traumatic stress that had been plaguing her. We got set up for the session, identifying Myra's feelings of dread when walking into A New Hope as the target.

As we began the eye movements, Myra started sobbing almost immediately. She described a very painful experience during rehab five years before regarding a very close friend named Jill. They'd been at the same halfway house and would attend meetings together every day.

"Jill was the first 'real' friend I ever had," Myra choked out through her sobs. After six sober months, Jill had relapsed and was killed a week later in a single car accident. "I believe she killed herself because she couldn't deal with the shame of using again… She couldn't handle facing all the people she thought she'd let down."

As we continued the EMDR process, Myra began to gain the insight that the trauma of losing Jill was intruding on her perception of every single resident she'd been working with at A New Hope. She was afraid that if she invested in them and believed in them, they—like Jill—would relapse and break her heart.

She said she'd completely pushed Jill out of her mind over the past couple years and hadn't even consciously thought about her for several months. Myra realized she'd done nothing to heal that pain, and as we went through the EMDR process, it became integrated (instead of suppressed) and she was able to feel longing and appropriate grief for the loss of the very first person she'd allowed to get that close to her.

As we went on, Myra started to retrieve amnestic memories of physical abuse from her father when she'd been five or six years old. She narrated several memories of his violent anger, and one of him choking her with his left hand while repeatedly slapping her in the face with his right.

"How could a father do that to his little girl? How could he hate me that much?" she whispered, wiping at the tears running down her cheeks. I had no answer for her.

As we finished our morning EMDR session, Myra described how she was having waves of compassion for herself and a growing sense of strength and resilience. "I've survived a lot of shit," she said. With tears in my eyes, I nodded in agreement.

We finished up the afternoon with her reading her mission statement, one that was focused equally upon service to others and self-care through her own recovery. She established principles of honesty, integrity, kindness, and self-acceptance, and points on her moral compass. Myra finished up the two days with the understanding that every time she violated her integrity, it was because she'd allowed her autonomic arousal to get too high and had acted compulsively. She was visibly brightened at the conclusion of our two-day intensive treatment and said she was excited to go back home and put into practice her new skills of self-regulation and intentionality.

We followed up two weeks later via videoconference, and Myra reported doing much better and feeling much lighter.

"Nothing has changed, but everything has changed," she observed poignantly during our follow-up call. Her life was still demanding and challenging, but she was now intentionally facing (instead of instinctively avoiding) these challenges armed with skills for resilience.

When I asked her about her depressive symptoms of hopelessness, fatigue, and suicidal ideation, Myra simply said, "I don't have time for that."

She also described how she'd started sharing the painful parts of her work with her sponsor and other women in recovery (after receiving their permission), to actively avoid accumulating secondary traumatic stress symptoms any longer.

She thanked me profusely and ended the conversation with this statement: "I'm very grateful to you, Eric, for all you've given me in our two days together. But I want you to know I'm *most* grateful for the gift you've given my daughter. Our work has helped me be more present, less angry, and allowed me to love her the way she deserves to be loved."

Chapter Summary

Compassion fatigue can occur in anyone who works alongside the suffering, and presents as negative effects resulting from this work and/or the perceived demands of the work environment. There are various models and programs such as the ARP and CCFST to assess and alleviate the symptoms of secondary traumatic stress and burnout associated with compassion fatigue, which is accomplished through a variety of resilience strategies and self-care.

The trauma-focused caregiver acquires these resilience skills in a variety of ways, all of which require diligent practice over time. The first step to developing personal resilience and being able to impart it to patients and clients is by understanding the concepts of perceived threat and its influence on the sympathetic nervous system (the fight-or-flight response). The most important facet of maintaining a regulated autonomic nervous system and preventing the sympathetic nervous system stress response is via specific and systematic muscle relaxation techniques that must be practiced regularly throughout the day.

Secondly, successful healers utilize the skills of intentionality, perceptual change, connection/support, and self-care to continually develop and enhance their resiliency. By becoming and remaining resilient, they are less symptomatic and more graceful in their work. They have a sense of purpose as they are able to engage in deep and powerful relationships with the people they help, and they are able to be compassionate, authentic, and congruent in their peer and client relationships. This congruency translates into the workplace, where integrity and personal maturation can flourish when self-regulation is maintained, connection and support systems are utilized, and self-care principles are regularly applied in the trauma-focused caregiver's daily life.

Chapter Three

Foundations of Trauma-Informed Care

Focus Questions:

- How did trauma-informed care emerge?
- What are the goals of trauma-informed care?
- What are the trauma-informed principles outlined by SAMHSA and NCTIC?
- As a caregiver, how do I start to practice trauma-informed care?

In this chapter you will learn more about:

- Defining trauma-informed care.
- The core principles (elements) that are central to trauma-informed care.

Trauma creates change you don't choose. Healing creates change you do choose.

– Michele Rosenthal

The History of Trauma-Informed Care

The trauma-informed care philosophy appeared as a result of research that began to highlight the long-term consequences emerging in the lives of people due to trauma. Medical doctors as early as 1985 began discovering that early-life traumas were impacting their adult patients negatively, and started thinking more in depth about what that might mean throughout someone's lifespan.

This discovery has emerged to the point that the World Health Organization (WHO) has proclaimed that a person's "mental health and many common mental disorders are shaped to a great extent by the social, economic, and physical environments in which people live" (2014, p. 8). We have long believed in American culture that the problem is "within the person," yet science has continuously shown that issues often arise due to environmental and relational factors.

This research can be found in studies like the Adverse Childhood Experiences (ACE) study, which pioneered an understanding of trauma's lifelong influence on health and well-being. Vincent Felitti, MD, and a representative from the Centers for Disease Control and Prevention (CDC) named Robert Anda, MD, began the ACE study in 1995 and discovered that both physical and mental health were easily compromised when individuals experienced a certain dosing of adversities, often labeled as developmental trauma, in their formative years.

The increasing amount of research regarding the symptoms of trauma ignited a shift in the field, as helping professionals recognize the importance of someone's developmental history in terms of retraumatization, possible reactivation of a traumatic history, and over-pathologizing of reactive adaptations due to a patient's prior trauma.

As a result of this shift and the increased understanding of trauma's lifelong impact, the National Center for Trauma-Informed Care (NCTIC) was founded in 2005. The NCTIC's overall mission was to change the culture of organizations so that they were not employing aversive interventions that activated a trauma history: "NCTIC uses a pragmatic, strengths-based approach to services and systems as well as to individuals, encouraging people to make whatever changes they can immediately, while also working toward long-range goals" (National Center for Trauma-Informed Care, 2012, p. 1). The NCTIC was created in conjunction with the Substance Abuse and Mental Health Services Administration (SAMHSA), and was later merged with SAMHSA's Strategic Initiative on Trauma and Justice to search for ways of treating individuals without reactivating their trauma histories.

From these humble beginnings a movement grew to provide better care in various mental health and primary care settings by taking a person's trauma history into account, and designing systems that didn't reactivate or retraumatize those seeking help.

The application of trauma-informed care has evolved into a language and thought process of trauma sensitivity in multiple settings. One such example of this sensitivity can be found in Massachusetts' school system, which created a program for educators on how to approach students' problematic behavior in regards to trauma: "As educators, we must be aware of the prevalence of trauma in the lives of the children in our schools. Children experiencing some type of trauma are likely to struggle in school with language and communication, attentiveness to classroom tasks, regulating emotions, and engaging in the curriculum" (Gilligan, 2011, p. 243). Massachusetts' initiative has helped to reduce mental health referrals, improved general educational outcomes, and increased the number of graduates overall.

Other areas where the philosophy of trauma-informed care has made an impact include the juvenile justice system, group homes, general mental and physical health services, the child welfare system, and even some community programs and corporate adoption agencies. Adopting a trauma-sensitive philosophy and incorporating it into daily practices can improve any organization with a focus on helping others, as the main elements include compassion, valuing human life, using nonjudgmental language, and viewing each individual as a collection of unique experiences to be engaged within creative, flexible, and accepting ways. Shame, criticism, or any form of humiliation are absolutely avoided in trauma-informed caregiving.

There are a host of writers who have composed lists of important elements for providing trauma-informed care. Two of the most common include a safe place, both emotionally and physically, and a helper who can prove themselves as trustworthy and reliable to the trauma survivor. Caregivers who communicate clearly, concisely, and set strong boundaries are received warmly by those they are helping. Several writers have also encouraged the creation and offering of choice in as many different aspects of treatment as possible, which requires a significant level of collaboration and capacity building between the caregiver and their patients or clients.

Trauma-informed care involves helping others with the mindset that everyone can heal and flourish, regardless of their history. It means that the helper believes that no matter how long someone has walked in the adversities of their own unfortunate past, they *can* move past it and live a life full of meaning and strength.

The NCTIC and SAMHSA are very clear in their four foundational criteria for classification as a trauma-informed and trauma-sensitive organization:

1. The recognition that trauma's impact is widespread, and that the consequences are felt throughout almost all human organizations. Also that whether a survivor's issues concern their physical health, mental health, or both, that reactive adaptations (those adaptations made in reaction to stress, arousal, or threat that manifest emotionally, physically, behaviorally, and with thinking) resulting from a history of adversity and trauma must be dealt with as part of any intervention.

2. An adequate awareness of the signs and symptoms of trauma in patients/clients, families, staff, and others involved within the system of care. Continued action in designing policies and operations to create a stable and compassion-oriented environment are pursued, with more focus on the process of healing than on punitive adherence to rigid policy and practice.

3. The implementation of knowledge into everyday practice. A trauma-informed organization not only trains their staff in providing quality trauma-informed care, but supports them in their daily practice of this approach.

4. Caregivers' deliberate avoidance of reactivation or triggering of traumatic memories in those being served. Healers are trained to avoid reactivation of trauma and understand the essential nature of this if their patients/clients are to prosper during treatment.

The Definition of Trauma-Informed Care

Trauma can be defined as anything that interrupts or interferes with the normal development of social, emotional, psychological, cognitive, spiritual, lingual, or physical processes. This interruption affects survivors physiologically, cognitively, behaviorally, emotionally, socially, and spiritually.

Many perspectives view the behavior resulting from trauma as an intentional act which, when rewarded or not, can be modified. This is a very limited approach, and one that does not include the principles we are advocating for in this text. Trauma-informed care recognizes that an undesirable behavior is the manifestation of an unmet need or a tool to relieve suffering that is been reinforced over time. In order to ameliorate it, the *whole person* requires attention throughout the healing process, and programs that focus on the origin of the presenting problem instead of the undesirable behavior itself are much more effective overall (Dezelic, Ghanoum, and Neale, 2016).

To define what makes care "trauma-informed," organizations such as the SAMHSA, the American Psychiatric Association (APA), the National Child Traumatic Stress Network

(NCTSN), the NCTIC, and the CDC have created their own criteria. Though there are small differences among them, all organizations require that practices attend not to the symptomology or the behaviors of the trauma survivor, but to the *person themselves*.

SAMHSA outlines three "R's" that define the goals of a trauma-informed approach as:

1. Realizing the impact that trauma has on personal and system-wide levels.
2. Recognizing the signs and symptoms of trauma within the system to avoid retraumatization.
3. Responding systematically through policies, procedures, and practices.

It also emphasizes the creation of an environment where empathy and compassion for one another is the norm, and enabling a community of individuals experiencing similar symptoms to support one another. This relational approach is common in rehabilitation centers, and allows trauma survivors to feel accepted and understood.

The APA requires that an organization consider the effects of trauma on behaviors and health. This includes an assessment of both the survivor and healer at the start of the process, so that both can gain awareness about their own biases and assumptions about the functions of behavior. This translates into the caregiver's ability to create safety for the client, and includes intentionality in language, empowering choice over compliance, and staying present in understanding the struggle of the survivor. Again, relationship and connection are prioritized over punitive measures.

The NCTSN requests that care addresses the totality of the healing system. Trauma-informed practice includes caregivers, children, peers, and service providers, all of whom are involved in the healing process. Education is integrated in all programming to increase understanding of the biological effects and overarching science behind trauma, which translates into an increased commitment to promote a stable therapeutic relationship and eliminate the potential for retraumatization.

Gabor Maté, a doctor specializing in childhood development, explained the relationship between parents who were not connecting with their children and the link to long-term symptomology in an interview: "The more stressed parents are, the more developmental problems you will find in kids" (as stated in Crowley, 2011, para. 2). Connection, control, choice, and trust must all be implemented in trauma-sensitive care for not only the families, but also the systems that serve them.

The guiding beliefs of the NCTIC are inclusive, and a diagnosis of mental health issues or substance use is not required for an individual or family to become a member. With the understanding that symptomology is not necessarily pathology, but adaptation to experiences, the NCTIC's focus is on meeting needs that the problem behavior is currently satisfying. Implementation of a structure throughout the healing process is led by peer supports. Families, professional caregivers, survivors, mentors, and those in recovery all make up the community, and this network increases the resiliency and effectiveness of the process before, during, and after healing.

The CDC looks to the ACE study for how trauma affects an individual's health over time, and has a significant influence over the standards of healthcare in America. Doctors assess early phases of treatment based off of the outcomes of the ACE assessment, and also provide education and prevention to communities that might be at risk. Their influence with policy has brought awareness to many factors that contribute to the downfall of a family's health and wellness.

According to these definitions, trauma-informed care allows for the professional caregiver, patients/clients, and their supports to come together as one, with a deeper understanding of how prior trauma influences current thoughts, feelings, and behaviors. When transparency and trust are promoted and retraumatization is avoided, individuals and organizations are able to connect with and support one another in a relationship that encourages resiliency, healing, and sustained growth.

Six Guiding Principles of Trauma-Informed Care

In addition to the four fundamental elements listed above, the NCTIC and SAMHSA require that specific principles be adhered to for identification as a trauma-sensitive organization. There are six philosophical principles that support trauma-informed care, and these practice beliefs are straightforward and imperative for good clinical practice, both within the organization as a whole and between an individual caregiver and their patients/clients:

1. **Safety:** Throughout the organization, staff and the people they serve feel physically and psychologically safe.

2. **Trustworthiness and Transparency:** Organizational operations and decisions are conducted with transparency and the goal of building and maintaining trust among staff, patients/clients, and family members of those receiving services.

3. **Peer Support and Mutual Self-Help:** The organization promotes peer support amongst

professional staff, between caregiver and patient/client, and for those seeking services. Opportunities for community involvement and stability are provided, and play an integral part in promoting the professional resilience of helpers while empowering and encouraging the helped.

4. Collaboration and Mutuality: There is a leveling of power differences between professional caregivers and patients/clients, and among the system of care's staff. The organization recognizes that everyone has a role to play, with the professional caregiver being more accessible and the helped being more participatory.

5. Empowerment, Voice, and Choice: The organization aims to strengthen the voices of the staff, patient/client, and family members, and recognizes that every person's situation is unique and requires an individualized approach. Instead of caregivers gravitating toward "fixing" individuals, the patients/clients are encouraged to be involved in their own recovery, and to have confidence in their ability to make choices that are personally beneficial.

6. Cultural, Historical, and Gender Issues: The organization actively moves past cultural stereotypes and biases (based on race, ethnicity, sexual orientation, age, geography, etc.), offers gender-responsive services, leverages the healing value of traditional cultural connections, and recognizes and addresses historical trauma.

Principle One: Safety

Since psychiatrist Judith Herman published her landmark book, *Trauma and Recovery*, in 1992, the mental health field has gained clarity on the need for safety and stabilization in trauma treatment. Far more than abstract concepts, these functional aspects of the treatment process help to provide safe, stable, nurturing relationships and environments so that recovery and healing can easily take place.

Safety has a great deal to do with the survivor's ability to predict, understand, and build a genuine connection to the caregiver. When a person experiences trauma—especially of high frequency or long duration—a natural shift occurs in the social engagement system of their brain (those areas that pick up interpersonal signals, including verbal and nonverbal; kinesics, proxemics, haptics, facial expression, and paraverbal communication; tone, volume, and cadence, etc.): it becomes biologically more difficult to trust. Stability is necessary in order to foster an environment of healing, and thrives when caregiving professionals, agencies, and organizations follow through on their promises to patients/clients and their families without judgment or criticism.

Those who wish to provide trauma-informed care must adopt a vision of assuring safety from the perspective of the *survivor*, not their own point of view. This promise of safety exacts a price on the healer—the sacrifice of their own ego, beliefs, and the value-based demands they might otherwise place on others.

A few years ago, a university held an event and offered a variety of health and wellness services and resources to its students. One of the agencies attending the event stated that they were solely dedicated to showing "love and compassion" toward young, pregnant women in financial difficulty. This organization held certain beliefs, however, that did not align with everyone. When several students asked the representatives what steps they would take if a young woman seeking their services did not agree with their particular beliefs, they said, "We'd try to convince her to accept them."

"And if she does not?" questioned the students.

"Well…then we'd feel she was lost, and beyond hope," answered the representatives.

Unfortunately, this type of response is not rare in regards to service offered by providers, and can leave those who need their help with feelings of alienation, guilt, shame, and even hopelessness. Many providers have an agenda, and feel driven by a personal sense of right and wrong that they have allowed to infiltrate the professional arena. Their attitudes and beliefs place extra demands on the already stressed and traumatized, and end up doing more harm than good in terms of healing.

The trauma-focused caregiver and trauma-informed organization understands how vital safety, stability, and the exclusion of judgment are when working with any trauma survivor seeking support and services.

What is Safety?

According to Merriam-Webster's online dictionary (2017), the term "safe" means to be "free from harm or risk," or "secure from threat of danger, harm, or loss." The perception of being safe is necessary for most types of meaningful human interaction, but *especially* therapeutic ones between a caregiver and a trauma survivor attempting to heal from their past.

Landes, Garovoy, and Burkman (2013) suggest that safety is an essential element in trauma treatment, and one that should be approached with an organized and policy-driven method or strategy. They designed a protocol called Skills Training in Affective and Interpersonal Regulation (STAIR) to facilitate a safe and stable environment for the client. The STAIR protocol is a form of CBT, though the initial phases of emotional awareness and emotional regulation are all about safety and stability.

Additionally, Kagan and Spinazzola (2013) suggest that safety requires attention to the environment, as well as an active, intentional, and deliberate management of all aspects of the service provision with those seeking to be helped. Kagan and Spinazzola state it is very unlikely that the patients and/or clients will perceive safety and become stable if the organization of services is not intentional, with deliberate decision-making by the professional caregiver.

Practical Ways to Create Safety

Creating safety begins with the thoughtful, deliberate practice of examining all therapeutic actions from the point of view of the person being helped. Many organizations have struggled with this due to a mindset steeped in economic proficiency and factory-level production, rather than the engagement and stabilization of the service seeker.

During a training workshop held in Oklahoma, our module went into safety and stabilization and we asked those attending whether they felt confident about their deliverance of such an environment.

"Of course my clients feel safe. They know I'm there to help them," said one therapist, to which several other participants nodded in agreement.

This was not an observation from the victim's perspective, but simply a report that the therapist felt safe, so their clients should as well. This is an egocentric view of safety, and one that is neither active nor deliberate in designing a stable treatment environment.

Another way of looking at the secure or safe environment comes from the work of Carl Jung, who suggested that the therapeutic frame is the "container" for the therapy experience (1907/1960). This frame is comprised of fixed "elements" for the therapeutic work—details like session times, the location they are held at, the way the office or building is decorated, etc.

These and other factors might seem small and insignificant in a general context, but for the traumatized individual they provide a sense of predictability and familiarity that is imperative for progress in treatment. Below are additional ways caregivers can create a safe environment, or "frame," which is conducive for healing:

1. Fully orient the patient/client. Describe the therapeutic process in detail to the person being helped. This process is often forgotten or ignored by agencies and organizations that are overly focused on presenting behaviors. In a well-meaning attempt to triage the immediate demands and dysregulation of the service seeker, these organizations skip or move quickly through the explanation part of the safety-creating process, which can result in greater dropout rates and less satisfaction with services.

A Balinese tale about Dewi Sri can provide guidance on how to help those seeking our services. The tale speaks of a young man who one day smelled cooked rice, which was the food of the gods. He approached Dewi Sri, the goddess of rice and prosperity, and asked for a taste, but instead of sharing the rice with him, she patiently taught him how to farm, harvest, and prepare the rice so he could feed his family for decades to come.

Orienting patients and clients before treatment is similar in nature to Dewi Sri's approach, in that preparing a person for action allows them to benefit the most from their endeavors. This builds a sense of hope and positive expectancy within them, and increases their capacity to trust the helper as each declared and achieved milestone is acknowledged throughout the treatment process.

2. Acculturate the patient/client. Acculturation creates a sequence, or process, through which the helped is likely to move. This involves exploring exactly what the nature of the organization's healing culture and processes are, and making it clear to the patient or client who they will be working with and how it will aid in their goals of recovery and wholeness.

The structure of treatment/appointments is discussed, as well as clinical rituals, routine paperwork, what movement through the treatment structure looks like, etc. It is important for caregivers to remind clients that every individual is unique, and to reiterate that although there are "norms" in treatment, however they choose to move through the process is correct for them.

A doctor at a family practice in North Carolina was especially skilled at acculturating his patients during appointments. At the start of any new intake, he would spend twenty minutes discussing his work methods and focus, and what he valued about his role as their doctor. Then he would dive into his philosophy on medications and medical procedures, and his viewpoint about natural, nonprescription approaches as the first avenue to explore for any diagnoses. This doctor's relationship development and explanations made it a very safe place for treatment, and his patients had the utmost trust in his abilities and feedback.

3. Believe the patient/client can and will improve. Safety can also be influenced by the caregiver's belief in the client's recovery. Many organizations claim to believe that people have the potential and possibility for relief, but often that is not clearly or consistently translated through their practices, language, or behaviors. Some might say that the compassionate heart is so wounded after hearing the traumatic story of another that they lose hope in the possibility of healing, but that does not occur in trauma-focused caregiving. The trauma-sensitive caregiver understands how *resilient* survivors are, and that certainty exudes from them during every therapeutic interaction.

4. Practice compassion/love of others. Safety and stability of the patient/client are greatly improved when the helper practices compassion and understanding.

A new counselor was receiving feedback from her supervisor about her shrinking caseload, who suggested she might try showing more compassion in sessions. "Perhaps your demands for client performance and results are beginning to overshadow your original desires to facilitate healing. They can create additional stress on your client, and might explain why they're not rescheduling with you," the supervisor said.

The counselor's response was reminiscent of her inexperience in the field, and her lack of comprehension about what trauma-informed care entails. "I can be compassionate and empathetic—as long as the client's doing what they should be doing."

Compassion is more than the fabricated pretending of care for someone else; it is an essential quality of character for those who desire to be healers. True compassion exceeds merely listening to someone and parroting back what they have just said. It involves being able to see into the world of another human being, and demonstrating that concern in an authentic way throughout a client's journey to recovery, regardless of how fast or slow it might be.

5. Practice empathy and attunement. Empathy is a vital skill and talent a caregiver must possess in order to help their patient/client feel safe. True empathy involves the intentional choice of being able to see things through the eyes of another and feeling connected to that individual. It is led by attunement, or the intuitive and reactive process a caregiver practices when relating to their client's emotional needs and moods. Dr. Theresa Wiseman (1996) outlines four defining attributes of empathy as:

1. The ability to see the world as others see it, not as we see it.
2. The ability to view others with a nonjudgmental mind frame.
3. The ability to understand the other person's feelings.
4. The ability to communicate to the other person that we understand their feelings.

Attunement is not possible when the helper has an agenda for the helped, nor is it sustainable unless the healer lets go of their own ego, demands, and personal schedule. An attuned and empathetic caregiver is dependable, protective, patient, and empowers their patients/clients to grow in all the primary domains of human life.

Principle Two: Trustworthiness and Transparency

Trustworthiness and transparency are two concepts vital to any sustainable, safe, and predictable relationship. According to Fallot and Harris in the newsletter *Trauma Psychology* (2008, p. 6), trustworthiness has much to do with consistency, and maintaining clear interpersonal boundaries. The newsletter also pointed out that explaining things in a meaningful way and providing a sensible, predictable order of operations enable a trauma survivor to trust in the healer and their competence.

Dependability is another attribute of trustworthiness, and is necessary to the successful application of healing principles and practices. It is interesting that something as divergent as Bushidō, the Japanese code of ethics for samurai life, should point the way to trustworthiness and transparency. One of the code's most important paragons includes living a life that holds "loyalty, courage, veracity, compassion, and honor as being important, above all else." Interestingly, these characteristics are the very foundation of trustworthiness and transparency in a healer as well.

Practical Ways to Display Trustworthiness and Transparency

The methods for building trust and transparency are simple, but require dedication and a commitment to the therapeutic relationship that transcends any discomfort the caregiver may feel when setting aside their ego and lowering any protective walls.

1. Be reliable. As part of the process of healing and recovery, those seeking help must be able to rely on the helper to follow through on what they claim they will do. That reliability can exist in many different ways, but it needs to be an ever-present part of any therapeutic relationship. A small act of reliability, for example, could be a service provider calling every other Friday at the same time, like they have promised to do. It is not a huge act, but communicates to the patient/client that the provider can be trusted.

2. Follow through on assignments, ideas, and expectations of the patient/client. When working with trauma survivors, they often experience fear and confusion throughout the process. To mitigate this anxiety, helpers must make every effort to complete the assignments they accept and meet the expectations they have created with the patient/client.

3. Do not make excuses if you fail or forget. This is where transparency comes in, and though it may go against your natural inclination, owning the mistake and apologizing will always go further than an excuse. Human error is unavoidable, and being honest with your clients will serve to strengthen the authenticity of the therapeutic relationship and "level the field" between caregiver and trauma survivor.

4. Be honest and avoid omission. Honesty during treatment represents maturity and confidence in one's practice, and the ability to stay focused on the welfare of others. Untruths or omissions can rupture a fragile therapeutic alliance, and are often the result of fear or defensiveness in the caregiver.

5. Speak from your core of authenticity. Sometimes professional caregivers get caught up in ego self-protection, or "impression management." They are invested in appearing a certain way to fellow employees or clients, and that interferes with their genuineness and authenticity. Allowing others to see you for who you *really* are (including fears, biases, patterns, and struggles) is an essential part of transparency.

One of the more interesting experiences we have encountered while training caregivers, especially counselors, is that some of them adopt a stiff "professional voice" when it comes to their work. In one particular instance, a graduate student who had adopted this style of speaking was having a hard time being relational with those he served.

We suggested that he affect similar tonal qualities in his professional interactions to ones he would use when speaking to his pet. The content of his conversations remained the same, but the tonal shift led to a transformation that was truly remarkable to watch. Once his clients felt he was approachable and transparent (rather than distant, judgmental, and uncaring), his effectiveness and efficiency in treatment skyrocketed.

6. Volunteer information that could be useful or helpful. In the field of mental health, many new therapists are terrified to say anything to a patient/client about their own beliefs, biases, or history. Vogel and Wei (2005) found that self-disclosure promoted the formation of a strong, healing relationship, while withholding information adversely impacted treatment.

7. Prepare all transitions before they arrive. Have an awareness of where people are going to have to shift or move as they begin and then proceed through the process of healing. Help them recognize and prepare for transitions, possible sticking points, or situations that might present an increased challenge to them.

8. Work daily to increase competence. This is a deliberate practice where the caregiver is constantly refining their capacity to bring healing to others. Developing one's character and honesty with others is an intentional and deliberate practice, with lots of room for growth.

Principle Three: Peer Support and Mutual Self-Help

Peer support and mutual self-help are very impactful modes of healing when conducted through a trauma-informed lens. Peer counseling and therapeutic communities have been an important part of the healing process in addiction programs since the early 1970s, with Dr. George De Leon writing extensively on these concepts as well as the modality of community as a "method" (1994). There has been recent evidence that peer support is associated with positive effects on hope, recovery, and empowerment, both at and beyond the completion of the intervention (Bellamy, Schmutte, and Davidson, 2017). Repper and Carter (2011) found that recovery was facilitated through peer support and self-help-type support groups. From a purely physiological perspective, there is a good reason why this might be so: the relational system, or the "social engagement" system of the body, is an access point to increase healthy physical functioning as well as to heal from trauma. Peer support is an established relationship that has healing properties.

There have been many recent studies exploring the "critical ingredients" of peer support, with findings suggesting both structure and process standards are two of them (Holter et al., 2004; Solomon, 2004; Hardiman, 2004). Structural standards are elements of peer initiatives that define the basic rules and how the group is constructed. They include being free from coercion (i.e., voluntary), consumer-run and directed (both governmentally and programmatically), and having an informal setting with a flexible, nonhierarchical, and non-medical approach (i.e., not diagnosing, etc.) (Solomon, 2004; Salzer, 2002; Holter et al., 2004; Clay, 2004; Campbell, 2004; Hardiman, 2004). Process standards are more like beliefs, styles, and values, and they include:

1. The peer principle (finding affiliation with someone with similar life experience and having an equal relationship).
2. The helper principle (the notion that being helpful to someone else is also self-healing).
3. Empowerment (finding hope and believing that recovery is possible; taking personal responsibility for making it happen).
4. Advocacy (self and system advocacy skills, choice and decision-making opportunities, skill development, positive risk-taking, reciprocity, support, sense of community, self-help, and developing awareness) (Campbell, 2004; Clay, 2004).
5. Peer support as a mindset and a way of being with people.
6. Peer support opportunities being created in a practical way.

We know from decades of psychotherapy research that "what is healing" has little to do with a particular therapeutic approach and everything to do with the relationship, trust, and connection between the person seeking help and the caregiver. Understanding, empathy, and intimacy are central "ideas in action" that help to create and deepen the meaning and strength of these therapeutic relationships.

Many hear the word "intimate" and begin to feel a little uncomfortable, but we are using it in the context of meeting the needs of those looking for help in an authentic way and offering them real contact and relationship. We are not recommending a "top-down" relationship between therapist and patient, but instead advocating for a co-created relationship that philosopher Martin Buber described as an "I-Thou" meeting of minds (1929/1958).

Once we as helpers realize we are not the agents or brokers of change in others, but merely facilitators offering real love, understanding, and support, the relationship between us and our patients/clients will change dramatically. We do not come to the meeting looking to change our clients through coercion or manipulation, but rather to build a co-relationship where felt trust and support allows for them to re-experience their past traumas in a way that promotes proper integration and desensitization, and encourages new relational support.

Meeting another person in their place of pain and struggle and offering nonjudgmental support and relational understanding is the foundation that creates the space for healthy dialogue, while providing patients and clients with a new source of internal strength and encouragement.

Practical Ways to Facilitate Peer Support and Mutual Self-Help

To accomplish the relational objective of peer support and mutual self-help, we must come to our clients with several important perspectives that dictate how we interact. Instead of committing to a theory of change that directs the outcome, we prioritize the process of relationship, contact, and support, acknowledging that change is inevitable when those are present.

1. Hold an all-encompassing view of the patient/client's disorder. In a relational, trauma-informed care model, we do not assume that the problem, addiction, or discontent resides solely within the individual. We always consider the whole environment and situation, including someone's cognitive, behavioral, emotional, physical, and social health in regards to their needs for healing. Trauma *can* occur alone on the side of a mountain, but it is usually a social event with an impact that carries on in our social lives. It is within this social realm and interaction that healing can also take place.

2. Have a greater awareness of yourself and others. The goals of peer support and mutual self-help are global changes in one's lifestyle, identity, and developmental process. There is a clear comprehension that recovery and healing are enabled through self-awareness, self-compassion, and acceptance of one's present experience.

3. Maintain certain ideals about "right living." These ideals include:

· Truth and honesty.

· Living in the here and now.

· Personal responsibility for self and what is co-created with others.

· Social responsibility (brother's or sister's keeper).

· Moral codes concerning right and wrong (categorical imperatives).

· Recognition that the inner person is good, even though behavior might be harmful.

· Change is the only certainty.

· A belief in "learning" to learn.

· Community involvement.

· Good citizenry (De Leon, 1997).

4. Take a* nonjudgmental *stance. Coming to a relationship without *any* judgments is impossible, and we want each of you to really understand this. When we talk about a nonjudgmental relationship, we are not saying that healers do not bring their ideas, histories, and concepts of "right living" to the interaction—we all have our subjective notions about honesty, morals, and so on. The nonjudgmental stance in a peer support modality has to do with how we treat others *with differing ideas and experiences from us*.

We are also not talking about the acceptance of things we do not like, know are harmful or immoral, or simply disagree with. We are referring to the recognition that the patient/client is coming to us as they are, with their own ideas about what is right and wrong, moral or important. We are to meet each struggling person with an open heart and mind, creating something together in the present moment that is meant to help them heal. Real friends tell each other what they think and feel. Real friends maintain the relationship through the good and the bad, and *this* is the nonjudgmental stance helpers must strive for and support.

Once the relationship is created, we might say to a patient/client, "Taking drugs seems harmful to you. You've described—and I can see—how it's negatively impacted your life. As your friend, I want to share this thought with you and support you in making better choices. If you don't make the choices I'm suggesting, I'm still here as your friend and support, always offering relationship."

The first sentence starts with the judgment, "Drugs seem harmful to you." It is not a judgment about who they *are*, or whether we approve or disapprove of the behavior. This is an important distinction. We are saying that we care about that person's well-being and want them to feel better and make safer decisions. Additionally, we are letting the individual know that no matter what they decide to do, we will remain a friend and a support to them regardless.

Our job is to see others for who and where they are in the moment, through relationship and dialogue, and let them know they are not alone. Through this support, the hope is that patients and clients will try healthier methods and ideas, while "throwing out" those that have not worked for them.

Principle Four: Collaboration and Mutuality

Collaboration and mutuality grew out of dissatisfaction with the medical community, and have since spread to many professional arenas including mental health, physical recovery, and resiliency programs. Alan Bleakley, PhD (2014) posits that collaboration and mutuality are absolutely fundamental to trauma-centered medical practice and care. In his book *Patient-Centred Medicine in Transition: The Heart of the Matter*, Bleakley proffers basic building blocks (Bleakley, 2014, p. 81) for this transition from a "therapist/patient" relationship to one of coordination, mutual involvement, and equality:

1. Patients are the catalysts or activators of change, and drive the healing process.
2. The foremost aspect of treatment is a sense of attachment or relationship between healer and the healed.
3. Therapeutic alliance is essential.
4. Treatments/interventions must be locally focused, fitting into the life and system of the patient.
5. The healer's role is one of building and encouraging capacity and competence in the patient.
6. The healer is the advocate when advocacy is needed, and the focus is on the good of the patient rather than systemic demands.

Practical Ways to Facilitate Collaboration and Mutuality

Gratton and Erickson suggested that the greater the complexity of the task, the less collaborative people become: "Members of complex teams are less likely—*absent other influences*—to share knowledge freely, to learn from one another…to help one another complete jobs and meet deadlines, and to share resources…" (2007, p. 102). This has often been the case in traditional mental health settings. When we move into the realm of the paraprofessional, however, we see that they often collaborate more effectively than the highly educated professional mental health worker.

Some of the practical methods for collaboration were covered thoroughly in our section on the first principle of safety, in regards to the orientation and acculturation process of relationship building between caregiver and patient/client. It is vitally important that the helped individual feels they are respected, cared for, and cared about, and this is more clearly conveyed when they know what is happening, why it is happening, and who will be most involved in their recovery.

Collaboration also has a great deal to do with the emergence of hope and faith on the part of the helped, due to the respect they are receiving, the belief others have in them, and the positive expectations they have begun to form about their potential for being healthy and whole.

Principle Five: Empowerment, Voice, and Choice

Empowerment, at its most basic level, means to increase one's ability to choose with intentionality so that they can deliberately act on that choice to obtain personally relevant goals. Additionally, this creates a greater internal attunement to their strengths and weaknesses without overly focusing on those weaknesses.

Stepping away from the written descriptions of empowerment that have circulated and been popularized today, we might say that as a character trait, it is simply the act of being kind to others. Those who practice kindness seem to be competent at expressing things in ways that encourage others, making them feel valued and possessed of worth. Most people are profoundly affected when they meet a truly kind person, and the insights and values of kind people tend to attract and draw others to them.

Empowering others means that you are not criticizing them, judging them, or making the assumption that they are doing all they can and there is no room for growth and betterment. Human kindness is often visible through the expression of praise, even when the success was a small one or required work to see. Kindness also asks that a person set aside the ego that directs so much of their daily life and allows themselves and others to just *be*, without the demands of the normative or "socially acceptable."

Practical Ways to Promote Empowerment

Helpers can support the development of empowerment in their patients and clients in a number of ways, all of which build off the previous principles of transparency, peer support, and mutuality:

1. Avoid the use of jargon or complex terminology.
2. Focus on the words patients and clients use, matching their language and usage as much as is reasonable.
3. Choose positive words.
4. Create statements that give choice to the helped.
5. Avoid criticism and negativity.
6. Use open questions when appropriate.
7. Assume that the helped have the capacity to grow.
8. Validate concerns and fears.

Having the Voice and Making the Choice

Oftentimes large agencies and service providers agree in principle that an individual seeking services should have a voice in the decision-making, but the value of those choices is unappreciated when the organizations limit the options available. Offering complete autonomy to patients and clients assumes that they have the capabilities to recognize what is correct for them, and that is a very empowering act.

Any time we offer a choice, we have to be willing to accept it. Nothing ignites people's dissatisfaction more than having a choice taken away, or being ridiculed for the choices they have made. Caregivers and organizations need to create opportunities for the individual to have choice, and encourage the expression of that choice as progress in their recovery.

Principle Six: Cultural, Historical, and Gender Issues

Merriam-Webster (2017) defines culture as "the integrated pattern of human knowledge, belief, and behavior that depends upon the capacity for learning and transmitting knowledge to succeeding generations; the customary beliefs, social forms, and material traits of a racial, religious, or social group; the characteristic features of everyday existence (as diversions or a way of life) shared by people in a place or time; the set of shared attitudes, values, goals, and practices that characterizes (a group)."

Put another way, culture is the social container that holds our shared experience, our heritage and history, our beliefs, and more: it is a group's way of being, from generation to generation. It includes communication styles, both lingual and physical, it establishes the basic "rules" by which relationships, gender roles, and familial structures are established and maintained, and it determines what is socially acceptable and what is "taboo." Culture shapes the way a group understands and communicates its history and interprets its experience. Therefore, culture exerts a powerful influence on a person or community's experience of trauma, and the path toward healing. The trauma-informed professional will seek to understand their own cultural context and that of others, and will respect the differences among groups as they utilize the resources of a client's particular culture to offer trauma-informed care. The healing professional will have a need and desire to step into the world of another and understand the realities of that world without judgment or criticism, using what is found there to help survivors build a pathway to recovery and health.

The Free Dictionary (2016) defines history as "a chronological record of events, as of the life or development of a people or institution, often including an explanation of or commentary on those events." While history may seem to present itself as a factual recounting of what happened to a person or community, it is shaped by culture, social location and belief systems, along with a myriad of other factors that may not be openly recognized or acknowledged.

It is often said that "the winners write history." And whether the identity of the group of which you are a part has a history shaped by "winning" or "losing," it is important to acknowledge and examine the role that history may play in any past or emerging trauma narratives. One of us witnessed such an example of historical trauma during a trip with a colleague:

> "I was traveling overseas with an African American colleague who received a phone call from home that his young daughter had been caught spray-painting a culvert wall with her friends. A cranky neighbor phoned the police, who came and spoke to the girls. While they were waiting for the parents to pick up the children, they placed the colleague's daughter inside the police car out of the hot sun.

The girls got a warning and were asked to help wash the paint from the wall, before being taken home. When my colleague heard this story from his spouse, he immediately cut his trip short and flew home. He was devastated by this mischievous incident, and fought back tears while sharing it with me.

'As a white American, you probably feel that this was an upsetting but essentially harmless learning experience for a kid. But as a black man, the image of my child in a police car…' my colleague said, becoming so deeply upset he could not continue.

The history of slavery and its aftermath, systemic racism, and perceptions around improper use of force by police toward African Americans contributed to feelings of shame, rage, and impotence that made this event a traumatic one for my colleague, whereas for me, it would have been concerning, but not devastating."

The following case study will further illuminate the role culture and history play in supporting the healing work of the trauma-informed caregiver. Following Super Typhoon Haiyan which devastated the Visayas region of the Philippines in 2013, one of us traveled on a solidarity visit with survivors and a local organization that was engaged in supporting the disaster recovery:

"Prior to the visit, the headquarters of the disaster recovery office that would be hosting us sent over a twelve-page document to help orient their visitors to the history, practices, and cultural norms of the Filipino people. The document offered a brief overview of the weather, geography, languages, and ethnic groups that constituted the Philippines—basic visitor information available in any guidebook, but knowledge a traveler is always grateful to receive before embarking.

The document then briefly reviewed the history, both economic and political, that had shaped that nation. The Philippines was a nation of islands with historically separate and sometimes competing tribal groups. Any of those islands and groups had frequently endured attacks and suffered domination from powerful nation-states, and when those occupation periods ended, they left behind languages, cuisines, practices, stories, and relationships that became a part of the tapestry of the islands and the nation it would become. Those 'outside' factors also included the trauma of war and strife, and the memories of shame, fear, and pain that accompanied such experiences.

The description included an overview of U.S. military intervention and domination in the region. There was no judgment nor commentary offered, but the information provided helped our group, all from the U.S., to be self-aware that although we saw ourselves as engaged in a relationship of compassion and healing accompaniment with the survivors of the typhoon, there was a history of colonial domination between our peoples that could interfere with our efforts to help, and at the very least would color the interactions between us and our disaster recovery leader. In order to be effective on the survivors' path to recovery, we needed to understand the history and habits of the people, and practice humility and respect for their self-determination and choice.

The document went on to offer a 'mosaic of culture' describing the many religions, ethnic groups, foreign influences, and some of the cultural etiquette and practices that would help our group become 'perfect strangers,' receiving and practicing hospitality in a place whose ways were unfamiliar to us. It stated that the Western practice of the familiar use of first names with acquaintances would be perceived as disrespectful, especially when used with someone of status, or an elder. What we might have reasonably assumed was a way to connect with a person after trauma—using their name and sharing our own—could've easily been misunderstood and prevented our connecting in a healing manner.

It was also shared that to encounter men urinating against a wall or by a roadside, burping, or spitting in public was not rude, but culturally acceptable. Behavior that we might have interpreted as indicating distress or traumatization was actually customary.

This document, offered with an open heart and spirit, supported our group in being a healing presence, and prevented us from making some incorrect assumptions about behaviors we were witnessing. It helped us to not make cultural missteps that would've interfered with our desire to offer trauma-informed care and exercise compassion.

Throughout the visit I found myself viewing the Filipino people through the corrective lens offered by my hosts, and wondered, *what would it be like if every time I walked with a traumatized person, I could look through the lens that would help me understand their worldview and ways more clearly?*"

Principles to Keep in Mind for Cultural Sensitivity

Not every trauma-informed caregiving situation comes with such comprehensive instructions as the ones mentioned above, but there *are* principles any healing professional can follow to refine their abilities in conducting culturally sensitive encounters:

1. Power. Remember that the survivor of trauma has had their sense of safety, control, and power taken away, perhaps violently. As a professional caregiver, you may be perceived as having more power than the person you are seeking to help. Based on your gender, size, age, education, background, etc., you may be unconsciously communicating a power dynamic that does not promote self-determination and empowerment for wholeness. Communicating confidence and positive expectancy is not the same as communicating that you are an expert who knows better than they do what they need to be healthy and whole.

2. Protection. Ask yourself what social structures, connections, and surrounding environmental factors contribute to the trauma survivor's sense of safety and normality. How can you as the healing professional reinforce a sense of safety by your stance, location, vocal tone, and eye contact? During a session, ask the patient/client, "What can we do, right here and now, that will help you feel safe?"

3. Practices. While the effects of trauma are physiologically and psycho-spiritually demonstrable, the notion of "being traumatized" (and particularly PTSD) is viewed as a Western construct. Though that is changing, many cultures in the Global South and developing countries express reactions to violence very differently. The pathologizing of trauma that is common in the U.S. and Europe and the dependence on psychotherapeutic approaches is strange to many people in other cultures. The experience of war, rape, displacement, loss of life, or injury to self or loved ones *is* traumatic, but the degree to which particular traumatic experiences are encoded or perceived by the survivor as disabling may vary widely depending on cultural context. Furthermore, trauma and grief may look different in different cultures and contexts. Ask patients and clients, "Can you help me understand how you express _________(sadness, joy, fear, etc.)?"

Much of the cultural personality that emerges in each community is reliant on these accepted general belief systems, even when the practice of those beliefs are slightly different from home to home. Culture influences how emotions are expressed and even how people communicate or give advice to one another on how to be healthy. What this loosely translates to is a sense of held beliefs some might call a "ready-made" set of solutions for problems that members of the community experience (Seibert, Stridh-Igo, and Zimmerman, 2002).

Trauma as an experience will then almost always be embedded in the cultural beliefs of the community, as well as to inform which treatment approaches would be acceptable. The responsibility of the paraprofessional healer is to ensure that the healing process and treatment that is delivered and used goes beyond being sensitive to an individual's culture to the actual *inclusion* of cultural beliefs and practices to bring about peace, restore balance, and increase resiliency.

Cultural sensitivity requires a true look at the unique nature of the individual, family, or group engaging in healing or recovery. This search for uniqueness opens the heart of the caregiver to greater levels of compassion and empathy, and marginalizes the assumptions and tendencies to overlay someone's healing process with our demands, expectations, or projections.

It is important to also realize that culture is a dynamic process, one that is continually adapting to the environment and the people in that environment. Immigration is a great teacher of this principle—when families that have been separated for many years are able to reassociate, there are many familiar and immediately apparent similarities, but there are equal numbers of differences that have grown into the culture during the intervening time. Over time, perceptions of health, illness, death, and what it means to suffer adapt, as does the family's rituals and customs.

Effective support and healing requires one to understand and be able to utilize the culture within which the trauma survivor lives and functions. It is unfortunate that many caring and heart-led people reach out to the hurt and wounded to bring relief, but do so from a culturally egocentric perspective that can lead them to underutilize those things that could be most helpful, while overutilizing behaviors, thoughts, or approaches that actually hinder the healing process.

The following items are modified from the work of Seibert, Stridh-Igo, and Zimmerman (2002) as points of learning that help with cultural sensitivity and understanding:

· The patient/client's theory of why things have happened the way they have.

· The patient/client's theories on illness and health.

· What the individual's cultural identification means to them.

· The way they view or see their traumatic situation.

· Their religious/spiritual beliefs.

· Which healing process the individual/family feels is acceptable and trusts.

· Make certain not to over-promise in your optimism to be helpful.

· Conduct evaluations or assessments with cultural sensitivity in mind, watching for biases and inaccuracies.

Questions to Ask Yourself and Others

In conjunction with these principles of cultural sensitivity, there are questions healing professionals should ask themselves during patient/client interactions to promote a strong therapeutic relationship and avoid alienation.

1. What are the basic ways of communicating in this culture/religious group? Caregivers should communicate using their clients' preferred methods, including things like culturally relevant stories and examples, metaphors that are consistent with the understanding of the helped, and utilizing functional aspects of communication held as common practice within the cultural belief system. In Arizona, for example, the Navajo Nation is more focused on family, clan, or the collective group rather than individualistic egocentric communication, and to maintain direct eye contact with them during conversation could be considered invasive and bordering on rudeness.

Recently, one of us was co-facilitating a trauma-informed care workshop in Kenya. Allow him to explain his experience learning new ways that some cultures communicate:

> "As part of the process of teaching self-regulation in this workshop, I was invited to share with a colleague sitting nearby a narrative of painful work experiences. After describing the exercise, I heard nervous giggles, and watched the body language of the group attendees become closed down and resistant.
>
> Trying to interpret those cues, I asked, 'Is everything okay?'
>
> One of the Kenyan attendees explained that sharing negative experiences, especially those that might be perceived as failures, was uncomfortable for their culture, almost taboo. 'It's like exposing my nakedness,' he said quietly.
>
> Those of us conducting the workshop had had no way of knowing this going in to our regular teaching agenda. Because of that interaction, we were able to learn more about the Kenyans' general communication style and tailor our teaching structure to be more effective for them."

2. How are gender roles understood, and what are acceptable interactions between and within genders? Many cultures, even subcultures and indigenous groups within North America and Europe, have strict social rules governing interaction between different gendered persons. Rules about social distance, touch, eye contact, and how to approach a married or unmarried person (especially female) can be unstated publicly, while observed strictly by the entire community. When in doubt, ask, and whenever possible, match genders when working in trauma care.

3. What physical cues will help you communicate respect and empathy? Observe the social distance practiced by the group with which you are engaged. What is the customary social space between individuals? What kind of eye contact is customary? Is touch taboo or permitted? Do differing or special rules exist between people of the same gender, of different genders? As much as possible, pay attention to cues from the other person, and match your stance to theirs. If you do not understand, ask. If you make a mistake, apologize.

4. What is ethically appropriate and socially acceptable behavior? In the Philippines, U.S. responders noticed while interviewing typhoon survivors in their village that they might giggle or laugh at what seemed like an inappropriate time. It was remarked later that Filipinos giggled when they were happy or pleased, but also when nervous, embarrassed, or confused.

Additionally, responders engaged in some joint project development with their Filipino colleagues noticed that no one ever disagreed with a presented idea, but following what seemed like an agreement, no action would take place for months.

When the responders were finally able to discuss the continued delay in project development, the local community shared that in their culture, it was rude to say "no" to anyone, and to disagree directly with the U.S. partners would be considered a publicly shaming act.

The Filipino colleagues had thought their U.S. partners understood that their "yes" had really been a "no"—they had sent the appropriate verbal and nonverbal cues in accordance with Filipino customs, and were puzzled as to why the same issue kept being brought forth by the U.S. responders.

Understanding what is socially permissible and how to politely work through a misunderstanding is an important skill for the trauma-informed healing professional.

5. What resources and approaches for healing are practiced in this setting? Trauma healing has universal elements, but it also features elements that are particular to a person or the community's own cultural context. Trauma-informed caregiving walks attentively alongside that person or community, building trust and demonstrating respect in ways that support those natural and cultural resources for health already present. If those resources are available to the patient/client it may be helpful to invite attention to them, and attempt to understand and embrace them as a part of the healing process.

6. How does culture shape the healing process? Writing in a compendium of psychosocial reflections following the war in the former Yugoslavia, Alastair Ager, PhD, described four phases of potential response to traumatized communities (Ager, 1997, p. 73). These phases are on a continuum, from the lowest level of community disruption to the most severe:

1. Minimal disruption of intact protective influences.
2. Reinstitution of protective influences.
3. Provision of compensatory support.
4. Targeted therapeutic intervention.

The phases, particularly the first two, provide a helpful framework for the nonclinical healer to understand the positive values of indigenous cultural resources and to support/reinforce such factors while providing care following trauma.

Avoiding Assumptions and Preserving Cultural Resources

The United Nations Research Institute for Social Development (UNRISD) describes "protective influences" or "protection" as preventing, managing, and overcoming situations that adversely affect people's well-being. Protection may include policies and programs designed to reduce poverty and vulnerability, diminishing people's exposure to risks, and enhancing their capacity to manage economic and social risks such as unemployment, exclusion, gender discrimination, sickness, disability, and old age.

Indigenous networks and understandings—that is, the way local people naturally connect for mutual support and what they know or believe to be true about the world, themselves, and their community—are powerful resources for healing and wholeness after trauma. Some of the common cultural influences that traditionally support wholeness and spiritual well-being are:

1. Family structures.
2. Meanings (spiritual, cultural, familial).
3. Networks.

Regardless of whether the healer personally understands, supports, or values those local structures, meanings/values, and networks, if they are valued by the traumatized person as a part of the "before" world of meaning, the healer should seek to preserve and safeguard those resources. It is vital for trauma-informed professionals to reserve judgment and "bracket" the assumptions that come from their own value system and cultural presuppositions, and not to impose these judgments on the one being supported.

During a trauma-informed care training in South Sudan, one of us was reacquainted with a young staff member of the South Sudanese disaster recovery organization co-sponsoring the workshop:

> "I'd met this particular staff member in a previous training, and had been impressed with her insight, intelligence, and commitment to the well-being of her people. When I saw her at the next one, she spoke of how glad she was that we had returned to share this information with a larger group.
>
> 'I'm happy to be here, and looking forward to working with all of you over the next two days,' I responded.
>
> The animation in her face fell away then, and she said, 'I won't be in the training with you. I'll be attending a nearby women's bible study.'
>
> Assuming that the bible study was primarily a support group, I pressed on, saying how much she'd contributed to the previous training, and how I hoped she'd benefit professionally and personally from the training we'd be conducting. She nodded, smiled, and embraced me—before disappearing for the duration of our training time.
>
> South Sudan is a strongly patriarchal, traditionally tribal society, and after twenty years of war and with continuing ethnic conflict, pushing this very well-educated and professional woman to violate the social norms of her culture regarding gender roles was inappropriate. Additionally, any benefit she may have received from the training would surely have been lessened by the discomfort of her male colleagues and herself, as well as the loss of social support being made available to her in that infrequent gathering of the women of her country.
>
> Those community structures formed part of the web supporting the well-being of her fragile new country and its leadership, or 'intact protective influences.' My invitation to her, though well-intentioned, was rooted in gender assumptions and practices that were familiar to *me*, but that did not recognize the differences in our cultural identities. The result of my request could've been harmful, rather than healing, for the entire group."

The trauma-informed healer who seeks to be effective in a different cultural setting will "walk alongside" survivors, tabling their own cultural assumptions and values. They will listen with their entire body: eyes, ears, and heart. They will ask questions and listen respectfully to the answers, and only *then* will they offer and practice trauma-informed care that reinforces existing community structures, meanings, and common practices, even when those practices differ from their own. Of course, this is sound practice even when working with trauma survivors from our own communities.

Caregiving after trauma is rarely the appropriate setting to attempt to engage in social reform or to amend a person's worldview, even if we think their world needs changing. When social and cultural structures have been compromised by communal trauma or conflict, it is appropriate to seek ways to restore and support those structures so the trauma survivor has something familiar to rely on as they rebuild their world. If that is not possible—for example, if the trauma has resulted in the rupturing or displacement of existing familial connections—helping the survivor to engage with an alternative support community can compensate, in the short term, for the loss of those connections.

Presently, there are thousands of women and children refugees from Central America who have been incarcerated for months in detention centers in the U.S.'s southwest region. Many have fled violence, been separated from their families, and endured further trauma during the passage north and following their detainment by immigration. Bereft of their families, churches, and neighborhood connections, many have formed alternative familial groups with other detained women and children whose stories are like their own. While not replacing what has been lost, the establishment of connections with other detainees creates a social and cultural resource. Caregivers and caseworkers visiting with these women and children should seek to support such relationships, and if the women are released, attempt to promote additional support through volunteers and housing programs.

When possible, building compensatory support for survivors should be done in consultation with the trauma survivor and knowledgeable indigenous leadership, who will then deepen their own ownership and participation in the healing of themselves and their community. All too frequently, well-meaning organizations allow their personal beliefs or viewpoints to dictate where they feel financial resources should go, as was the case for one of us when he participated in a disaster relief project:

> "In the midst of a multi-year project supporting refugee families fleeing war in a neighboring country, it was suggested to our disaster response team that we commit substantial funds to renovating a school into a temporary apartment building for five displaced families. We argued that the funds could support many more families if we instead gave them to a nearby, state-of-the-art United Nations refugee settlement. We could 'save' more families if we did it our way!

Our partners suggested—more gracefully than we probably deserved—that families forced to flee war and then placed in a refugee setting where they were isolated, dependent on handouts, and surrounded by the religious group whose aggression had displaced them in the first place would never begin to recover. They continued that 'saving' more families via the settlement would instead save none, only deepening the traumatic wounding of the refugees we were hoping to support.

In the end, we recognized that providing five families with a safe dwelling as a source of pride and self-reliance would much more effectively promote recovery."

Cultural Humility

Without careful and continuing attention to cultural norms, even the most generous of acts can become problematic. In a similar way, a culture's fragmentation or weakening can negatively impact the resilience of a traumatized individual or group, and the trauma-informed caregiver must respectfully accompany these people during the dark period when they face the loss of such resources.

For example, some years ago, a specific Christian congregation in the Midwest committed to sponsoring a Hmong refugee family. They secured an apartment for a man and his family who had been assigned to their resettlement project, arranged language lessons, and provided them with friendship, care, and nurturing before their journey. The congregation worked with unusual diligence to see to it that none of the family's needs would go unmet.

When they arrived with only two changes of clothing, the congregation brought more, as well as other goods and materials. The man thanked them, but said that they really only required two outfits: one to wear and one to wash. Still, the congregation members persisted in their generosity, reasoning that the family had suffered so greatly that they deserved to have much more than two simple changes of clothing.

So each time an additional gift came, the man accepted it with thanks. What the members of the congregation did not know was that in his culture, to say "no" when offered something was considered extremely rude, and he had attempted to communicate already that the family's two outfits were not a sign of deprivation, but rather customary and sufficient possessions.

If they had been aware of his cultural norms or the clues he had been broadcasting, they would have realized that he was overwhelmed by the unnecessary excess, guilt-ridden by his inability to assist those he had left behind, and filled with shame. Every gift to which he said "yes" when he really meant "no" only deepened his sense of survivor's guilt. Unable to communicate his dilemma to the well-meaning community, a great tragedy resulted when the man hung himself in his apartment a few months after his arrival.

These days in the corporate and academic worlds, much is being said and written about the practice of "cultural competency." As racism, sexism, and all the other "-isms" continue to create divisions and sometimes violence in our communities and workplaces, management teams and leadership groups striving to develop these skills of "cultural competency" must first admit that our natural inclination as human beings is not to have it. That is to say, all of us are filled with unexamined assumptions about the world, ourselves, and other people that we have deemed "acceptable," but that might not fit someone else's reality. Thankfully, we can be humble, attentive, and open to learning from those we hope to help, and this practice of cultural humility is extremely helpful for those who work in trauma healing.

Ways to Practice Cultural Humility

The *Journal of Counseling Psychology* defines cultural humility as the "ability to maintain an interpersonal stance that is other-oriented (or open to the other) in relation to aspects of cultural identity that are most important to the person" (Hook et al., 2013, p. 353). According to Tervalon and Murry-Garcia (1998):

> Cultural humility incorporates a lifelong commitment to self-evaluation and self-critique, to redressing the power imbalances in the patient-physician dynamic, and to developing mutually beneficial and nonpaternalistic clinical and advocacy partnerships with communities on behalf of individuals and the defined population. (p. 117)

What does cultural humility look like in the work of the trauma-informed professional, and how can you practice it?

1. Know yourself, and do not allow your ego to get in the way of the care you are trying to provide.

2. Bracket your judgments, prejudices, assumptions, and beliefs, rather than assuming "everyone" shares them. Be willing to have your own world shaken up a little bit—if you do this, you are opening yourself up to being challenged and changed for the better.

3. Be aware of what you do not know about the person, their experience, or its context. Admit to yourself—and to the individual you are trying to help—that even when you know about

their traumatic event, you still do not have a complete understanding of what it means to them in the context of their culture, history, and faith expression.

4. Remain in a relaxed body and do not perceive threat as you welcome the unknown, and the sacred opportunity to learn from another and accompany them in their pain.

5. Listen with all parts of yourself: your ears, eyes, body, and heart.

Put another way, we need to avoid a "colonial" way of thinking and seeing. Just because someone's practices, resources, education, and experience are different than ours does not give us license to assume we are smarter than them or know what is better for their recovery. Ask questions and embrace the answers. Be patient and respectful. Invite correction. When you make a mistake, apologize and be grateful. Do not be afraid of silence; much is communicated without words. Trust the other person—and trust yourself—to communicate care and facilitate healing and growth together.

Attunement to Gender

Here's a brief explanation on the difference between the terms "sex" and "gender" and how they are defined: "sex" describes the biological characteristics of a person who is male or female, or as it is coming to be understood, characteristics anywhere on a continuum between the two. Biological sex generally influences gender and gender roles, especially in traditional societies, but gender is fluid, influenced by culture, and because it is socially determined, can and does change. Oxfam International (1994) offers this "working definition" of gender:

> People are born female or male, but learn to be girls and boys who grow into women and men. They are taught what the appropriate behavior and attitudes, roles and activities are for them, and how they should relate to other people. This learned behavior is what makes up gender identity, and determines gender roles. (p. 4)

Gender roles vary widely from culture to culture, and among particular social groups within cultures. Females and males who do not conform to traditional gender roles—in any culture—can be subject to criticism, stigmatization, or violence, and being forced to conform may cause traumatization. For those who have also experienced an acute trauma, this nonconformity may deepen traumatic effects and complicate healing.

Gender looks at roles, activities, and relationships, answering questions such as:

1. Who does what.

2. Who makes the decisions.

3. Who benefits from these decisions.

4. Who uses and controls resources (credit, money, land, materials).

5. What the culture practices regarding inheritance, property rights, and access to justice.

Race, class, education, socioeconomic status, and age all influence gender roles. As these factors shift or change, gender roles may shift as well. Trauma, war, disaster, and other crises may alter gender roles temporarily or permanently. During WWI and WWII, the demand for soldiers drained the work force in the U.S. and parts of Europe, and women became employed outside the home in great numbers for the first time. This emergence into the work force changed how women saw themselves and their traditional roles, and eventually spurred a dramatic shift in gender patterns, many of which became permanent.

Gender helps us to "tune in" to other kinds of differences, and when we increase our awareness of genders and gender roles in varying contexts, we also sharpen our skills of attuning to other influences on people and communities after trauma. Race, social status, ethnicity, age, and more all impact the cultural practices of individuals and groups, and inform/affect the way they respond to and recover from trauma.

Difficulties Faced by Women Across Cultures

Worldwide, women have a variety of specific struggles and challenges they face in their day-to-day lives, and in the wake of a traumatic event:

1. Women and emergencies. Women and children comprise up to eighty-five percent of those displaced by conflict and disasters. When men leave to fight wars or seek work in times of economic deprivation, the number of women heading households increases dramatically, with eighty to ninety percent of family groupings in refugee settlements being headed by women. In male-dominated cultures, these women are often excluded from the decision-making following catastrophes, and home-keeping women may be "invisible" to those delivering aid or working to redevelop the community. In many cases, their vulnerability to the effects of trauma is intensified. The protection issues regarding women and children in times of conflict, war, and disaster are serious, as incidences of violence and the breakdown of social structures both increase in circumstances of perceived and real threat.

2. Women and childbearing. Though critical to the survival and thriving of families, peoples, and societies, the woman's central role in childbearing and childrearing is undervalued. Work in the home is frequently unrecognized and without remuneration. Even in developed countries, women who have chosen to focus their labor in the home describe themselves as "not working." Childbearing women who work outside the home frequently lose access to status positions, pay equity, and access to promotion when they "take time off" to focus on reproductive work, whereas with men in many cultures, the ability to produce children and support a large family is a positive indicator of status.

3. Women and employment. Productive work can be understood as work that is done for remuneration and/or recognized by the community as valuable and necessary. In most cultures (with rare exceptions), men hold the status positions, are better paid for comparable work, and have the power to make decisions for themselves and others, while women tend to be under-rewarded in all of these areas. While men enjoy the benefits of this lack of equity, they can also carry an intensified sense of responsibility and stress that increases their threat perceptions.

Meanwhile, women deprived of status and the real or perceived rewards of productive work may struggle with feelings of shame, guilt, and powerlessness that make them more vulnerable to trauma and its effects.

4. Women and community work. "Community work" includes social organization, caring for children, the sick, and elderly, organizing/lobbying authorities for social change, and securing needed services to benefit the community. While men and women share this labor, women's workdays across the world are longer than men's, as they often integrate reproductive work and the tending of household and family needs. For example, in many countries where access to water is scarce, women shoulder the difficult task of finding and securing water for nourishment, cooking, hygiene, and gardening. Their efforts require physical exertion for long periods of time, even spanning several days.

5. Women and resources/benefits. UN statistics demonstrating the variance in resources between genders are as follows:

· Women perform two-thirds of the world's work.

· Women earn one-tenth of the world's income.

· Women comprise two-thirds of the world's illiterate community.

· Women own less than one one-hundredth of the world's property.

In cultures where women's status is distinctly less than that of men, the work of a trauma-informed professional will want to balance attentiveness to the intensification of the effects of trauma that may result from gender imbalance, with respect for the traditions and intact social structures that also may support healing.

6. Women and access to human rights. The Human Rights Watch (2014) says:

> Despite great strides made by the international women's rights movement over many years, women and girls around the world are still married as children or trafficked into forced labor and sex slavery. They are refused access to education and political participation, and some are trapped in conflicts where rape is perpetrated as a weapon of war. Around the world, deaths related to pregnancy and childbirth are needlessly high, and women are prevented from making deeply personal choices in their private lives. (p. 1)

In some cultures, genital mutilation, maiming, and other forms of violence including the murder of women is perpetuated and sanctioned by cultural tradition or religious practice, and this exacerbates the effects of trauma for victims and perpetrators alike.

7. Women and religion. Among the world's religions, doctrine and practice frequently enshrine preferential treatment and status to males. Many religions teach a subordinate role for females, forbidding women's access to hierarchy, and directing a limited role for women in marriage and the household. Some religious traditions license domestic violence against women as a way of maintaining traditional gender roles and access to power. Alternatively, religious practice can be a potent source of hope and connection for women as well as men, offering solidarity, inspiration, and a vision of justice and equality.

Religion in Trauma-Informed Care

Everyone who is seriously involved in the pursuit of science becomes convinced that a spirit is manifest in the laws of the Universe—a spirit vastly superior to that of man, and one in the face of which we with our modest powers must feel humble.

– Albert Einstein

As we have noted throughout the text, the real goal of the healer is a spiritual (but not religious) activity aimed at helping the individual reveal the fullness of the being they truly are. Dr. Robert Grant (1999) connected the caregiver's work to spirituality when he said that in spite of trauma's brutality and destructiveness, it still has the power to expose survivors to profound existential and spiritual significance. A survivor's displacement of their ego forces them to confront much more deeply the various levels of self and reality. Grant observed that trauma can often force survivors on a path that many mythic heroes, spiritual seekers, shamans, and mystics have been traversing for millennia.

It is not uncommon that the aftermath of a traumatic event ignites a fundamental drive to fulfill a spiritual need. Traumatic events can shatter our current view about the world, others, and self, and negatively shift our core assumptions about purpose and safety. We seek new explanations for the horrors of life, with many turning to spiritual sources for insight and inspiration. Since our psychological and/or emotional sense of security has changed, it is natural for humans to seek comfort in time of pain, which many attempt to fulfill with the outlets of patriotism or spirituality (Brethour, 2001).

Religion is an important element in the healing process that may contribute to or inhibit trauma recovery since it is one way that humans fulfill their spiritual need. Reza Aslan, an Iranian-American professor of creative writing and author of the book *Zealot: The Life and Times of Jesus of Nazareth*, tells us that religion is not just about beliefs, but is a statement of identity that incorporates culture, nationality, and rituals. Trauma-informed caregivers must attend to the messages, both positive and negative, that the religious identity of the trauma survivor affirms, and find ways to establish connection and support in its positive assertions while treating cautiously and tenderly those that are not.

The use of the survivor's religious practices in the therapeutic setting may be looked down upon or criticized, even with contempt, by many professionals or academic researchers. This can be a missed opportunity, however, if caregivers overlook the power of a survivor's religious beliefs in their recovery. All religions have powerful emotional and spiritual resources for health, healing, and hope, and for many religious people, the primary source of hope and positive expectancy is rooted in their belief system and/or their relationship with the divine.

The sacred texts of most religions offer potent narratives of hope and redemption—stories of being lifted from despair, disaster, or death into a new life, one filled with depth and meaning. For example, Psalm 41:3 of the New International Version of the Bible states "the Lord sustains them on their sickbed and restores them from their bed of illness" (NIV), and in the Qur'an, the supplication of the Prophet Ibrahim [Abraham] says, "And, when I am ill, it is He who cures me" (Qur'an 26:80, Sahih International). In addition, many of these sacred scriptures offer sound medical advice, including recommendations for professional help and mental health treatment to those contending with trauma. In the New World Translation of the Holy Scriptures (NWT),

Jesus of Nazareth [Jesus Christ] states to his followers that "those who are strong do not need a physician, but those who are ill do" (Mark 2:17, NWT).

For many religious practitioners, their community of faith is a rich resource for connection and support, one that contributes positively to the individual's healing. These stories can provide a path or a place of grounding in which the patient/client can find new meaning, restoration, and respite after their experiences.

In addition, there seems to be empirical support that shows religious practices used as coping resources can increase resiliency. Religious orientation and positive future orientation, as well as novelty seeking, were related to resiliency and post-traumatic growth (Seidmahmoodi, Rahimi, and Mohamadi, 2011; Schaefer, Blazer, and Koenig, 2009; Ai et al., 2007; Ano and Vasconcelles, 2005; Ai et al., 2005). It is worth noting that some studies have shown mixed results on the efficacy of religious coping and resiliency toward stressful events (Bryant-Davis, Wellman, and Tsong, 2012), but a subsequent meta-analysis seemed to confirm that poor outcomes with religious practices were related to negative religious psychological adjustment, while good psychological adjustments were related to positive religious coping (Ano and Vasconcelles, 2005).

Negative influences present potential pitfalls to caregivers and healing companions. These influences may be direct or indirect (assumed); additionally, they may be uncritical assumptions held by the practitioner and unconsciously imposed on the patient/client, sometimes to their detriment. A person's religious tradition may, for example, teach that those who experience trauma or disaster are being judged by God and punished for wrongdoing or sin. The tradition may invite shame or guilt as a normal response to the experience of a traumatic event, in essence "blaming the victim." Religion may affirm that pain and suffering are good or purifying experiences that are somehow inherently redemptive. A religion may hold a doctrine that all that happens is due to predetermination, and is a part of the "will of God." While this may seem comforting to some, for others, such an affirmation could silence natural expressions of grief or anger, effectively shutting down a survivor's emotional grieving process and impeding their recovery.

The Role of Indigenous Spirituality

In many communities, particularly those where indigenous spiritual practices have been overlaid by the group's conversion to an outside religion such as Christianity or Islam, indigenous practices that have been suppressed by the mainstream religion may emerge in times of trauma and acute grief. Finding ways to incorporate, affirm, and help the survivor utilize those traditional resources is an important gift a healer can offer, whether or not they find such practices personally helpful or appropriate.

Cultural and religious considerations should help to facilitate resilience with compassion as they educate, equip, and empower survivors. Trauma-informed care embraces the basic principle that all people deserve respect, compassion, and empathy for the support of their emotional and physical well-being—*all* lives are sacred and of value. Thus, as a form of this respect, the caregiver should seek to embrace with attentiveness those parts of the survivor's religious tradition that support recovery. Healing trauma relies on cultural humility, collaboration with the survivor, and an attentive and nonjudgmental spirit that brings the best understandings of science and religion together to serve the whole person.

Showing respect for the religious perspective of the survivor helps to facilitate trust between the professional caregiver and the one they are seeking to help, and this openness builds a valuable bridge across differences.

There are five principles the trauma-informed caregiver should strive to master when it comes to religious understanding, respect, and humility:

1. See the good in all people and traditions.
2. When in disagreement, be respectful.
3. When in doubt, ask and learn.
4. Know enough about basic religious norms that you avoid violating them.
5. Build trust, reserve judgment, find and build bridges.

It is important for the healing professional to provide the survivor access to sacred texts and rituals, and to demonstrate respect for their religious traditions. Provision of access is not the same thing as providing instruction. The healer can help those they serve discover these materials, but direct teaching often sends the message that the helped should already know or understand them in a certain way, which can lead to them feeling ostracized or their pain minimized.

Sacred stories can offer a place to identify and universalize the personal experience of trauma, and finding one's experience in a sacred story validates it while pointing the way to recovery. From a religious perspective, trauma healing promotes the restoration of spiritual wholeness and supports an integrated spiritual journey marked by awe and wonder, which reconnects an individual to their ability to experience joy, peace, purpose, meaning, and love. It can contribute to the survivor's work of meaning-making, while helping to reintegrate the personal mission narrative that was shattered or disrupted by the trauma.

Personal Bias in Trauma-Informed Care

One of the most important things we have learned over the past several years studying the outcomes of treatment is that an excellent relationship between the trauma-informed caregiver and patient/client is *crucial* for recovery. Helping care providers to develop, maintain, and enhance their relationships with the people they serve is always beneficial to treatment efforts and outcomes, and it is important to address any impediments to this right away. Care providers have an ethical responsibility to identify and attend to any behaviors or attitudes that might diminish the quality of the therapeutic relationship, as personal biases, conscious or unconscious, have the potential to severely handicap this important component of treatment.

Racism, sexism, ageism, classism, and homophobia are all examples of biases that can potentially contaminate the therapeutic relationship. Marginalized populations have become acutely sensitized to the judgment and ridicule of others, and can frequently perceive these biases in others even when no overt signs are present. Trauma survivors are usually overrepresented in these marginalized populations, and when they encounter care providers who are judgmental, critical, or dismissive, their physiological threat-response system is activated. When this happens, the environment no longer feels safe and inviting for them, and they may begin to avoid certain providers or treatment all together because of this discomfort.

It is important for care providers to first become *aware* of their biases and prejudices, so that they can be resolved. Supervisors can help by gently directing staff members to identify the times when their biases were activated during interactions with patients or coworkers, and can collaborate to formulate a plan for resolving these potentially dangerous prejudices. Finally, management can assist in this mitigating process by creating and supporting policies and expectations among direct care and supervisory staff that judgmental, critical, and disrespectful attitudes and behaviors will not be tolerated.

Below are four excerpts from various sources regarding counselor bias and what the profession says about it, with the first written by Dr. Jeremy Sherman (2012) in "Counselor Bias: A Dumb Reason We Think We're Smart" at Psychology Today:

> Business consultants, editors, psychotherapists, social workers, teachers, we all are prone to counselor bias. With less skin in the game we pretend we're putting ourselves in the shoes of people with more skin in the game. We can't believe how irrational they are, and we're impressed by how rational we are in comparison. Counselor bias comeuppance arrives when we find ourselves in similar situations to theirs. Then what consolation is our supposed all-weather rationality?
>
> One argument I've heard for spiritual practices is that they prepare you for just such rough situations ahead. If you meditate every day for ten years, then you'll be able to keep from losing your mind if you end up with horrific cancer. I think I invested in my philosophical interests for a similar reason—the consolations of philosophy I thought would carry me through tough times.
>
> But all the people I know who have undergone terrific stress or are still in it say nope, they gain little comfort or peace from the equanimity they cultivated during times of peace. The simulated fire drills don't do much to keep them calm during their fires.
>
> I believe them. I'm impressed by how little my hard-earned equanimity helps even in what relatively modest turmoil I've suffered in the 15 years. It's humbling to realize that. And humbling is good. (para. 14-17)

The University of Missouri's student newspaper, *The Maneater*, posted an article written by Abbey Sussell (2010) titled "School of Education Works to Eliminate Bias from Counseling Sessions":

> Laurie Mintz, professor of Counseling Psychology at the Education, School and Psychology Program in the College of Education, has been active in dealing with value clashes in counseling training programs.
>
> The clash between students studying to become counselors' personal beliefs and university counseling programs has continued to generate controversy. In the past year, multiple colleges have fought lawsuits in which student counselors claim discrimination of their beliefs.
>
> Counseling students have been reprimanded when expressing personal values in a counseling session that frown upon the client's sexuality, race or socioeconomic status.

> "We realized this was a huge problem across training and we needed some guidance in the field as to how to deal with this," Mintz said. Mintz, along with other university professors, drafted a model values statement for counseling psychology.
>
> The statement has been endorsed by many associations, including the American Psychology Association Division of Counseling Psychology and the Society of Counseling Psychology and was published by The Counseling Psychologist. The "Counseling Psychology Model Training Value Statement Regarding Diversity," aims to assist training programs and trainees.
>
> "Our code of ethics is clear," Mintz said. "A counselor needs to be able to work with a diversity of people and not bring in your own value judgments. This is not about the counselor's needs, it's about the client's needs." The values statement does not seek to change counselors' personal values, but instead provide guidance, Mintz said.
>
> "We cannot dictate your values and we do not want to," Mintz said. "But we do want to know that you will be able to set your own values aside at the counseling door and help the client grow and change. You must be willing to examine your own values and struggle with them to the point of making sure you can provide good services to a client." (para. 1-9)

On the American School Counselor Association's (ASCA) blog, Dr. Rhonda Williams (2011) answered a question about bias in the caregiver's workplace in "The Duty to Address Personal Bias":

> *Scenario: My school counseling colleague and I were recently having lunch together when she began to tell me about a 15-year-old student she was working with who identified as gay. As she told me about this student she described how strongly her religious beliefs went against everything this boy was talking about. She said that based on her religious beliefs she felt compelled to counsel the boy "out of being gay." She shared that normally she keeps her religious beliefs out of the school counseling office, but in this case she sees her efforts worth saving this boy. To me this seems unethical. How should I approach this?*
>
> First and foremost, our mission as school counselors is to advocate for all students, not just those with whom our personal values agree. Our professional mission based on the ASCA Ethical Standards for School Counselors clearly identifies advocacy,

leadership, collaboration and consultations as a means to provide equity in access and educational success. Given that 64 percent of lesbian, gay, bisexual, transgender or questioning (LGBTQ) youth report feeling unsafe at school on any given day, how might they feel when the school counselor confirms that lack of safety and support?

Research states that four out of five LGBTQ students report they can't name one supportive adult in their school. These students suffer from lower self-esteem, struggle with academics and often exhibit depression. They are more likely to run away from home and have a higher rate of substance abuse than the general population of students. The Gay, Lesbian and Straight Education Network (GLSEN) reports that students hear anti-gay epithets 25 times a day, and 97 percent of the time teachers do or say nothing about this type of harassment. This marginalized group of students, who represent 5 percent-10 percent of any given student body, is two to three times more likely to commit suicide. Almost 30 percent of completed suicides among youth are related to sexual identity.

The first tenet of the ASCA Ethical Standards preamble states, "Each person has the right to be respected, be treated with dignity and have access to a comprehensive school counseling program that advocates for and affirms all students from diverse populations including: ethnic/racial identity, age, economic status, abilities/disabilities, language, immigration status, sexual orientation, gender, gender identity/expression, family type, religious/spiritual identity, and appearance."

The Ethical Standards are clear regarding the school counselor's role in providing equity, social justice and self-determination. The preamble also states that students be affirmed in the groups with which they identify "with special care being given to students who have historically not received adequate educational services." (para. 1-4)

Finally, the American Psychological Association provided this tip sheet on counselor attitude bias and lessons learned from HIV/AIDS, authored by Dr. Paula Britton (n.d.):

Overall, the research suggests that the personal attitudes and biases of psychologists may affect their professional treatment and decision making. The impact of HIV/AIDS to this area of literature is illustrated below.

Psychologists may be vulnerable to negative biases toward clients. Mental health workers have demonstrated biases against persons with AIDS. Crawford et al. (1987)

> found that mental health workers indicated that persons with AIDS were more responsible for their illness, less deserving of sympathy, and more dangerous to the general public than clients with leukemia. These workers reported less willingness to attend a party or work where a person with AIDS was present. (Lesson Learned from HIV/AIDS, para. 1-2)

Personal and Professional Growth

The consequences of caregiver bias are far-reaching and damaging, and in the field of trauma-informed caregiving, our mission is first and foremost to provide acceptance, safety, and an environment for a trauma survivor that is free from judgment or perceived danger.

In order to foster this type of environment and therapeutic relationship for a person seeking help, it is vital that we are not only expanding and evolving our personal perceptions of what is "right" or "normal" or "acceptable," but also that we are pushing ourselves to continue learning in our chosen helping career.

Professional development and growth are required in many fields as part of an ethical or legal licensing requirement, and are especially important in trauma caregiving work where complex and challenging situations are faced every day. According to the International Association of Trauma Professionals (IATP), professional growth needs to be more than just "getting a certificate for sitting in a seat for so many hours so you can sustain your employment." Personal and professional growth are essential to providing increasingly better and more effective help to those recovering from trauma, and should never be undervalued or shirked.

Personal growth and development are transformational, leading us to make consistent improvements in multiple domains such as our emotional, social, relational, physical, spiritual, and intellectual life. Oftentimes this type of development is initiated by some life event that triggers dissatisfaction with the status quo, and a desire to "never have to deal with that event or situation again." This is a reactive form of personal growth, however, and is usually limiting in that it only provides motivation to overcome that particular situation. What we are recommending is a type of personal and professional growth that is an *engaged* process of seeking mastery in all domains of life.

Human beings have the potential to improve and grow regardless of their histories, experiences, deficits, or personalities. This idea of human potential is the foundation of healing principles for both the professional and layperson alike, and is one of the basic tenets of all work with the traumatized. Human beings are capable of creating and maintaining healthier lives, if they can achieve acceptance, possess faith and hope for the future, and have adequate attachment and support from others.

One of the primary tasks of the healer is to become more fully who "they" are through acts of personal creation. From this perspective, personal creation is founded in the idea that the healer is on their own journey of personal and professional growth, making incremental improvements in motivation, character, skill, and compassion, while moving away from the demanding nature of their own egos and refining their global charity or love for others. Creation is not the chaos of happenstance, or careless conception of one's life. Creation carries with it a certain intentionality that is not simply a reaction to the hurtful, annoying, or painful events of life.

There are several avenues to travel in the journey of personal and professional growth, and no particular pathway is necessarily the right one—but we do believe several basic skills are fundamental to the process. This list is by no means exhaustive, but is a good starting point for developing your abilities as a trauma-informed caregiver:

1. Self-control/self-regulation of our own emotions.
2. Courage to believe in others and act on that belief.
3. Attitude of service.
4. Compassion (awareness of others without critical judgments).
5. Integrity (living by your value system and allowing others the same privilege, even if you do not agree).
6. Self-awareness (physically, psychologically, emotionally, and spiritually).
7. Persistence in learning, practicing, and skill-building.
8. Development and fine-tuning of your sense of purpose.
9. Patience (having it for others and yourself).

Developing as a healer releases us from the fear of our own egoic demands and increases our personal intimacy with our own wholeness, integrating all of our formerly incongruent parts into the tool we use to reach out to those around us in love and compassion.

Change is inevitable, and does not depend on an individual developing insight or taking any certain action. Life at all levels is in a constant state of change, alteration, and adaptation. In clinical settings change takes on more of a creational meaning, which is found in the transformation of a survivor becoming more fully what they have the potential to be. The healer becomes the custodian of skills that bring creation into their own lives, and then extends those abilities to the lives of others through acts of co-creation. More than any other reason, personal and professional growth is necessary to increase the efficacy of this co-creation process.

Traditional helping models have taken the position that the patient/client must have a certain understanding, often labeled as "insight," before effective change can successfully occur. This view appears inadequate and based on the ego-driven needs of the therapist, who "evaluates" when and how much insight is present in the patient/client and whether it is adequate enough to provoke the change. It is not uncommon for helpers to take a posture of judgment and even at times denigrate the patient/client for not seeing what the helper sees or feeling things the way the helper thinks is appropriate. Personal and professional growth will reduce this tendency, so the helper can avoid inadvertently demeaning those seeking relief and help. A caregiver is less likely to erode the fabric of rapport necessary to provide the best care and healing if personal and professional growth is an ongoing activity.

A healer's actions should help the patient/client identify and connect with the creational aspects of living, while assisting in their development of hope and faith so they can act intentionally and move in a direction that produces the desired results. Human beings appoint meaning to the actions they take in their lives, and each decision and choice carries with it a creational quality. Sometimes people are actively creating health, and sometimes they are impacting their lives for ill. For a healer to be effective at helping another construct change and generate positive life outcomes, they must be actively involved in their own healthy creative process. Remember that the single most important tool the healer possesses is *who they are* and how they are in the world, with these elements being refined through personal and professional growth.

Case Study: Hannah

Hannah was a twenty-three-year-old Caucasian woman living with her eight-year-old son, Joshua, in a small two-bedroom house in upstate Michigan. Though unemployed currently, Hannah worked to pay her rent by cleaning properties for the landlord.

Hannah had been put into CPS care three times before the age of eighteen, for reports of neglect and sexual abuse. She'd never finished high school nor taken her GED test, and had had a lot of contact with the local police department in her Michigan town due to domestic violence from various boyfriends over the years. The local hospital staff was also familiar with Hannah and Joshua, since she'd been hospitalized several times due to injuries inflicted by her boyfriends, while Joshua had a chronic asthma condition that flared up severely every few months and required emergency care.

Joshua's father was a thirty-nine-year-old cousin of Hannah's father, and he only interacted with the two of them if they accidentally bumped into one another at a large family function. A court investigation and paternity test had stated that the man was indeed Joshua's father, but he'd remained unemployed for years and had yet to pay any child support.

One morning in May, Joshua found Hannah on the floor of the bathroom, unresponsive, and called 911. After several days of stabilization during which it was found that she'd overdosed on her mood stabilizer medication, Hannah was moved to the behavioral unit of the hospital. Her sister reported to the unit's presiding psychiatrist that Hannah had been hospitalized four or five times already for similar episodes, and had been diagnosed at different times with schizophrenia, bipolar disorder, suicidal intentions, major depression, and epilepsy.

The psychiatrist believed that Hannah had taken the medication in an attempt to kill herself because she was depressed, lonely, and overwhelmed by the intense conflicts she'd been having with her mother that week. During his interview with Hannah, the psychiatrist reported that she was "alert, angry, belligerent, guarded, and uncooperative" when questioned about whether it had been a suicide attempt, and that she continued to assert that she had overdosed by accident. After consulting notes on Hannah's previous hospitalizations, the psychiatrist suggested that until Hannah was no longer in denial about the suicide attempt, she wasn't equipped to be a safe and competent parent to Joshua.

CPS was then involved, and the assigned caseworker met with Joshua the next day during his lunchtime at school to ask him some questions.

"My mom is nice and takes good care of me. She always talks to me if I've done something bad; she never hits me or anything," Joshua reported.

"What about any drug use?" the caseworker asked.

"I don't think so…no."

"Your house was very clean when we stopped by; does your mom keep it tidy?" the caseworker continued, making notes in her file. "Do you have things like toothpaste and shampoo most of the time? Do you have to help your mom out with things like cleaning and groceries?"

"I help Mom clean and wash the clothes when she's not feeling good, and she *has* been feeling sick a lot lately. I wish Grandma would stop fighting with Mom. It makes her cry when Grandma hurts her, and that's usually when Mom gets sick and sleeps a lot."

"Your grandma hurts your mom?"

"Yeah. She hits her and leaves bruises."

When asked specifically about Hannah's suicide attempt, Joshua said that he'd seen his mom take her pills the night before her overdose, but that she'd been in a better mood than the preceding days. "She said the doctors had given her new pills to take. They're always giving her new ones."

The interview concluded with Joshua telling the CPS caseworker that he helped his mother a lot, and hoped she'd be better soon. Once the caseworker returned to her office, she wrote a report stating that she thought Joshua was being untruthful to protect his mother, and that even though the home was clean and his immediate needs seemed to be met, that he should be removed for safety reasons.

After reading the case study, what principles of trauma-informed care would you apply to help Hannah and Joshua's situation?

Chapter Summary

Trauma can be defined as any experience that interrupts an individual's normal social, emotional, psychological, cognitive, spiritual, language, or physical development, and has long-ranging and widespread effects. The history of trauma-informed care is nested in the study of these effects, many of which were discovered during the Adverse Childhood Experiences (ACE) study initiated by Drs. Vincent Felitti and Robert Anda. This study as well as many others led to the formation of groups like the NCTIC and SAMHSA, all of which made it their mission to properly define trauma-informed care and enable organizations to carry out new protocols for staff and clientele that alleviated suffering while avoiding retraumatization.

These protocols and systems are guided by six overarching principles that comprise trauma-informed care to be practiced amongst caregivers and between the caregiver and their patient/client: safety, trustworthiness and transparency, peer support and mutual self-help, collaboration and mutuality, empowerment, voice and choice, and sensitivity to cultural, historical, and gender issues.

Religion and indigenous spirituality can also be valuable factors in a trauma survivor's recovery, especially in those individuals who have been displaced by war or disaster, and the trauma-informed caregiver is to practice cultural humility, acceptance, and a respect to the importance of these customs at all times. Personal bias and opinions are not entirely preventable during client interactions, but trauma-informed caregivers are aware of these beliefs within themselves and never allow them to dictate their demeanor, suggestions in treatment, or the strength of the therapeutic relationship.

To combat the possibility of personal bias and continue to strengthen one's abilities to provide trauma-informed care to the suffering, those in caregiving fields should consistently be developing themselves personally and professionally, by furthering their education as well as intentionally working to better their own emotional, physical, spiritual, and social lives. This dedication to continuous growth and mastery renews the caregiver, allowing them to inspire clients to pursue their own paths of recovery with hope, positive expectancy, and creational autonomy.

Chapter Four

Trauma and Traumagenesis

Focus Questions:

- How do professionals define trauma?
- What are some of the complications with the current definitions of trauma?
- What is a broader and more complex definition and understanding of trauma?
- How does a broader understanding of trauma help improve trauma-informed care?

In this chapter you will learn more about:

- A comprehensive definition of trauma.
- The categories of trauma: "Big T" and "little t."
- The nature of traumagenesis and how to understand it.

You can only go into the unknown when you have made friends with yourself.

– Pema Chödrön

Post-Traumatic Stress

Despite historical progressions in the field of traumatology and psychiatry, professionals are still unable to agree on a conclusive definition of trauma. Many mental health professionals are still debating on what constitutes psychological trauma, and heated arguments have arisen due to definitions that have minimized or excluded many traumatic experiences.

Post-traumatic stress disorder (PTSD) has been known by many names in the past, such as "shell shock" or "war neuroses" during the years of World War I, "combat fatigue" or "battle fatigue" during World War II, and "Vietnam Syndrome" after the Vietnam conflict. PTSD does not just happen to combat veterans—it can occur in all people of any ethnicity, nationality, culture, or age. PTSD affects approximately three and a half percent of U.S. adults, and an estimated one in eleven people will experience PTSD in their lifetime.

The American Psychiatric Association (APA) first recognized the symptoms that would later be known as PTSD as a syndrome that occurred among relatively normal survivors of intolerable traumatic stress. The first iteration of the *Diagnostic and Statistical Manual of Mental Disorders* (DSM-I) published in 1952 labeled this syndrome as a "gross stress reaction." In the second edition of the DSM (1968), "gross stress reaction" was replaced by "adjustment reaction to adult life" and "transient situation disturbance." "Adjustment reaction to adult life" was limited to three forms of trauma, however, and overlooked the effects of exposure to traumatic stress (Friedman, 2013), while "transient situation disturbance" had a negative connotation and was not recognized as a disorder.

It was not until the publication of the DSM-III in 1980 that the APA labeled and recognized PTSD as a disorder with an outlined diagnostic criterion "which stemmed from research involving returning Vietnam War veterans, Holocaust survivors, sexual trauma victims, and others" (U.S. Department of Veterans Affairs, n.d., para. 13).

In the DSM-IV-TR, trauma or PTSD was categorized as an anxiety disorder, which did not take into account the impact a traumatic event has on an individual. The DSM-5 now defines traumatic stress as "a psychiatric disorder that can occur in people who have experienced or witnessed a traumatic event such as a natural disaster, a serious accident, a terrorist act, war/combat, rape, or other violent personal assault," with trauma and PTSD being listed under a new category called "trauma- and stressor-related disorders" (American Psychiatric Association, 2013, p. 265). In this new category, five diagnoses of trauma- and stressor-related disorders are clustered together, including "reactive attachment disorder, disinhibited social engagement disorder, post-traumatic stress disorder, acute stress disorder, and adjustment disorder."

Creating this category in the DSM-5 may have been beneficial to the destigmatizing of PTSD sufferers, as it now connects those symptoms to *outside* events. On the other hand, the DSM-5's criteria also limits the definition of trauma—as it is currently written, the diagnosis requires a person to have exposure to an intense traumatic or stressful event. This does not easily account for prolonged or frequent low intensity events like bullying, body-shaming, or family discord, which can generate enough physiological arousal in the body to equal that of someone who has experienced a significant traumatic event.

Criteria for PTSD in the DSM-5

We are going to present a very brief overview of the diagnostic criteria developed by the APA (2013) for PTSD in the latest version of the DSM, all of which are required for the diagnosis:

1. Criterion A (one required): The person was exposed to death, threatened death, actual or threatened serious injury, or actual or threatened sexual violence, in the following way(s):

· Direct exposure.

· Witnessing the trauma.

· Learning that a relative or close friend was exposed to a trauma (in cases of actual or threatened death of a family member or friend, the event(s) must have been violent or accidental).

· Repeated or extreme exposure to aversive details of the traumatic event(s) (i.e., first responders collecting human remains; police officers repeatedly exposed to details of child abuse).

2. Criterion B (one required): The traumatic event is persistently reexperienced, in the following way(s):

· Intrusive thoughts (i.e., repeated, involuntary memories).

· Nightmares.

· Flashbacks (these may be so vivid that the individual feels as if they are re-watching it).

· Emotional distress after exposure to traumatic reminders.

· Physical reactivity after exposure to traumatic reminders.

3. Criterion C (one required): Avoidance of trauma-related stimuli after the trauma, in the following way(s):

· Trauma-related thoughts or feelings.

· Trauma-related reminders.

4. Criterion D (two required): Negative thoughts or feelings that began or worsened after the trauma, in the following way(s):

· Inability to recall key features of the trauma.

· Overly negative thoughts and assumptions about oneself or the world (i.e., "I am bad," "no one can be trusted").

· Exaggerated blame of self or others for causing the trauma.

· Ongoing fear, horror, anger, guilt, or shame surrounding the trauma.

· Decreased interest in activities.

· Feeling isolated, detached, or estranged from others.

· Difficulty experiencing positive affect.

5. Criterion E (two required): Trauma-related arousal and reactivity that began or worsened after the trauma, in the following way(s):

· Irritability or aggression.

· Risky or destructive behavior.

· Hypervigilance.

· Heightened startle reaction.

· Difficulty concentrating.

· Difficulty sleeping.

6. Criterion F (required): Symptoms last for more than one month.

7. Criterion G (required): Symptoms create distress or functional impairment (social, occupational, etc.).

8. Criterion H (required): Symptoms are not due to medication, substance use, or other illness.

There are subtypes of PTSD as well, one of which is for those who display an elevated representation of adult dissociative behavior, while the other is for children aged birth to six years old. If you serve either of these populations, you may wish to become familiar with these subtypes in more detail.

Criticisms of the DSM-5's Criteria

Despite the DSM-5's detailed and inclusive diagnostic criteria, it has been criticized for overlooking the larger context of exposure that can lead to traumatic stress. For example, Criterion A's requirement that a survivor has been exposed to "actual or threatened death, serious injury, or sexual violence" (American Psychiatric Association, 2013, p. 271) limits the DSM-5's definition of trauma, and minimizes the traumatic experience of someone who has endured emotional or mental abuse that didn't meet these stipulations.

The DSM-5 now includes two new disorders that address childhood social neglect, referred to as reactive attachment disorder (RAD) and disinhibited social engagement disorder (DSED). The Criterion C for both of these disorders requires that the child has experienced a pattern of extreme insufficient care, as evidenced by at least one of the following:

1. Social neglect or deprivation in the form of persistent lack of having basic emotional needs for comfort, stimulation, and affection met by caregiving adults.

2. Repeated changes of primary caregivers that limit opportunities to form stable attachments (i.e., frequent changes in foster care).

3. Rearing in unusual settings that severely limit opportunities to form selective attachments (i.e., institutions with high child-to-caregiver ratios).

These disorders address the extreme emotional neglect of a child, but may not adequately include inconsistent emotional neglect and the sporadic mental abuse of a child. As a result, the presentation of typical behavioral symptoms observed in children who receive inconsistent support for their emotional needs or intermittent mental abuse (but not to the level of these "extremes" criteria) are classified as experiencing an adjustment disorder or another specified trauma- and stress-related disorder.

The DSM-5 also seems to minimize the traumatic experience of a wife who has undergone years of emotional and mental coercing without physical violence (i.e., threatening to take the children away, threatening deportation, etc.), degradation and humiliation (i.e., verbal mortification, urinating on someone to humiliate them, etc.) from a man who made a vow to love and cherish her for the rest of their lives. Would you consider it to be traumatizing for a child to be cyberbullied or coerced, without physical violence, or to have to do things against their will because they are being threatened or blackmailed? These are topics that create controversies on the definition of trauma in the mental health field.

According to a scripture written approximately 3,000 years ago by King Solomon (Ecclesiastes 7:7, ESV)—"surely oppression drives the wise into madness"—these aforementioned circumstances of prolonged cruelty, unjust treatment, or abuse are traumatic incidents that cause mental pressure or distress, which can result in many of the symptoms of PTSD. In our "modern era" of medicine and mental health treatment, however, the wounds caused by these traumatic incidents can be overlooked or minimized, and in defense of our medical/psychiatric view of trauma, the array of influential variables makes it almost impossible to predict if an event or circumstance will result in the traumatization of an individual.

Trauma as a Physiological Response

Defining trauma is a complicated task, especially with the enormous latitude—based on everyone's unique resiliency—to what can be traumatic for a person. Nonetheless, it is unarguable that humans inevitably experience stressful events throughout their lifespan. Many individuals have developed emotional resilience and the ability to self-regulate as a way to overcome and flourish in the face of those challenging and stressful moments, but there are times when particular stressful events, both catastrophic and common, can overwhelm someone's natural defenses. As a result, the autonomic nervous system may process that event as traumatic stress (Rojo Aubrey, 2015).

The individual's resiliency and mental architecture are factors that contribute to the scope and difficulty to constitute what can cause traumatization. Earlier in the text, we defined trauma as any experience (a.k.a. "traumatic activators") that interposes or impedes with the normal physical, psychological, emotional, mental, social, and/or spiritual development of a person. These experiences are perceived as a threat (real or fictional) to self or others and overwhelm the individual's physiology, resulting in a disruption of their normal human development. Trauma, therefore, is a physiological or neurobiological reaction to unbearable experiences that can be influenced by a number of factors, including the person's resiliency as well as the intensity, duration, and frequency of these experiences.

For years, the focal point of trauma service delivery was the emotional and psychological impact of an event upon the psyche of an individual. As the field of trauma and traumatic stress—and our understanding of neurobiology—has matured, there has been a shift from the traditional emotional and psychological into the neurobiological when exploring the effects of trauma, with a strong emphasis on the physiological, or body-based, experience. This does not minimize the reality of emotional and psychological impact from trauma, but grounds it in a context of overall bodily responses that are predictable and explainable. One of the advantages of approaching trauma as a normal and predictable neurobiological response is that it allows for the reduction of stigma and pathologizing.

Viewing trauma as psychological or emotional pain caused by external events may lead to an attempt to erroneously diagnose or judge adaptive and mitigating behaviors (ones we will discuss later in the chapter) that are an *appropriate* response to physiological changes in the body. In addition, this viewpoint can result in us demanding that boundaries or environmental changes be enforced to stop the survivor's mitigating physiological behaviors. This is an unreasonable request, akin to asking someone to stop their body's natural process of digestion after eating food.

The trauma-informed caregiver understands that these congruent adaptive and mitigating behaviors are the survivor's attempts to resolve their overactivated physiology, even when those behaviors might be unpleasant, damaging to the patient/client, or even illegal.

According to our definition, traumatic activators can be an infinite array of traumatic and aversive events ranging from divorce or separation to a traumatic sexual experience (i.e., rape, molestation, incest, etc.) that activates the body's natural physiological responses to a perceived threat and dysregulates normal human development. This normal homeostatic neurobiological dysregulation in the body, nervous system, and brain is the result of changes in the serum levels of neurochemical-peptide-hormonal cocktail mixes (i.e., corticotropin; corticosteroids such as cortisol, arginine vasopressin, glucocorticoids, catecholamines, growth hormone, and prolactin; reduction in neurotransmitters such as serotonin), which create immediate physiological changes and can eventually result in altered anatomic pathways (Popoli et al., 2011; Ranabir and Reetu, 2011).

The body's inability to manage traumatic activators can hinder the brain's hippocampus from integrating and/or processing a traumatic event as an explicit memory. Explicit memories are declarative memories that require conscious thought, and include the autobiographical memories that connect us to our past occurrences. Conversely, implicit memories do *not* require conscious or even cognitive realization of remembrances, allowing us to perform tasks without conscious awareness of previous experiences (driving a car does not require conscious thought, for example).

During a traumatic event we may dysregulate and/or dissociate ourselves from the overwhelming nature of the occurrence as a way of self-preservation, which can result in the encoding and integrating of implicit memories about the event, but fails to integrate the corresponding explicit memories (Siegel, 2008). Exposure to a stressful event also hinders the medial prefrontal cortex's ability to encode an integrated association between the event, location, contacts, and even the time-stamp. As a result, professionals who lack the neurobiological understanding of how traumatic memories can be encoded with errors may misevaluate a survivor's inconsistent recollection of past events as lies or manipulations.

During a traumatic event, different parts of the brain that usually work in an efficient and integrated way can become unlinked or disconnected. When this linkage is broken, it sets the stage for incomplete or partial learning that is unfiltered through a lens of reality checking and is likely to be volatile and highly reactive. Louis Cozolino, PhD, has written that when this disconnection happens, emotional memory can be overly accessed and not well evaluated for authenticity (Cozolino, 2016). These errors in memory can be activated by environmental triggers that resemble past traumatic experiences (i.e., a survivor of abduction is filled with terror when a male approaches to ask her for directions). As a result, our bodies become flooded with powerful and painful emotions that are not consciously connected to past memories, due to a failure to encode and/or integrate the traumatic experience as an explicit memory. Most of the time we perceive the current situation to be a danger or real threat (since we *feel* threatened), and display protective or mitigating behaviors that others may not understand.

Sherin and Nemeroff (2011) stated that:

> The classic fight-or-flight response to a perceived threat is a reflexive nervous system phenomenon that has obvious survival advantages in evolutionary terms. However, the systems that organize the constellation of reflexive survival behaviors following exposure to perceived threat can under some circumstances become dysregulated in the process. (p. 263)

What is being proposed is that these physiological processes in response to the threat are natural, reflexive, and meant to be helpful. Take, for instance, a paper cut. It is nowhere near life-threatening, but the instant someone's finger is cut by the paper, the body goes into an immediate response process to mitigate the "threat." Bleeding may or may not occur, but the body still sends a chemical cocktail to the damaged tissue area to seal the wound by creating inflammation, followed by those elements that will heal the wound and prevent infection. The autonomic nervous system—without conscious input from the individual—has already begun to marshal various bodily processes to adapt to and heal the wound.

Blisters are another example of the body's healing process at work. They form in areas where skin has been damaged, collecting with fluid to create a protective layer between the tissue and further injury. As the discomfort from a blister increases, it is not unusual for one's gait to change. This modification in stepping or walking is not generally a conscious choice at first, but a mitigating response to reduce the distress being generated. If the pain persists long enough, it may become elevated to our conscious awareness, but the body's initial reactions are not intentional or consciously decided upon.

Similarly, trauma follows the same trajectory of unconscious-before-conscious physiological mitigating responses to try and heal from the wounds of a traumatic experience. By moving the focal point of trauma toward these bodily processes, a reduction in shame and stigma is possible because the symptomatic behavior is understood to be a *naturally occurring* response rather than the result of disease, disorder, or intentionality. This sets the stage to approach healing and recovery from a more holistic and strength-based perspective, where the patient/client no longer feels defective or "broken," but grasps that their body is behaving exactly as it was designed to (just to an overactivated extent).

"Big T" and "Little t" Trauma

Trauma includes the natural neurobiological and physiological occurrences in the body as a result of a traumatic activator (a real or perceived threat to self or others). Traumatic activators can be categorized in two ways, commonly referred to as "big T" and "little t" trauma.

"Big T" trauma is a primary traumatization, and represents traumatic events that are more commonly associated with the diagnostic criteria of PTSD (i.e., war, being held at gunpoint, a physical assault). While a "big T" incident is viewed as a high intensity event that disrupts normal human development, the accumulation of "little t" traumas—also primary traumatizations—can insidiously and incrementally raise one's traumatic stress levels to worrying heights.

"Little t" traumas, sometimes referred to as complex traumas, can be overwhelming, but are not necessarily classified as traumatic for the first few incidences. Some examples would include bullying, harassment, emotional abuse, threats that are non-life-threatening, etc. The first couple occurrences of emotional abuse (name-calling, criticizing, gaslighting, etc.) in a relationship might not be viewed as traumatic, but the frequency of these "little t" incidents can emotionally and mentally disrupt an individual's normal development by chronically dysregulating the body's homeostasis, and offsetting the experience of positive emotions. Eventually this dysregulation becomes the norm, due to the structural changes in the brain that these "little t" events have created.

As one may imagine, these categories can have grey areas in regard to severity and resulting dysregulation. Infidelity and divorce would technically be labeled a "little t" trauma (due to the fact no one's life was directly threatened, no physical injury took place, and there was no sexual violence), but they may only occur once and still result in severe post-traumatic stress. Depending on a person's level of resiliency, an accumulation of "little t" traumas, or even reminiscing on one "little t" event, can result in suicidal ideation, hopelessness, and a plethora of other serious symptoms. Biologically speaking, this overactivation of the threat-response system (the fight-or-flight response) is altered through cumulative harm—every time a "little t" trauma occurs, the autonomic nervous system responds with changes to the body's neurochemicals. As a result, repeated activation creates a greater propensity to react, a greater neurological readiness to reactivity, and more fluidity and speed in reacting.

From this perspective, the results of "little t" trauma can subjectively rival or even exceed those of "big T" trauma in terms of physiological activation, dysregulation, and resulting traumatic stress. The trauma-focused caregiver must pay careful attention to the fact that while the "big T" traumas tend to be easily visible, they are no more important than the subtle, often minimized "little t" traumas that impact people's lives. We must remember that an individual does not need a "great big bad event" to generate a physiological response to their environment or the experiences in their life.

Systemic Traumatization

Besides primary traumatization (both "big T" and "little t" experiences), larger systems can also experience a form of trauma known as tertiary, or systemic, traumatization. This form of traumatization can occur at the global, geographical, organizational, and/or familiar level.

Examples of systemic traumatization include the Rwandan mass genocidal slaughter imposed on the Tutsis by the Hutus in 1994, which accounted for 800,000 deaths (BBC News, 2011). On September 11, 2001, a terrorist attack cost the lives of 2,977 individuals in New York City, Washington, D.C., and Shanksville, Pennsylvania. The mass shooting in Las Vegas,

Nevada, on October 3, 2017, took the lives of fifty-eight people and injured nearly five hundred others.

Natural traumatic disasters have also claimed the lives of many people and left billions of dollars' worth of damage to be repaired by governments and communities. On December 26, 2004, in Sumatra, Indonesia, an earthquake that measured 9.1 in magnitude killed a reported 230,000 people. The Australian Geographic (2011) outlines nine more of the biggest natural traumatic disasters in history:

1. March 11, 2011: A tsunami that hit the North Pacific Coast of Japan killed approximately 230,000 people.
2. November 1, 1755: An earthquake in Lisbon, Portugal killed more than 18,000 people.
3. August 27, 1883: A tsunami that hit Krakatau, Indonesia killed approximately 40,000 people.
4. September 20, 1498: A tsunami that hit Meiō Nankai, Japan killed 31,000 people.
5. October 28, 1707: An earthquake in Nankaido, Japan killed approximately 30,000 people.
6. June 15, 1896: A tsunami that hit Sanriku, Japan killed approximately 22,000 people.
7. August 13, 1868: A tsunami that hit northern Chile killed approximately 22,000 people.
8. April 24, 1771: An earthquake in Ryuku Islands, Japan killed nearly 12,000 people.
9. January 18, 1586: An earthquake in Ise Bay, Japan killed approximately 8,000 people.

These are a few examples of historical traumatic activators that impacted an entire nation, which created a systemic dysregulation that undoubtedly changed entire belief systems regarding personal safety.

Although war, terrorism, and epidemics certainly do create systemic traumatization, there are also traumatic activators that do not involve disasters of a great magnitude or high mortality rates. In 2016, whether perceived or real, the U.S. presidential election created a national systemic dysregulation that altered many Americans' sense of security and personal safety based on the biased and repeated comments made against Muslims, Latinos, and other minorities. As a result of tertiary traumatization, these and other grand-scale environmental activators are not just affecting individuals but are also impacting our geographical communities with identity-based crises (i.e., questioning our nation as one of equality, acceptance, and tolerance of other cultures).

Traumatic activators can also offset the homeostasis of a family system. There are an infinite number of activators that do this, including divorce, death, illness, crimes or community violence, homelessness, natural disasters, etc. Even joyful events such as marriage or the birth of a child can be traumatic activators, based on who is being affected and how it unfolds.

The family members' resiliency and mental architecture and the level of systemic functioning (i.e., stability) all have an influence on what might cause tertiary traumatization in the family unit. The onset of a traumatic activator can put considerable stress on the family unit, and if the family members are not able to function at their previous level, the system will begin to break down. As a result, overwhelming and dysregulated emotions can drain members' abilities to provide basic needs (emotional support, safety, love, food, etc.) and maintain day-to-day activities (hygiene, work, school, etc.) for others in the family unit.

Problematic communication patterns can arise, further alienating family members instead of bringing them together to support one another. It is in these moments that family members will be reactive and will display behaviors that can be destructive to the emotional bonds holding the family together. When families are overwhelmed by stressful circumstances the disruption is widespread, including but not limited to physical, behavioral, genetic, cognitive, hormonal, and relational development.

As with individual behaviors, it is important for the trauma-informed caregiver to view familial interactions as the natural response to the neurobiological and physiological changes of the members' dysregulated autonomic nervous systems. Said in another way, the symptoms labeled as "dysfunctional family behavior" are frequently the consequences of accumulated/layered circumstances, stressors, and reactive responses, all of which are normal rather than volitional behaviors. This view can help us provide trauma-focused and compassionate caregiving that is conducive to change and healing. In addition, it is important to understand that real or identifiable traumatic events are not necessary for the emerging of symptomatic behaviors. Real or not, we must understand that these symptoms are primary adaptations to adverse environments.

Traumagenesis

The concept of traumagenesis explores the origins of trauma (Rojo Aubrey and Gentry, 2019), and in order to understand these origins we must first look at trauma as a *physiological* phenomenon. Trauma professionals need to realize that it is not necessarily the events or experiences themselves that are destructive or disturbing—it is the body's physical reaction to them. The unfortunate truth is that each person responds uniquely to such overwhelming stressors based primarily on their developmental trajectory, and the consideration of traumagenesis can help us to broaden our understanding of traumatic stress.

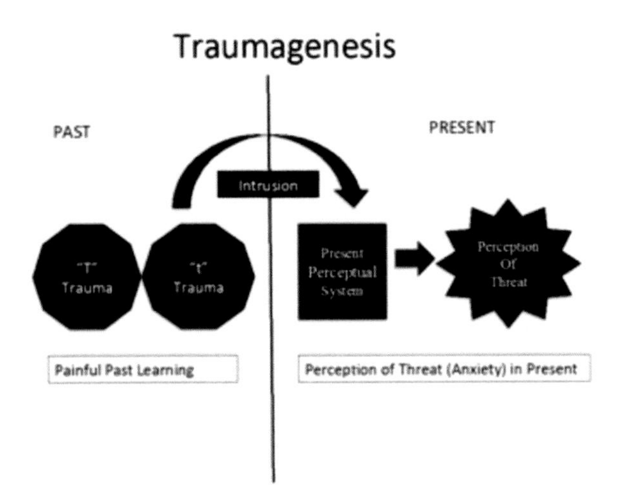

Traumagenesis is a concept that widens the traditional view of trauma, which in some circumstances has proven to be too narrow. Restrictive or narrowed traditional definitions of trauma can limit the many approaches to healing that may prove very effective, which is not beneficial for trauma survivors or the treatment as a whole.

One of the primary factors of traumagenesis is that it can occur in anyone's life, but the young are more vulnerable to permanent and indelible neurological as well as biological impact that changes or alters them at a molecular and/or epigenetic level. The brain experiences the world by receiving energy (i.e., photons, vibrating molecules, etc.) or information through our senses, and then converting these forms of energy to electrochemical energy for processing.

Thinking—although unknown exactly how—takes place through the mind's different forms of testing and comparing those thoughts with the experiences happening in the environment. The frequency, intensity, and duration of experiences inform the brain and body on how to react, without evaluation or a critical eye. We "see" pictures, "hear" sounds, and "feel" sensations, categorizing and construing their meanings or schemas. This journey of development begins before conception—and not just as a fetus growing in the womb. In most circumstances, human beings also receive a generational transmission of family culture, which may be free of abuse, but is still filled with trauma-generating behaviors, attitudes, and interactional patterns.

Rojo Aubrey and Gentry (2019) have outlined four major categories of traumagenesis (the first two of which were discussed in Chapter Two), with the latter two listed below showcasing the field's recent broadened explorations of the origins of trauma:

1. Primary traumatic stress.
2. Secondary traumatic stress (STS).
3. Environmental trauma (a.k.a. emotional contagion).
4. Epigenetic trauma.

Micah Leshem, PhD, and Alice Shachar-Dadon, PhD, from the University of Haifa, and Jay Schulkin, PhD, from the Georgetown University School of Medicine (2009) published an article that has reset psychological thinking about trauma's origination, when they found that adversity in female rats *before* conception impacted the social and affective behaviors of their progenies. Although further research is required to conclusively generalize these findings in humans, they suggest the possibility that trauma may begin for a child before they are even conceived, based on the life experiences and stress levels in the life of the mother. This is a vital point to understand: The trauma or stress experienced by the mother in her lifetime might create environmental pressures of an epigenetic nature that can negatively impact an unconceived child.

Psychiatrist Bruce D. Perry of the Child Trauma Academy has long established that exposure to stress, accident, poor neonatal care, or maternal substance abuse can have a severe impact on the developing fetus and create novel brain patterns and sensitivities that may later manifest in odd or ineffective child behaviors. Perry's research coupled with that of Leshem, Shachar-Dadon, and Schulkin's would clearly warn that trauma can begin through the creation of stressors that are significant in the life of the future mother, or the family functioning and future mom's ability to cope with stressors.

An additional factor that complicates the question of when trauma begins is found in individual resilience and adaptability on the part of the mother. Not all experiences are created equal; different people experience the same situation in an idiosyncratic or unique way, which challenges the ability to be definitive or absolute about when and at what specific point trauma was initiated. While the specific moment may be unrecognizable, there are elements that can exacerbate the impact of trauma on the mother and increase the likelihood of post-traumatic stress. These primary factors of acuity are intensity, duration, and frequency, and would be the same for the mother as for the fetus or newborn child.

In an effort to understand the genesis of trauma, we need to understand how the mother perceives the intensity of the stressors she is experiencing. Many researchers feel hesitant to use such an ambiguous measure, because it is a challenge to create good statistical analysis when each person possesses a highly personalized view of what intensity is like for them. Duration, or the length of time between the beginning and end of an episode is a little easier to grasp and quantify, but even that is somewhat personalized by the perceptions of the individual experiencing the stressor. The final factor of frequency represents how often a stressful or distressing event occurs, and is oftentimes the easiest factor to measure.

How intensity, duration, and frequency interact collectively becomes vitally important to understanding where trauma begins. A disturbing experience can have a low level of intensity, but if it lasts for long periods of time, or occurs quite often, this combination can begin to generate stress that potentially overwhelms the future mom's ability to adapt or cope. If an experience was one of high intensity, with long durations and frequent occurrences, it would be easy to significantly devastate the emotional, psychological, and even to some extent the physical reserves of the future mother. It is also likely that adolescent mothers might be at a greater risk of generating epigenetic trauma effects in their offspring, because of the natural instability of adolescence.

A cautionary note must be expressed—we are by no means declaring in any way that a child's behavior should be blamed on the mother. This is just a simple recognition that a highly stressed future mother being subjected to an environment that overwhelms her ability to adapt could engender epigenetic activation of trauma for the child. It should also be mentioned that the father or other supportive relationships play a huge role in creating a safe haven and pleasant environment for the mother-to-be.

Based on these results, however, we can conclude that it is possible for trauma to manifest itself in the life of an individual sometime before their conception, or even that it can be passed down through generations. According to epigenetic studies done by Dr. Marcus Pembrey and his team, stress experienced by a child's grandparents and parents is a great determinant for their own genetic expression, health, and development. One such finding was that changes in a paternal grandmother's early food supply influenced the cardiovascular mortality of her female grandchildren (Pembrey, Saffery, and Bygren, 2014).

These discoveries would suggest that creating more stable environments that are within a tolerable range of stress just prior to conception, and maybe significantly before conception, might be an important factor in supporting the healthy emotional and psychological development of children.

In summary, the emergence of trauma in an individual might be impacted by the life and environment of the mother before she gets pregnant, the level of stress during pregnancy, distress in the environment postnatal, and/or transgenerational factors of stress experienced by grandparents and parents. This should initiate a thought process about how we can collectively foster and maintain a supportive and stable society to give as-yet-unborn children a greater opportunity to thrive and prosper.

Reactive Adaptation and Reactive Mitigation

Most books and articles on trauma focus heavily on outlining a series of signs and symptoms to recognize if someone has been traumatized. This can be an endless list, one that is inclusive or exclusive depending on the individual's unique resiliency. Instead of focusing on a daunting list of symptoms and signs, we felt it was more important that trauma-focused caregivers understand the processes that occur when the body's physiological arousal systems are activated.

As we learned in Chapter Two, when someone is exposed to a traumatic stressful event, real or perceived, their sympathetic nervous system becomes charged and activated. This creates an unbalance in the body's homeostatic status, which will then need to be stabilized in order for the body to return to a state of "normalcy." In order to accomplish homeostasis, the body will become reactive and automatically, without conscious thought, force us into a state of reactive adaptation and/or reactive mitigation. Some of the common observable behaviors during these states are anxiety- or fear-based symptoms. Many survivors of trauma, however, often present with a combination of anhedonic and dysphoric symptoms, aggressiveness or externalized anger, and/or dissociative symptoms (American Psychiatric Association, 2013, p. 265). It is important to remember that these behaviors are symptoms of trauma, and are neither conscious nor deliberate.

In order to differentiate the states of reactive adaptation and reactive mitigation, we are going to refer to psychologist Martin Seligman's experiment with dogs. In 1967, Seligman conducted an experiment with three groups of dogs, where each group was placed in a cage and given random electric shocks to their paws with electrical floor grids. The dogs assigned to groups one and two were able to avoid the electrical shocks by jumping over a low partition to the other side of the cage. The third group of dogs, however, was not able to escape the electrical shocks because their partition was too high (Seligman, 1972). In this traumatic experiment, the dogs assigned to groups one and two used an adaptation process—they moved to an area where no pain was felt. This is a similar response to when you might jerk your hand away from a hot stove, and has an obvious survival value.

Mitigation, however, occurs when we cannot escape the distressing situation that is activating our body's physiological arousal system. In the case of the third group of dogs, if they ran away and hid every time they saw or heard Seligman's assistants, this would have been a reactive mitigation response. This is similar to a female rape survivor avoiding all males with mustaches or beards since they resemble her perpetrator.

Both the reactive adaptation and reactive mitigation processes are normal, involuntary physiological responses to alleviate the pain and discomfort associated with an actively charged arousal system. Thus, it would be unreasonable for a caregiver to ask someone to stop these automatic and reactive systems, and the trauma-informed healer is aware that the key to recovery is not to "stop" these normal physiological responses, but to regulate them. As a result of helping patients and clients self-regulate their physiology, they are better able to gain optimal neocortical access, which will allow them to avoid maladaptive behaviors while intentionally choosing those that are more likely to be successful.

Alarm and Threat-Response System

Many homeowners, and even those who rent, have made wise choices to invest in various types of home security systems (carbon monoxide poisoning detectors, smoke detectors, etc.). Although no one desires or hopes for an incident to occur, these investments create a sense of safety and can end up saving someone's life. Human beings also have a miraculous security system that is diligently working to protect us from any kind of environmental danger. At times, however, this system might not be functioning adequately, and can end up robbing us of that feeling of safety.

Similar to the smoke detector—which alarms everyone that there is a potential danger of fire—our body has a natural security system that alarms us when we are faced with danger from our environment. Let us turn our attention to two major biological components of the human security alarm and threat-response system. The amygdala (Latin for "almond") has received a lot of publicity for its association with fear. Specifically, based on the research of neuroscientist Joseph LeDoux, neurobiologist James McGaugh, and others, it has become known as the "panic button in the brain" (Arden and Linford, 2009, p. 31). The amygdala is associated with many other functions as well, including learning, emotions, memory consolidation, regulation of the autonomic nervous system, activation of the startle response, interpretation of facial expressions, arousal, and other functions. There are two bilateral amygdalae, which are a complex group of nuclei, located deep in the medial temporal lobes of the brain that are considered to be part of the limbic system. This is one of the major structures involved in our security system, and as part of that security system, the amygdala is highly responsive to fear and primed to recognize any stimuli that can be a potential threat. This recognition activates the corticosteroids and adrenergic systems, leading to the stimulation of the sympathetic nervous system (Arden and Linford, 2009).

This is accomplished through one of the two neural pathways, which LeDoux (1996) dubbed the "low road" and the "high road," out of the amygdala. The fast track (low road) relays messages with speed and precision from the amygdala to the thalamus, and on to the subcortical areas of the brain. This pathway does not connect to the cortical regions of the brain or even require conscious awareness, because it relies on speed for survival purposes. In other words, if you were hiking and heard a rattle, any message sent to the cortical regions of the brain (which we will discuss in the next paragraph) that caused you to stop and ponder—even for a moment—about whether it was the sound of a baby rattle or a poisonous rattlesnake could be costly or life-threatening. Arden and Linford (2009) stated that the "speedy reaction on the part of the amygdala is more important than fine-grained distinctions," and there are many deadly situations that validate this statement (p. 32). Conditioned responses or even internal stimuli such as perspiration, tunnel vision, increased respiration rate, etc. also activate low-road circuitry. The downside to the speed and sensitivity of the low-road circuitry out of the amygdala is that it can result in fear or terror within the context of a perceived threat that is not a real danger, which may have a phenomenological adaptive purpose but no survival purpose.

If the amygdala identifies the internal or external stimuli as nonthreatening, the activity in this area of the brain starts to diminish. This is accomplished through the slow track (high road), which relays messages from the amygdala to the thalamus and then to the cortical regions of the brain, such as the orbitofrontal cortex (OFC), dorsolateral prefrontal cortex (DLPFC), dorsal medial prefrontal cortex (dmPFC), ventrolateral prefrontal cortex (VLPFC), and the anterior cingulate cortex (ACC), before going back to the amygdala. This high-road neural pathway from the amygdala to the cortical regions is slower and more complex than its speedy sister, the low road, and the complexity of this circuitry causes a delay for electrical messages traveling through it. The high-road neural pathway from the amygdala to the cortical areas of the brain is more robust compared to the high-road pathway back to the amygdala. When signals are sent from the amygdala to the cortical areas of the brain, the cortical regions start to produce conscious awareness and thinking, including reality testing, about the current situation. This meticulous cognitive process creates a complexity in the alarm system as the result of the conscious thinking and reality testing being relayed back to the amygdala.

It is the cortical areas that can modulate or inhibit the activity in the amygdala, which can prevent the cascading of biological occurrences that stimulate the fight-or-flight response of the sympathetic nervous system, and the subsequent parasympathetic nervous system response for returning to homeostasis. The challenge, however, is that the amygdala can bypass or ignore the top-down inhibition process and continue to stimulate the sympathetic nervous system. This may be one of the reasons why thoughts (i.e., positive affirmations) are less effective or take more time to mediate strong emotions, while strong emotions seem to easily heighten negative or pessimistic thinking (Arden and Linford, 2009).

Keep in mind that the amygdala's function is part of our alarm system, and gives us an evolutionary edge as it protects us from threats that pose a risk to our lives. Things become problematic only when that threat system is *chronically* charged and activated. Another issue is that chronic activation of the system enhances the speed and functionality of the body's alarm system, resulting in what is called the Hebbian theory or cell assembly theory—"cells that fire together wire together" (Lowel and Singer, 1992, p. 210). In other words, every time the alarm system becomes activated, the capacity to generate reactive adaptation gets stronger "so we react rapidly to danger rather than to think about it" (Arden and Linford, 2009, p. 33).

In the case of a married couple, this process is clear when a husband becomes snarky after his wife asks him whether he took his vitamins ("Stop treating me like a child!" he might snap). This is the result of the charged low-road circuitry in the amygdala, and a failed top-down inhibition of the amygdala modulated by the cortical regions of the brain through the high-road circuitry. On the other hand, the husband could also turn to his wife and say, "Thank you for taking the time to care for me. I know I can be grouchy and it seems like I'm unappreciative, but sometimes I just feel incompetent. I know that's not what you intended, but it's how I've felt all my life because of everyone telling me what was best, while never listening to my needs. I want to feel capable, and I need your understanding to do that."

This type of response requires the cortical regions of the brain and the amygdala to communicate via the high-road circuitry. Throughout this process, the cortical areas integrate the emotions generated from the amygdala with conscious thinking, reality testing (i.e., "I dislike my wife telling me to take my vitamins, but my life is not in danger"), and other sources of information. As a result, the cortical areas of the brain can inhibit the activity in the amygdala and allow us to have access to the cerebral cortex, which is involved in higher brain functions, to plan out the most effective behavioral response. Let us take a closer look now at a particular area of the brain involved in reality testing.

The anterior cingulate cortex (ACC) plays a key role in a variety of autonomic and higher-level functions, but various studies also allude to the ACC and dorsal anterior cingulate cortex (dACC) being involved in shifting our attention toward social or environmental threat (Dedovic et al., 2016; Lin, Wu, and Wu, 2015; Klumpp, Angstadt, and Phan, 2011; Milad et al., 2007; Spunt et al., 2012). In essence, the ACC functions as a filtering system or threat assessment that turns our attention to any relevant threats in our environment. Besides acting as an alarm system to protect us from real or perceived physical and emotional pain, including exclusion, rejection, or ostracism (Eisenberger and Lieberman, 2004), "the ACC is reciprocally connected with the amygdala" and "participates in assigning both positive and negative valence to events" (Hayden and Platt, 2009, p. 887).

Although there has been some debate and controversy about the specific roles of the ACC and dACC, it appears they play a key role in the modulation of autonomic nervous system activity (Shenhav, Cohen, and Botvinick, 2016; Critchley et al., 2003; Luu and Posner, 2003). The ACC, which helps regulate the body's threat response, is a fast and efficient system that can save our lives when presented with a real environmental threat.

Another way these threat systems are strengthened (for better or worse) is through the natural process of generalizing or collapsing classification systems. Let us say that an individual has a near-death medical reaction after ingesting the castor oil plant, sometimes called the "palm of Christ" and known to be more poisonous than cyanide. Surviving this severe toxic reaction would later activate the body's alert system (i.e., the amygdala and ACC) and survival response (the sympathetic nervous system) to any plant that looks remotely similar to the castor oil plant. A later allergic reaction to another plant or flower may collapse all plants and flowers into a single dangerous category. This generalization decreases reaction time by eliminating categories of the kingdom plantae (good for survival), while increasing the amount of potential threats that exist in the environment (bad for the autonomic nervous system's regulation). This can cause hypervigilance, heightening an individual's state of anxiety when in the backyard or park, until it eventually occurs any time they step outside. Thus, the survivor loses the ability to distinguish elements that are safe and those that truly pose a threat, and the world becomes exponentially more dangerous. As a result, survivors have to focus more of their energy externally (outside of oneself) to prevent or avoid potentially dangerous environmental elements, which leaves them with little to no energy to do any self-reflection.

This is all too commonly observed when survivors are disconnected and unable to pinpoint why they are feeling anxious, upset, or are adversely reacting to environmental triggers. One of the side effects of this state of chronic external hypervigilance is that the individual becomes self-centered, exhibiting symptoms that resemble narcissism. This is an appropriate and normal physiological process of self-preservation, resulting from the collapsing or generalizing of categories that increase perceived potential threats in the environment.

When a threat is perceived, the alarm system is alerted, and the sympathetic nervous system is activated to address the threat. The sympathetic nervous system immediately prepares the body to do one of two things: 1) neutralize or mitigate (fight) the threat; or 2) escape (flight) the threat. At times, these systems can become so overwhelmed that they freeze, which is a function of a specific component of the autonomic nervous system known as the vagus nerve.

The dorsal vagal complex (DVC), or the dorsal branches of the vagus nerve, play a role in this stress or threat response. Dr. Steven Porges proposed in his Polyvagal Theory that the tenth cranial nerve and two branches of the vagal nerve elicit two types of behaviors: 1) withdrawal or immobilizing; or 2) self-regulation and effective social communication (Porges, 2011; Beauchaine, Gatzke-Kopp, and Mead, 2007; Porges, 2001). The behaviors associated with the sympathetic nervous system and dorsal vagal system are discussed below.

Table 4. Sympathetic Nervous System and Dorsal Vagal System Behaviors

Sympathetic	Dorsal Vagal
Anger	Freezing, being "stuck" or paralyzed
Aggressiveness	Dissociation
Overly manipulative	Covertly manipulative
Defensive	Emotional numbing
Reactive	Reactive
Impulsive	Impulsive
Hostile	Emotional and psychological distancing
Self-centered	Self-centered

When our survival system is activated, various neurobiological systems are suppressed (i.e., the sub-diaphragmatic system, the ventral vagal complex which dictates our relational/social engagement system and executive function, etc.). The electrical activity is diverted from the neocortex (where executive and higher-order brain functions take place) to the posterior part of the brain, the brainstem, and even the diencephalon (located in the caudal part of the forebrain). This part of the brain has various functions and is mainly concerned with keeping us alive. It will instinctively result in reactive behaviors that are adaptive or mitigating and not concerned with deeper processes like self-reflection and intentionality.

Ultimately, the trauma-focused caregiver is set apart from others due to their thorough understanding of the physiological factors regarding trauma and post-traumatic stress in individuals, families, and nations. Effective trauma-focused treatment works *with* these factors instead of against them, acknowledging their natural place in human survival and promoting new ways to combat an overactive autonomic nervous system and the resulting post-traumatic stress symptoms so that lasting recuperation can be achieved.

Post-Traumatic Stress Injury (PTSI): Reducing the Stigma

In the book *Unlocking the Code to Human Resiliency* (Rojo Aubrey and Gentry, 2019), Drs. Rojo Aubrey and Gentry discuss the importance of trauma-informed sensitivity when using the term "post-traumatic stress disorder." They propose that despite the limited inclusion and exclusion criteria of PTSD when it was first described in the DSM-III in 1980, this then-new diagnosis helped millions of people in diverse ways including:

1. Giving a name to the frightening experience.
2. Increasing awareness and compassion.
3. Permitting insurance coverage for treatment.
4. Providing disability benefits.

Although the official diagnosis of PTSD has its benefits, it also has its subjective pitfalls. The "D" for disorder in PTSD perpetuates a bias that alludes to a preexisting pathology, which may connotate a mental weakness that can discourage professionals, including military personnel, from seeking help on a path to recovery when experiencing symptoms of PTSD. This includes over sixty percent of physicians who are reluctant to seek help for fear of losing their license if they were to pursue treatment for mental health struggles (Shanafelt et al., 2015).

In order to help alleviate the stigma attached to the label, advocacy has arisen to replace PTSD with Post-Traumatic Stress Injury (PTSI), especially since traumatic stress is commonly incurred in the line of duty for professionals helping, serving, and protecting others.

The use of the term PTSI might be more appealing to first responders and military personnel who are often less apt to seek help for a "disorder." In the case of military personnel, this is understandable since they are often honored for a *physical* injury earned in battle (i.e, the Purple Heart Medal awarded to those wounded or killed in action), but never for putting their emotional and mental states at risk to keep their country safe.

Please understand that we are not advocating that the American Psychiatric Association rename PTSD, but do support the fact that some individuals may prefer to use PTSI rather than PTSD. Our goal is to help those suffering from symptoms of PTSD/PTSI, and not to hinder anyone's motivations to seek help toward recovery. We are hopeful that as the field continues to evolve and grow decade by decade, that the integration of this revised term will lead to reduced stigma and a more productive and fruitful collaboration with patients/clients.

Chapter Summary

The current psychiatric definition for trauma in the DSM-5 is limited in certain ways regarding its ability to encompass the true challenges and complexities trauma survivors face. This definition is broadened via the identification of traumatic activators, which include any experience that overwhelms the body's physiology and disrupts normal human development. Trauma, therefore, is a physiological or neurobiological reaction to unbearable experiences.

PTSD is a result of this trauma, and is categorized and diagnosed by a list of criteria (Criterion A through H). There are some criticisms regarding the DSM-5's criteria and its applicability to other types of trauma that do not fit the requirements exactly, and additional disorders and diagnoses have resulted because of this.

Traumatic activators can be further categorized into "big T" and "little t" experiences, both of which vary in a number of ways. "Big T" traumas are defined as single or infrequent incredibly disruptive incidents such as natural disasters, physical assault, displacement due to war, etc. "Little t" traumas are those smaller experiences that create a disturbance over time, like bullying, emotional and verbal manipulation, name-calling, etc. A single "big T" trauma can certainly disrupt a person's normal development, but the accumulation of "little t" incidents can result in significant emotional and mental dysregulation as well.

An individual's unique mental architecture and personal resiliency both determine how and when an experience is traumatic to them. Even more interesting, the concept of traumagenesis explores how susceptibility or resiliency to trauma is partly dictated before conception—that is, the personal stressors a mother experiences long before she is ever pregnant can influence her child's adaptability to potentially traumatic situations and/or environments.

The human body has a perfectly designed set of systems and processes to identify and survive threats (perceived or real), with the sympathetic nervous system taking over and responding through adapting/neutralizing behaviors or escape when danger is sensed. A third reaction of "freezing" can arise as well, which is a result of the brain's dorsal vagal system and presents as dissociative or avoidant symptoms. Trauma survivors' adapting and mitigating behaviors, although challenging, are congruent with the way our bodies were designed to behave, and in order to be treated successfully, should be viewed as such by an understanding and compassionate trauma-focused caregiver.

Finally, as the mental health field continues to embark on new trauma treatment development, a strong wave of advocacy to refer to the diagnosis of post-traumatic stress disorder (PTSD) by the less stigmatizing post-traumatic stress injury (PTSI) has been brought forward in recent years. This is in the hope that individuals working in highly traumatizing fields such as medicine, the military, and first response will be able to come forward for treatment without judgment, shame, or a lack of support from their employers and coworkers.

Chapter Five

The History of Traumatic Care and Current Trends

Focus Questions:

- How has the care of individuals who are suffering from traumatic stress evolved over the years?
- What key historical events have influenced the innovative improvement of traumatic care?

In this chapter you will learn more about:

- The history of traumatic care and the evolutionary course of the field.
- Current evidence-based practices for treating traumatic stress.

Honorable errors do not count as failures in science, but as seeds for progress in the quintessential activity of correction.

– Stephen Jay Gould

Early Influences on Trauma Treatment

In the early years of psychotherapy, neurologist Jean-Martin Charcot was one of the first pioneers to reconceptualize the historical understanding of the ethology of hysteria. The term stems from the Greek word ὑστέρα, meaning uterus, and made reference to a woman with ungovernable emotional excess due to a "wandering womb."

Charcot hypothesized that hysteria was psychological rather than physiological in nature. This was a revolutionary historical event, since up until that time the symptoms of hysteria had been thought to stem from outside variables. For example, during the second century a physician named Aretaeus of Cappadocia believed that hysteria was caused by displacement of the uterus, hence the "wandering womb" reference (Adams, 1856). Physician Soranus of Ephesus opposed Aretaeus's view of a wandering uterus, arguing that "hysterical suffocation" was caused by inflammation. Later, Greek physician and philosopher Galen of Pergamon hypothesized that it was caused by substances being retained in the uterus (Gilman et al., 1993, p. 42). Thus, Charcot's innovative suppositions shifted the understanding of psychological trauma to a new paradigm.

One of Charcot's students, neurologist Sigmund Freud, concluded that the cause of hysteria was related to the patient's emotional life as a result of a traumatic event. Although the cause of hysteria remained psychological, Freud's attention was on the origins of internal deficit and how someone reacted internally to external events. There was a lack of focus on the impact that a traumatic event had on an individual, with Freud stating that the propensity for exhibiting traumatic symptoms was ingrained in a person since childhood.

During the same time period, Pierre Janet, a pioneering French psychologist working on what is now known as traumatic memories and dissociation, believed that the events that occurred in a person's life impacted how their personality developed and the behaviors they exhibited. In the 1940s, anthropologist and psychoanalyst Abram Kardiner studied the so-called "traumatic neuroses of war," or cognitive reenactments that are now referred to as flashbacks. In many ways, Kardiner can be thought of as an unknown pioneer in the philosophical development of trauma-informed care, since he viewed the symptoms of post-traumatic stress as a normal response to an unbearable situation, instead of treating patients and clients as though they were ill or exhibiting a psychological abnormality. Unfortunately, at some point in history there appeared to be an ideological regression to pathologizing individuals suffering from traumatic stress.

Prior to the 1970s, professionals implicitly blamed and placed responsibility for the development of chronic traumatic stress symptoms on the survivor of the traumatic event. During this time, it was not uncommon for professionals to view the development of psychological trauma (post-traumatic stress disorder) as a rare occurrence that only manifested among individuals with a family history of mental illness or a predisposition to it. It was believed that if healthy individuals were exposed to a traumatic event, they might suffer from acute psychological distress, but would innately recover or heal from the wounds with no long-term effects. It was during the Vietnam War that professionals observed the "delayed stress syndrome" among healthy soldiers, which forced another paradigm shift on how they conceived of and managed psychological trauma. In addition, other historical events influenced both the movement toward trauma-focused care and improved treatments for those suffering from traumatic stress.

Long before the use of the term "trauma-focused care," the feminist movement in the 1970s played an influential role in creating a trauma-sensitive and safe environment for survivors of traumatic incidents. Through a series of political campaigns, the feminist movement advocated to empower women and minorities (i.e., gay men and women), shining a light on the excruciating injustice of sexual violence, sexual harassment, and domestic violence. This movement led to the development of domestic violence shelters, rape crisis centers, and prevention awareness for sexual, relationship, and domestic violence (Burgess and Holmstrom, 1974). In the 1970s and '80s, men and women participated in marches and events to increase awareness about child abuse, and fought for the establishment of child advocacy centers (Wilson, Pence, and Conradi, 2013). These historical events resulted in the evolving innovation of trauma-informed practices, which in the 1990s were supported by the growing body of trauma-specific empirical research on the causes, effects, and treatments of traumatic stress.

Current Trends in Trauma Treatment

Currently there is a vast amount of empirically supported and promising practices for the treatment of traumatic stress. Many of the existing models overlap in their content, since research has shown that particular elements are necessary for any effective treatment of trauma. Though covering *all* existing models of trauma-focused treatment would be beyond the scope of this book, we have highlighted a few commonly used treatment models that are supported by strong empirical research:

1. Trauma Focused-Cognitive Behavioral Therapy: Trauma Focused-Cognitive Behavioral Therapy (TF-CBT) is an evidence-based model for both male and female children and young adults aged three to twenty-one. This model has been "recognized as one of the most effective interventions" available, with the strongest and most rigorously tested research to support the treatment of traumatized children (McMullen and O'Callaghan, 2012; Deblinger et al., 2011; Cohen et al., 2011; Weiner et al., 2009; Cohen, Mannarino, and Deblinger, 2008, p. 6; Cohen, Mannarino, and Staron, 2006; Cohen, Mannarino, and Knudsen, 2005; Cohen et al., 2004; Deblinger et al., 2001; King et al., 2000). On average, treatment is about twelve to twenty-five sessions for sixty to ninety minutes, and involves the following elements, summarized by the acronym PRACTICE:

· **P**sychoeducation (for both children and parents) and parent skills.
· **R**elaxation (self-regulation) and stress management (for both children and parents).
· **A**ffect expression and modulations (for both children and parents).
· **C**ognitive coping and processing (for both children and parents).
· **T**rauma narration (children).
· **I**n vivo mastery of trauma (cognitive processing).
· **C**onjoint child-parent sessions.
· **E**nhancing safety (present and future) and social skills.

TF-CBT addresses the relational component that is essential in psychotherapy for children, which explains its effectiveness in the treatment of emotional or behavioral difficulties "related to traumatic life events" (The National Child Traumatic Stress Network, 2012, p. 1). The model offers individual sessions for both the child and their parents or caregivers, and also includes joint parent-child sessions.

The Medical University of South Carolina offers free online training for TF-CBT through its National Crime Victims Research and Treatment Center: **www.tfcbt.musc.edu**.

Other free TF-CBT trainings include:

TF-CBT for childhood traumatic grief: **www.musc.edu/ctg**.

TF-CBT consultation program: **www.musc.edu/tfcbtconsult**.

2. Eye Movement Desensitization and Reprocessing: Eye Movement Desensitization and Reprocessing (EMDR) has become a popularized one-on-one approach to effectively treat trauma. Francine Shapiro, PhD, developed EMDR after an epiphany in 1987 while she was walking through a park. As she moved her eyes bilaterally to watch the birds in the park, Shapiro became aware of the self-soothing effect and diminution of negative emotions associated with her distressing memories (Shapiro and Forest, 1997; Shapiro, 1989). Later she included additional therapeutic treatments (i.e., cognitive therapy, hypnosis, etc.) to augment the standard protocol of desensitizing (decreasing) anxiety and other symptoms related to PTSD, called Eye Movement Desensitization (EMD), which she altered in 1991 to include the reprocessing element.

EMDR has been empirically and exhaustively studied "to reduce traumatic-related stress, anxiety, and depression symptoms associated with post-traumatic stress disorder" in people aged eighteen and up (Substance Abuse and Mental Health Service Administration's National Registry of Evidence-Based Programs and Practices, para. 1). Various meta-analytical studies have shown EMDR to be just as effective as cognitive behavioral treatments in reducing PTSD symptoms (Bisson et al., 2013; Seidler and Wagner, 2006; Bradley et al., 2005; Davidson and Parker, 2001), and more recently studies have actually found that the bilateral eye movements are a contributing element in the overall effectiveness of treatment (Lee and Cuijpers, 2013).

Typically, EMDR treatment sessions are sixty to ninety minutes; however, shorter sessions have been successfully developed. EMDR can be considered a brief form of psychotherapy, with the length of treatment depending on the complexity and extent of traumatic exposure. EMDR treatment attends to the past (disturbing memories and related events), present (situations that are causing distress), and future (skills and attitudes that a patient/client needs to develop for a positive future). The attention to the past, present, and future is addressed in eight phases of treatment:

1. History-taking.

2. Learning self-regulation skills (i.e., visual imagery, some of which have been adapted from clinical hypnosis "self-place exercises").

3-6. Identification of target (i.e., image related to the traumatic memory, negative beliefs about self, and/or emotions and body sensations related to the traumatic memory).

7. Closure (documentation of material that may arise) and reminders about self-soothing techniques learned in phase two.

8. Examination of progress related to the past, present, and future.

Although researchers have theorized that the adaptive information process (the diluting of traumatic memories with adaptive memory [neuro] networks) is the key contributor to healing, currently the underlying mechanism of how EMDR works has yet to be empirically identified. This does not hinder either its effectiveness to treat traumatic stress or its widespread use among psychotherapists.

3. Cognitive Behavioral Therapy: In relation to the treatment of PTSD, Cognitive Behavioral Therapy (CBT) has been used to treat it for many years, and still remains the most widely used treatment based on its effectiveness (Lopes et al., 2014; Mello et al., 2013).

CBT is a form of psychotherapy that attends to the cognitive (thinking and beliefs) aspects of an emotional response or action. Treatment helps survivors use behavioral strategies (i.e., relaxation techniques) to overcome symptoms (i.e., anxiety and fear) associated with a traumatic experience. It also takes a look at subjectively protective but maladaptive behaviors (i.e., isolation to avoid triggers that result in anxiety or fear associated with past traumatic memories), and encourages patients and clients to cognitively reflect on more adaptive behaviors. In essence, CBT treatment helps individuals who have been exposed to a traumatic incident to change their way of feeling, thinking, and acting.

4. Other Treatments: As stated earlier, there are an overwhelming abundance of trauma-specific models that effectively address trauma, including:

- Parent-Child Interaction Therapy (PCIT).
- Child-Parent Psychotherapy (CPP).
- Narrative Exposure Therapy (NET).
- Prolonged Exposure Therapy for PTSD in adults (PE).
- Cognitive Behavioral Intervention for Trauma in School (CBITS).
- Alternatives for Families: A Cognitive Behavioral Therapy (AF-CBT).
- Attachment, Self-Regulation, and Competency (ARC).
- Cognitive Behavioral Therapy for Acute Stress Disorder (CBT for ASD).
- Structured Psychotherapy for Adolescents Responding to Chronic Stress (SPARCS).
- Trauma Adapted Family Connection (TA-FC).

There has also been promising research evidence to support future evidence-based trauma-specific treatments such as Brief Eclectic Psychotherapy for PTSD (BEPP), Progressive Counting (PC), Trauma Affect Regulations: Guide for Education and Therapy in Adults (TARGET), and the Trauma Recovery and Empowerment Model (TREM). You can read more about additional trauma-specific treatment models for children and adolescents at the National Child Traumatic Stress Network: **www.nctsn.org/training-guidelines**.

This book does not endorse any specific model; instead we will focus on those common elements found in all empirically supported treatments that promote healing in the trauma survivor.

Chapter Summary

Traumatic care has a millennia-old history, dating back to the time of the Greek philosophers who claimed that emotional excess, hysteria, and post-traumatic behaviors stemmed from physiological issues like a "wandering womb." When Jean-Martin Charcot hypothesized that these behavioral symptoms might be occurring due to a psychological influence rather than a physical one, the field of trauma treatment was revolutionized.

From there, prominent researchers like Pierre Janet, Sigmund Freud, and others explored new avenues of psychologically based care, and events like the Vietnam War and the feminist movement of the 1970s instigated a movement toward trauma-informed care, advocacy programs for minorities and the LGBTQ community, and children.

Several popular methods of treatment have arisen in the past few decades, all of which possess similar elements supported by empirical research that shows quantifiable results in trauma healing. Among these well-known treatments are EMDR, CBT, narrative therapy, and various subsets of these, tailored for different age groups and trauma needs.

Chapter Six

Working with Trauma Survivors

Focus Questions:

- What is the application of trauma-informed principles?
  What key historical events have influenced the innovative improvement of trauma
- Are we holding survivors of trauma accountable for undesirable behaviors?

In this chapter you will learn more about:

- The application of trauma-informed principles
- Effective ways to create a climate of healing.
- How to be strategic and intentional in trauma-focused treatment.

You're not a victim for sharing your story. You are a survivor setting the world on fire with your truth. And you never know who needs your light, your warmth and raging courage.

– Alex Elle

So far we have discussed the role of a trauma-focused caregiver, how to build resiliency against compassion fatigue, the application of trauma-informed principles, the physical and neurobiological effects of trauma, and how trauma care has evolved over the years. This chapter will put the concepts you have learned into perspective, guiding you on the trauma-sensitive way of caring for trauma survivors.

Ineffective Interventions

Adaptive and mitigating behaviors—which are, at times, the reason survivors are voluntarily or involuntarily seeking professional help—may or may not be socially appropriate or legal. Trauma-focused caregivers must remember that these behaviors and biological changes are a *natural* adaptive or mitigating process as a response to the environment. Professionals with a lack of understanding of trauma expect survivors to function more effectively than the environment they are experiencing by setting boundaries, rules, and harsh or punitive ways to address behavioral concerns. These are unreasonable expectations, and would be similar to a physician asking one of their patients to reduce their gastric acid secretions to treat hyperacidity and balance the pH levels in their stomach. As a patient, you wouldn't be thinking, "Sure Doc, let me tell my body to reduce its gastric acid secretions." Instead, you would turn to your doctor and ask, "How? Are you going to give me something like an antacid to treat this, or recommend a diet to reduce my gastric acid secretions?"

In a similar way, as a trauma-focused caregiver you will be supporting the individual seeking help by providing them with skills—in an appropriate way and during an appropriate time—to assist them in healing.

As trauma-sensitive professional caregivers, part of the process is showing compassion to survivors of trauma. Because of our compassion, many professionals inaccurately believe that a trauma-sensitive approach is "coddling" those seeking help. That is not the case whatsoever—trauma-focused caregivers have a deeper comprehension of the survivor's overly active physiological and neurobiological system, and understand that their behaviors are an instinctual response to an environment that is perceived as threatening.

This does not mean that a trauma-focused professional condones behavior that is socially or legally inappropriate. We understand that a healthy society needs to preserve a social order to create both stability and safety for its citizens. Trauma-focused professionals are strategic and intentional while providing treatment, and are aware of the fact that harsh or punitive demands will do nothing to help the trauma survivor. In fact, professionals who use these types of methods to address behavioral concerns risk arousing strong emotional responses (fear, anxiety, disempowerment, etc.), which could cause the patient/client to generalize/collapse their categories of threat, and cause further complications or dysregulation that lead to relapsing into self-defeating behaviors (i.e., a sober survivor regressing back to drinking or past maladaptive self-soothing behaviors such as cutting).

As discussed throughout the book, one of the common mistakes when working with a trauma survivor is a professional's failure to treat those seeking help with compassion by labeling them or passing judgment based on adaptive or mitigating behaviors. In other words, professionals can make the mistake of viewing a trauma survivor through a deficit lens, which disconnects the trauma from the behaviors. As a result, their focus is on dealing with these behaviors in a way that is ineffective, and may even activate the survivor's threat-response system.

Once again, it is necessary to note that we are not teaching the acceptance of social or legally inappropriate behavior. We are stressing that the current way of treating mitigating behaviors is abortive. For example, it is not uncommon that court-ordered treatment for assault charges requires clinical treatments such as anger management or cognitive behavioral treatment. Nonclinical educators may try to change thinking by using growth and fixed mindset workshops. While these treatments and education have merit, teaching the Activating Event + Beliefs = Consequences (ABC) Model, or any other rationalization method, requires access to higher cognitive functioning. A person with an activated sympathetic nervous system due to perceived threat *does not currently have optimal access* to those levels of cognitive functioning and self-reflection, and will not until they are able to stabilize and allow the parasympathetic nervous system to take over.

Stabilization

Statistician Paul R. Rosenbaum compared the outcome results of therapeutic treatment and stability, finding that stability in the absence of treatment is almost equal to the results of treatment (2001). Therefore, as professional caregivers, our primary goal is creating stability in survivors' lives (i.e., creating safety and predictability) and helping them stabilize their biological survival system. There are four essential interventions that the trauma-focused caregiver uses to create healing:

1. Demonstrating their own ability to self-regulate.
2. Creating an environment of safety.
3. Helping the survivor regulate in their presence.
4. Helping the survivor regulate without their presence.

1. Caregiver's Ability to Self-Regulate: In Greek philosopher and scientist Aristotle's best-known work on ethics, *The Nicomachean Ethics*, he wrote:

> Anyone can get angry—that is easy—or give or spend money; but to do this to the right person, to the right extent, at the right time, with the right motive, and in the right way, that is not for everyone, nor is it easy. (Aristotle 350 B.C.E./1893)

Although it is not easy to get angry with the right person, to the right extent, and in the right time, as professional caregivers we have higher standards to help create an environment conducive to healing. What this means is that professional caregivers must be able to regulate themselves no matter what the survivor of trauma says or does. The moment that we as professional caregivers become dysregulated—and as a result, reactive—we are no longer effective in creating a safe environment for survivors to heal, and we may fall short at helping them stabilize.

There are various ways that caregivers can help survivors stabilize their biological system, and the first and primary intervention is mastering the ability to self-regulate their own alarm or threat-response system. As a result, the professional caregiver becomes a conduit for soothing energy.

It is likely that you have experienced a contagious type of echophenomenon while watching someone yawn, only to find yourself yawning. Echoparaxia, the imitation of someone's actions, is another powerful occurrence that can be used by professional caregivers. Helping those who seek your help with biological stabilization involves being able to soothe them by modeling self-soothing behaviors. This means that during your sessions it is okay, and encouraged, to find moments to openly self-regulate your biological system as a behavioral model for patients and clients. It can be as easy as noticing that the survivor is becoming more anxious, and taking a second to tell them, "Remember how I mentioned there are times I get a little nervous or anxious, and need a second to gather my composure? Well, this is a moment when I need a second," followed by verbally walking them through the process of self-regulation. This will allow them the opportunity to witness self-regulation in practice, and vicariously experience a sense of relaxation. The latter part is very important, because it creates the right moment for you to be able to teach them how to self-regulate. Once you are able to see a decrease in anxiety levels, you can help them learn those same self-regulation skills to prevent the chronic activation of their biological alarm (survival) system.

2. Creating an Environment of Safety: Since the etiology of these biological changes can be the survivor's environment, caregivers should attempt to help stabilize the survivor's environment. Even if your job duties grant you limited access to their environment outside of the office, you can provide a sense of safety to survivors from the moment they set foot in your office to the moment they leave. It is your ethical and moral duty to be intentional in everything you do to keep them as regulated as possible.

Your services of care must always operate under the premise of trustworthiness and transparency. Trust is really about predictability, and for a caregiver this means that you intentionally provide services in a predictable way (i.e., consistency, clear instructions, guiding them with what to expect and what will happen, etc.) to build a sense of trustworthiness. In practice, what this looks like is an orientation and acculturation process. As trauma-focused professional caregivers, you will outline the healing process, discuss what it is like to work with you as a professional, explain the format of the sessions, go over concurrent documentation, mention any biases that exist (personally or systemically in your agency), describe your healing philosophy, and declare any limitations as a result of the settings and rules of the organization. Although this may sound similar to informed consent, it goes above and beyond what is required with the goal of creating this vital, unshakeable level of stability.

Another part of practicing trauma-focused caregiving is to be transparent. This means you will never do anything without discussing it with your patient/client, and includes components of informed consent: what the treatment/services look like, the likelihood of it working and how it will work, etc. Since healing happens in relationships, trauma-focused caregivers intentionally build collaboration and mutuality with those seeking their help. Thus, decision-making is a shared process instead of a hierarchical structure. In turn, this leads to the survivor feeling empowered. Empowerment, involving voice and choice, does not mean that clients can do anything they want or nothing at all. The aim is to strengthen their experience of choice. As trauma-focused caregivers, we explain the process and how we can help the individual seeking help, but it is up to them to choose whether they will continue with services or seek someone else to help them.

Another important element in stabilizing is helping survivors build resiliency. In order to help survivors in the process, we need to believe they have the ability to heal from the wounds of trauma and possess the capacity to build resiliency. This capacity of building resiliency involves teaching survivors how to stabilize their alarm and threat-response systems, and to remain, as much as possible, out of those systems.

Care services are always provided in a culturally sensitive manner, but move past cultural stereotypes and biases. This means that instead of treating an individual as male or female, or as Hispanic, African American, or Caucasian, we treat that person as entirely unique based on their own individual and family history.

Safety in the survivor's relationships and environment. Stabilization and safety should also be created within the survivor's environment. Teaching the survivor's support network how to self-regulate can contribute to fostering an environment that is conducive to healing. Besides the self-regulation skills taught throughout this book, methods derived from research on relational therapy can improve relational (i.e., friends, family, etc.) stability.

"Harsh startups" are discussions that begin in a harsh way, usually with criticism and/or contempt (i.e., sarcasm, lopsided sneer, eye-rolling, etc.), and are a good predictor that a conversation will end with a negative outcome (Carrere and Gottman, 1999). Given that survivors' alarm systems are hyperactive to any perceived (real or not) danger in their environment, it is also safe to say that harsh startups can effortlessly activate the stress-response system. As a result, they can lead to adapting or mitigating behaviors that are reasonable given the activated system, but socially destructive to a relationship.

Using the work of Gottman (1999), caregivers can teach the survivor's support network how to soften their startup by learning how to state a complaint without blame. This can be accomplished through using "I" statements, followed by a positive need. Instead of someone saying "you're so inconsiderate" or "you never think about others," show the survivor's support system how to reframe these statements to something like, "I'm feeling ignored, left out, or unappreciated. Can we please buy things together?"

Besides showing the support system how to turn criticisms to complaints, it is also helpful to teach them to avoid defensive conversation. As with other mitigating behaviors, defensiveness is a form of self-protection to ward off a perceived attack (Gottman, 1999). For example, if a wife tells her husband that he is a "hopeless drunk" (criticism), the husband might perceive that as an attack of his character and worth as a husband and defensively state, "Maybe if you helped me out with paying the bills, I wouldn't be so stressed out that I needed a drink" (defensiveness). Of course, even though both of their behaviors are reasonable given the context, the behaviors are socially destructive to the relationship since the conflict is likely to escalate further without any resolution. As caregivers, you can help create some stability by instructing survivors and their supports on how to accept full or partial responsibility to avoid the destructive communication pattern of defensiveness.

Gottman also provides an antidote for another form of destructive communication: contempt. Contempt includes behaviors that allude to the individual's perceived sense of superiority (i.e., name-calling, sarcasm, hostile humor, sneering, eye-rolling, etc.). His advice is to create a culture of respect and appreciation by finding moments throughout the day to verbally express those things ("I'm really happy that we went to the ballet today. I know you have a busy schedule, and this really showed how much you care about me," for example).

Stonewalling is another pattern that Gottman noticed in ineffective relationships. This is a behavior that occurs when someone withdraws from the relational interaction, typically as a sign that they are becoming flooded or overwhelmed with emotions. Gottman proposed that the antidote to stonewalling is practicing psychological self-soothing, which is one of the key elements in treating survivors of trauma (1999).

3. Helping the Survivor Regulate in the Presence of the Caregiver: Based on our understanding of physiological and neurobiological changes (i.e., activated alarm and threat-response systems, memory system, and changes in the serum levels of neurochemical-peptide-hormonal cocktail mixes), when faced with traumatic environmental activators, we strategically and intentionally help survivors stabilize their biological system. Once they are able to do this they will be better equipped for the capacity of self-reflection, which could lead to better insight and a desire to make changes.

When is the appropriate time to help someone reflect on behaviors? Teaching those seeking your help is a challenging task. When the threat-response system is activated, we are naturally reactive, behaving with the need for immediate resolution without comprehending the lasting consequences of our actions. Take a second and think about the last time you did something inappropriate, or maybe even awful. At what point in time were you able to self-reflect and feel remorse for what you did? Was it at the moment you did it, or after some time had elapsed and you were able to calm down?

All too often, professionals provide moral or life lessons to survivors when they are functioning in a dysregulated body, with high access to the survival parts of their brain and minimal access to the neocortex. As a result, many professionals will pass judgment and assume that the individual is resistant and unwilling to change.

To explain this nonsensical logic further, imagine you were in a cave and a salivating, hungry-looking tiger sauntered in with his big, black eyes trained on you. How likely would it be that you could memorize the periodic table at that time? It would be next to impossible! The point we are making is that it is unreasonable to expect someone functioning with a charged or activated survival system to be able to absorb such self-reflective information as life lessons and steps for change. The least of their concerns is to process and encode into memory what you are trying to teach them; their survival system is acting in the "here and now."

As trauma-focused caregivers, you grasp the futility of such an attempt without the proper self-regulation and relaxation beforehand, acknowledging that there is a time for everything, including "…a time to be silent and a time to speak" (Ecclesiastes 3:7, NIV).

4. Helping the Survivor Regulate Without the Presence of the Caregiver: Once the survivor is able to regulate in the presence of the professional caregiver, the next step is to assist them in self-regulation outside of the therapeutic setting. One of the main ways this can be accomplished is through homework. This is a critical element that not only extends the therapeutic session, but also solidifies that the survivor plays a key role in their treatment and recovery (Cummings and Sayama, 1995).

It is worth noting that we have not mentioned homework as an early part of the treatment process, since that might set survivors up for failure or feelings of hopelessness. They must first be able to demonstrate autonomy over their autonomic nervous system, and an ability to regulate and self-soothe while in the presence of a professional caregiver. Once that has occurred, homework assignments can teach them to generalize these skills outside of the professional setting.

An example of a homework assignment would be something similar to what one of us does whenever he goes in for his monthly orthodontics visit. The visits include a braces adjustment that is sometimes uncomfortable or a little painful, so the author practices scanning his body and relaxing his muscles throughout the procedure. In the same way, we can teach a patient/client how to do this whenever they feel themselves becoming overactivated due to a perceived threat.

Now that we have outlined the four essential interventions to creating a healing environment for your patients and clients, we are going to present a case study for your practical application of these concepts. Remember—as you read Isela's story, take a second and scan your body for any tensed muscles, so you can intentionally relax them and avoid absorbing the traumatic energy involved in the narrative. If needed, go back and reread Chapter Two for assistance in this process of self-regulation.

Case Study with Dr. Rojo Aubrey: Isela

Isela was a Spanish-speaking woman from El Salvador in her mid-thirties when I met with her for a mental health assessment and treatment. At the time she was involved with CPS, and in the reunification process with her daughter. It had been a year since she had been paroled from prison for child endangerment; she had been charged with child endangerment for shoving a small cucumber up her eight-month-old daughter's vagina, reportedly after a discussion with her husband about creating a legal guardianship form to have the husband's brother care for their child in case of death. CPS had provided reports of Isela making statements that she'd been protecting her daughter, and expected me to testify that she was psychologically unfit to parent her child. During treatment with Isela, however, another side of the story developed as she shared her narrative and trauma timeline with me during treatment.

When she was about nine years old, military soldiers invaded her home and killed her father, and both Isela and her sister were forced to hear their mother being raped and begging for her life before being murdered while they hid in a closet. After the death of her parents, Isela's aging grandparents could only afford to take care of one of the girls and chose her sister, so Isela was put in the care of her uncle.

For the next two years, Isela's uncle sexually fondled her, without vaginal penetration, and forced her to perform oral sex. He would tell her repeatedly to be careful not to break her hymen, because her virginity was very valuable and would get them out of poverty. He would tell her that he had requested to take care of Isela instead of her older sister, since it had been public knowledge that Isela's sister had already had sex with her boyfriend.

Right before Isela's twelfth birthday, her uncle auctioned off her virginity and she was forced to have sex with a man she had never met while her uncle watched. Thereafter, her uncle would sell her for sex and at times in exchange for food. When she was sixteen, Isela befriended a young man in his mid-twenties who promised to take her away from her uncle. She eventually ran away with him to Mexico; while in Mexico, however, they struggled to afford food and shelter. The boyfriend convinced her to prostitute herself for enough money to cross the border to the U.S., with the goal of him finding a good job and them starting a family. Eventually she agreed, and the boyfriend made a deal with a member of a local gang. The local gang took Isela and used her for their gang-rape ritual, but then refused to pay Isela and her boyfriend, even threatening their lives.

The boyfriend spoke with the gang members again, and they all decided to begin trafficking Isela for sex. When she refused, they threatened her life and the lives of her sister and grandparents back in El Salvador. She was forced to have sex with over twenty men per day, including English-speaking customers from other countries, and she would be beaten whenever customers complained of her "just lying there" without any movement or excitement. After most of the members of the local gang, including Isela's boyfriend, were arrested for various crimes, she found her way to the U.S. and continued prostituting in order to make money to survive. Eventually Isela befriended some Christians at a local congregation near the street she worked. With their help she was able to find a different line of work, and ultimately got married.

Cases like Isela's are tragic, traumatic situations that happen all too often to individuals worldwide. According to the International Labour Organization, from 2002 to 2011 approximately 20.9 million children and adults were coerced into commercial servitude, including 4.5 million victims of sex trafficking (p. 13). In the United States, it is estimated that 150,000 to 300,000 children are at risk of commercial sexual exploitation (Goldberg et al., 2017).

While it is a living nightmare for a child or an adult to be forced to have sex with twenty or more customers a day, the inhumane cruelty of these acts has a lasting effect on the neurobiology, including the belief system, of the individual. Taking someone's traumatic history into account helps us understand why it is reasonable for them to hold negative beliefs (intellectually, emotionally, spiritually, psychologically, physically, socially, academically, etc.) about themselves, others, and the world. Without the healing of her traumatic wounds, it is difficult, if not impossible, for a woman who has been sold for sex by family members and partners to feel talented, valued, accepted, etc. What would her views and beliefs about relationships look like? Would she see her family and friends as warm, supportive, caring, nurturing, and loving people, or as dangerous and selfish? What would her beliefs about the world be?

Given Isela's traumatic history, those beliefs would be 100 percent accurate. It might not be a healthy belief system or one we want her to have, but it is reasonable based on her experiences. Distorted belief systems and an overly charged survival system will undoubtedly result in behaviors that are not socially or legally appropriate, but make sense in the context of the survivor's history.

Assignment: After reading this case study, write out a plan on how you would best serve Isela and help create healing in her life.

Concepts to Remember in Trauma Treatment

Although horrific events are certainly devastating, the aftermath can lead to smaller traumatic events that frequently activate the alarm and threat-response systems. We can compare the differences in these "Big T" and "little t" traumas to the severe breaking of a bone that receives a cast and is able to heal, versus a small incision made in the same spot every day that the body never gets the chance to repair. Ultimately, the tiny incision takes a larger toll on the body than the broken bone ever did.

Here are some additional concepts to remember when providing treatment for trauma survivors, all based on clinical experience:

1. People with histories of adversity have less cognitive processing capacity. Be brief and clear, give many examples of success, and ensure goals are realistic and reachable.

2. Understand that working memory is usually poor in people with a history of adversity. Do not rely on memory—write it down.

3. Recognize that functional verbal processing and verbal memory are usually poor in those with trauma histories. Do not rely on verbal instructions or directions, and try to keep your sentences fewer than ten words.

4. Do not write lists, instead addressing one item at a time. As the trauma survivor develops the ability to self-regulate, you may be able to incorporate several tasks at once.

5. Remember that in almost all work-related interactions, one or more parties are likely to be dysregulated.

6. Practice your own self-regulation skills, modeling them for patients and clients, and talking about the benefits you experience in your thinking (i.e., "my thinking is clearer") and emotion (i.e., "I feel calm, safe, etc.").

7. Self-monitor changes in your emotional and physical states, and talk about what your body is experiencing and how it is impacting your thinking, emotions, and behavior.

8. Speak slowly and control your breathing, exhibiting a relaxed state that can translate to your patient/client.

9. Understand that an activated sympathetic nervous system does not allow for a planning brain, nor is it self-reflecting or self-evaluating. Things discussed must have immediate action, not "ten minutes from now" action.

10. When providing information, follow this format:

· Overview/orient the patient/client.

· Show how this activity fits into the overviewed material.

· Give examples of how people are successful in achieving this activity.

· Summarize by embedding them in a success story.

· Ask for their feedback (i.e., "As you move through this situation, what do you expect you'll experience?").

A Reminder to Professional Caregivers

As professional trauma-focused caregivers, we entered into this field because of our big hearts for helping others. Unfortunately, this empathy, compassion, and desire to help others can leave us vulnerable to the effects of compassion fatigue, secondary traumatic stress, and burnout. Our desire to help the suffering can lead to discouragement if it does not actualize, but we need to humbly remember that no one, not even so-called experts, can solve the world's problems. There will be times that, despite all of our energy and investment, we cannot fully help someone stabilize. This does not mean we should give up or stop trying; it just means we need to show compassion for ourselves. Do not forget that many survivors have experienced complex traumas, and possess a long, generational history of traumagenesis. It may be unreasonable to expect to fully stabilize a survivor and their environment, but the progress we are able to facilitate can certainly result in a diminishing or reduction of harm, and move the patient/client closer to recovery.

Chapter Summary

Trauma-informed care is founded on the principles of trust, compassion, and accepting a patient/client for where they are in that moment, even if their behaviors are inappropriate or illegal. That is not to say trauma-focused caregiving condones such behaviors, or is a "coddling" type of therapy—but trauma-informed professionals understand that these types of adaptive and mitigating behaviors have arisen due to a survivor's overactivated survival response, and the consequential neurological and physiological changes that occur from those activated alarm and threat-response systems.

Trauma-focused caregivers utilize four methods of stabilizing patients and clients so that this survival response can be deactivated, which include exercising self-regulation as an example for the patient/client, creating an environment of safety, helping the patient/client to regulate in their presence, and teaching the patient/client how to regulate outside of the therapy office. Besides these four methods of stabilization, there are ten other concepts to remember when working with individuals who have a history of adversity so they can be set up for success and not failure.

Trauma-focused caregivers should bear in mind that their work is incredibly strenuous, and that symptoms of compassion fatigue, burnout, and secondary traumatic stress are not uncommon. Self-care and self-compassion are essential in order to combat the negative effects of helping those who are suffering, as well as the belief that a patient/client's progress, without a "fully realized recovery," is still progress nonetheless.

Chapter Seven

Empowerment and Resiliency Structure

Focus Questions:

- How can I improve and enrich the quality of care provided to my patients and clients?
- What stages will I be able to practice as a trauma support specialist?

In this chapter you will learn more about:

- The stages of treatment in the Empowerment and Resiliency Structure.
- An overview of Stages One to Four.

Life doesn't get easier or more forgiving, we get stronger and more resilient.

– Steve Maraboli

A Vehicle to Enhance Healer Excellence

A few years ago Dr. Rhoton was working with a client who was an engineer, and the man's requests during treatment started all three of us on a new trajectory for patient/client collaboration:

> "Since he was an engineer, his thought process was systematic—and for the first time, it became clear that there was a need for an explainable structure that could be shared with him and others. This engineer helped me reorganize the concepts of safety, structure, and transparency due to his need to understand the entire process of service before he committed himself to it.
>
> Many of the things explained to him were very basic, such as the length of a session, collaboration on note writing at the end of a session (known as "concurrent documentation"), and collecting feedback to correct the focus of what was being done in service. Additionally, I discussed in detail the discrete stages of the service process, and what needed to be accomplished in each stage as well as what he could expect in moving through each stage. This allowed for the creation of positive expectations regarding his ability to achieve success during the delivery of service.
>
> One of the questions the engineer was deeply concerned about was how he might move through this service compared to other people, and whether he was "too broken" to benefit from service delivery.
>
> My response to that question opened up possibilities for him, which became the common feature in each transition of service after that: 'Some people get into this part of service delivery and it's amazing how they can hit it out of the ballpark, it makes sense to them, and they immediately benefit. Most people, however, have to work on things, think about them, and allow themselves to experiment with the ideas and concepts before they really get the benefit. Still others have to put in some hard work, and may struggle for a while before they experience the benefit they're hoping for or expected.'
>
> This was an example of how having a structure propelled the client to feel safer and in control of the process. In the end, the engineer did very well in service delivery."

Being prepared for transitions and providing an expectation of what they might look like helps patients/clients and their families feel more in control of treatment, and evidence shows they participate more fully and successfully when they know what is happening and why.

Being able to explain and create predictability and a sense of control for the patient/client does a couple of outstanding things: 1) it increases the safety of working with the caregiver; 2) it allows the patient/client the ability to monitor themselves and feel more in control of the entire process; and 3) it allows the professional caregiver to be transparent so that treatment really is a collaborative process.

All of these benefits turned into our search for a simple clinical pathway that could be used with any model of treatment, and we began to develop and fine-tune this structure through collecting and evaluating the client experience. We might think of treatment as an organic process, one that has certain fundamental guidelines to ensure success. When those basic guidelines are violated, then the organic system cannot prosper maximally. Compare it to planting and harvesting a garden: To be a successful gardener, particularly with the variety of environments that people place gardens in, requires an understanding of the entire process, from picking the soil and location of the garden all the way through to the harvest. Mental health frequently tends to focus on the "seeds used in the garden," or models of treatment, rather than the entirety of the process. The treatment structure is a way to increase effective growth of those seeds, by having the process well laid out.

Playing with the idea of creating a clinical pathway to improve treatment quality and sustainable outcomes has given rise to a loose structure for therapy in the trauma treatment world. In 1992, Dr. Judith Herman's introduction of the Tri-Phasic Model revolutionized the treatment of trauma for individuals. In 1989, Dr. Charles Figley developed a Five-Phase Treatment structure for families. Clearly the idea that structure improves clinical outcomes has been around for a while; many caregivers, including therapists, can even parrot the stages or phases of treatment. But what is equally apparent is that while professionals know that structure increases the efficacy of treatment, many develop an almost religious conviction to a specific model of treatment—holding aloft a "holy hammer" toward EMDR or TF-CBT rather than incorporating the fluidity of an overarching structure that would allow the treatment to be employed more effectively.

What efforts would you be willing to make as a counselor, therapist, coach, or peer support to know that you were competently and consistently gaining enhancement and enrichment in providing care for those you served? Using a clinical pathway accomplishes the following (Rotter et al., 2012):

1. Improves care.
2. Improves outcomes.

3. Improves clinical governance.

4. Improves clinical competence/supervision.

5. Reduces variability of services and treatment, and minimizes the impact of having inexperienced staff.

6. Is inclusive of trauma-informed care and trauma-sensitive treatment.

7. Reduces costs, because treatment is consistent and has a process.

8. Creates a structure that facilitates measurable improvement based on criteria.

9. Translates guidelines or policies into applied and functional operations specifically designed for the population and individual patients/clients.

10. Builds a cohesive workforce.

11. Builds familiar and predictable patterns for staff and patients/clients.

12. Minimizes the impact of clinical ignorance when dealing with a diverse workforce (paraprofessionals to medical staff).

13. Improves treatment team communication.

14. Enhances and supports formal legally recognized assessment tools (CAPS, CANS-T, MMPI, etc.).

15. Increases patient/client confidence and hope in treatment.

For the clinical administrator, the instituting of a clinical pathway should be very attractive since it will better organize chart audits and can serve as a strong part of the quality improvement process (Kinsman, 2004). There are also advantages in the uniformity of service delivery and a reduction in variation (Panella, Marchisio, and Di Stanislao, 2003).

Drs. Rhoton and Gentry have spent years presenting workshops on a generic practice structure called the Empowerment and Resilience Structure that supports the sequencing of service processes to maximize the outcomes of those services. Wampold and Imel (2015) wrote extensively that the model of treatment is secondary to the context or structure of treatment. This does not invalidate models of treatment, but it *does* suggest that there are many aspects that need attention and focus to enhance change and healing. The Empowerment and Resiliency Structure of treatment was built primarily from the clinical work of Dr. Rhoton over a fifteen-year period, with the use of Feedback-Informed Treatment (FIT) and constant fine-tuning. Through this persistent activity, a structure emerged that enhanced clinical outcomes and successful treatment completion, and reduced recidivism.

This structure was built on clinical research that demonstrates the effectiveness of a trauma-focused treatment model (i.e., EMDR, TF-CBT, Progressive Counting, etc.) when embedded with a trauma-sensitive delivery system like the Empowerment and Resiliency Structure. This structure is versatile and applicable to any preferred model of treatment, resulting in enhanced and improved outcomes for all.

The following section will provide an overview of the Empowerment and Resiliency Structure for trauma treatment service delivery, which provides the aforementioned outlined benefits of clinical pathways.

The Empowerment and Resiliency Structure: An Active Ingredients Approach

1. Preparation and Relationship Building.
2. Psychoeducation and Self-Regulation.
3. Integration and Desensitization.
4. Post-Traumatic Growth and Resilience.

Stage One: Preparation and Relationship Building

Goals:

1. Patient/client will feel safe physically, emotionally, and psychologically.
2. Patient/client will be indoctrinated about how service delivery is carried out.
3. Patient/client will experience an increased confidence in positive service delivery outcomes.

Objectives:

To accomplish the three goals above through orienting patient/client to the service delivery process to build positive expectancy and confidence in a desirable outcome, and completing the formal and informal assessment process.

Orientation:

This is the mechanism for delivering information, building hope and expectancy in a future positive outcome, as well as building capacity, normalizing service experiences, grounding the patient/client and their family, creating transparency, and facilitating engagement.

Introduction to the Healing Process (Service Delivery Structure Explained):

It is essential to be explicit in orienting the patient/client and their family from initial contact if we want to create a safe, predictable process. To build hope and positive expectancy, we will convey clearly that we have a plan and a system that works, and talk about what is contained in each stage.

We might say something like, "We'll start by describing the orientation and what will be covered, then we'll talk about the assessment process, including formal and informal assessments that are likely to be used…" We will provide an explanation of each portion on a broad scale, narrowing the plan to more specific details as the time grows closer.

We will allow choice whenever possible. For example, we might say "would you like to do this section or this section first?" or "would you prefer option one or option two?"

When describing the service delivery stage, we will briefly discuss the possible models of intervention that can be used, and again let the patient/client know that when it is time, we will revisit these models and as much as possible allow them to choose the one they feel they will benefit most from. We will state and define the ultimate goal of the therapeutic process as a level of resilience that can allow for the termination of services, so that there is a clear beginning, middle, and end.

What is the Real Benefit of the Structure of Service Delivery?

In order for the healer to create intentional and deliberate transformation in the lives of those they are serving, they must not only help patients and clients to be free from psychological and emotional pain, but also propel them toward a future of choice and personal integrity. Without a structure, it is difficult to produce consistent results that can be reproduced, while having one empowers the therapist to build his or her own believability for the patient/client.

Structure supports and enhances a co-created, intentional learning and experiencing environment that speeds the emergence of transformational change in the life of the patient/client, rather than the slower or incremental change process often associated with the average counseling process.

What is the Healing Process?

We will describe the process that people move through during healing in exquisite detail and in order. We say things like, "When people first start in service they have some concerns about whether this is going to work, and are often afraid that their situations are so awful that nothing can be done. They sometimes worry whether they are up to the task, and that if they fail or fail again, what that means about them. But as they progress through the work, these fears and concerns lessen and a confidence begins to build."

We want to clarify to patients and clients how people will likely move through the service emotionally and psychologically, and detail what their bodies might experience, how their perceptions may change, the relational changes and growth to expect, etc.

We lay the process out the first time from beginning to end, then go back through it and describe what it looks like when it is done quickly, slowly, etc. We want to integrate the "theory of somes," giving detailed examples of how various people move through service delivery. We will say, "Some people move through counseling and it looks like this"—followed by a description of the average pace—"while others go more quickly or slowly. I don't know how you'll move through it, but I'm confident it'll be exactly the way that's best for you."

When we use the theory of somes, we are conveying to the patient/client that they are right regardless of how they move through the structure, and confirming our belief in their capacity to be successful. That service is an organic process, and cannot be shortchanged.

Acknowledging the Value of Personal Pacing:

Unless consciously regulated, a healer may exhibit a drive to prove their own value to themselves or supervisors by pushing patients or clients through the service too quickly. This is often supported by the demands of dysregulated individuals and systems of care that want to see the symptoms and behaviors of post-traumatic stress be resolved in a rapid way.

We will need to remember that human beings are organic systems, and therapeutic protocols must follow reasonable, organic processes of preparation for successful movement through treatment. The removal of pain is not recovery, nor is it health.

Providing Choice Points:

A choice point is the creation of multiple options that have been adequately explained and have had examples delivered in such a fashion as to allow a patient/client or family the ability to choose a course of action. This also generates knowledge that more than one course or direction is possible, and that if this choice does not work, they are still all right and can move forward with another one that still leads to positive and beneficial outcomes.

Highlighting Transparency of Process:

There is no doubt that professionals have an obligation to inform the patient/client about service deliveries and processes so that they can make an informed choice. This is often seen as a legal obligation rather than a solid and significant part of the service delivery process, but in the Empowerment and Resiliency Structure, it is a necessary and strategic part of treatment.

Assuming Capacity for Health and Wholeness:

By providing choices and explaining the process of healing, we are assuming that the patient/client has the ability to execute choice in their daily life. We are also believing that they are self-reflective and self-aware enough to make intentional choices, and follow through on those things selected.

Explaining the Beginning, Middle, and End of Service:

We will explain that the goal of treatment is for the patient/client to fully complete it, and leave having the skills necessary not to have to return in the future (as it relates to the current issues being worked on).

Talking About Working Together:

We will expose our weaknesses, biases and tendencies, exploring them together and modeling what it looks like to recognize these. We will focus extra attention on how to learn as the therapist to be five times better for the patient/client in five sessions, and ten times better in ten sessions. We will say, "I want to tailor everything for you, and even though that's my goal, I will sometimes fail and slip up. When that happens, I'll pause and you can help me get back on track."

Explaining Timing for Setting and Achieving Service Delivery Goals:

It helps to talk about the fact that human beings are organic organisms, and just like a seed, we cannot expect to fully blossom overnight. We will explain to patients/clients that when they are in a state of overactivation, they are always going to want an immediate solution to their discomfort. Sometimes that desire is so strong that it allows us to engage in "magical thinking," which is common in everyone. We will normalize this for the patient/client, and draw on our own experiences of "magical thinking" in the past, preferably with humorous or humanizing anecdotes.

Going Over Session Formats:

This is important because it builds in routine, ritual, and expectancy. We will always start each session with a review of the patient/client's feedback from the prior session (which we have already gone over alone beforehand), and provide the patient/client suggestions on how we can improve for them and their families. Improving our intentionality as healers will help us reconnect after the last session, and show our prioritized movement through the service process. We will address the rationale for our suggestions with concurrent documentation, and this sharing of the patient/client's records increases transparency and allows the opportunity for any conflicts in perception to be identified and processed on the spot. Things to be discussed in this step include:

1. Prior session feedback, with several possible things that the helper can do to improve.
2. Providing the things that can be done to improve, and letting the patient/client and their family choose which one they think would be beneficial.
3. Talking about how we will implement that in the future.
4. Talking about the kinds of things that will be accomplished.
5. Discussing the concurrent documentation process, and giving multiple examples of the kinds of things people may say about what they have done in service that day.
6. Setting of the next appointment.
7. Feedback paperwork.
8. Asking "how can I do the best job possible?" (Providing feedback-informed service delivery.)
9. Using feedback from our patient/client to fine-tune and improve the process of service delivery.
10. Saying things like, "Feedback helps me be better each time we meet. I'll review this, and when you come into the next session, I can tell you how I'll be changing to fit your needs and family culture better."

This is a good time to go back and tie in the magical thinking explanation given before, and then address other situations that sometimes challenge us moving forward. It is important for us to own these challenges, and we should say things like, "Sometimes in the process of service, clients experience fear in what they're being asked to do, or think, or see differently. I've come to notice that the roadblock is me—the therapist. It means I haven't been focusing on their unique situation enough, and I might be pushing them a little too fast and not designing things well enough for them. If that should happen, I will always apologize and make certain I improve my focus and attend to you better."

Choosing a Meeting Place:

Organizational structure and culture greatly influence the environment where services are provided. In understanding that many agencies experience limited space, our role is to create as much safety as possible through predictability, while recognizing that unpredictability can also occur. When working with a client or family, we will say, "I'll do my best to make sure we have the same room. If that's not possible, I'll let you know as soon as I know of any changes."

It can be helpful when working with those patients/clients who are more sensitive to provide a tour of the facility, showing them where the rooms are and what they look like. We might schedule the room for the next appointment as well, whenever possible. Other notes to improve the consistency in care include the rooms to be laid out exactly the same, with the same furnishings, color, and decoration, so that a feeling of familiarity and safety is always present.

When meeting in a home environment, we need to make sure to discuss how the patient/client can best benefit from our coming into the home to provide services. We will need to iterate that the home therapy process should have predictability, and that chaos makes service more difficult. We will ask the patient/client and their family to do the following:

1. Not to answer the door during a session.
2. Not to answer a phone call or text message during the session (most smart phones allow for notification of who it is, so they will know whether it is likely to be an emergency or not).
3. Not to allow friends or neighbors to attend, unless they are going to participate in all sessions.
4. To decide on the room that will be used each time.
5. Not to have the TV or radio on during a session.
6. To have the family/parents be present and participatory during the session if working with children. (If no agreement is given on the point of parent participation when working with children, then it is likely the home environment will not be conducive to service delivery. We will discuss this with the patient/client, and possibly turn down the in-home option.)

Case managers and other healers may choose to be less formal about the environment, though the expectation of providing consistency must be considered.

Setting both personal and professional boundaries is part of good healer practice, and when we fail at that task, it is an opportunity to model our redirection for the patient/client. This might sound like, "Wow, did you see how I reacted so quickly? I was so dysregulated there." We will follow that with modeling a self-regulation activity, and say, "Okay, now that I'm back in order…" Then we will discuss the process of the failure, and what we plan to do in the future to prevent it.

Laminated signs for the door are always a useful item to bring to home visits, or other materials that can help the family manage the environment more effectively. When the home's organizational structure is not conducive to the creation of a safe environment, then we will be sure to address this in supervision and possibly decide on another location for treatment.

Building Relationships:

In this first stage of service delivery, goals are not as collaborative as they will become in each following stage. We will remember that dysregulated systems are not good at logic or reasoning, so we will not add to the discomfort of early service delivery by demanding patients or clients to have a goal. We will make the first goal accomplishing the orientation and assessments, and explain to the patient/client that once these are done, we can collectively decide on the next steps and strategies for achieving other goals. The proper steps for relationship building in the first stage of the structure are as follows:

1. Review of the service delivery structure to build commitment to service delivery.
2. Orientation and acculturation around the service process.
3. Creation of safety (felt and real) as well as predictability in the service process by being transparent and descriptive to increase patient/client involvement and choice, and enhance decision-making ability.
4. Discovery of capacities and strengths associated with behaviors, thoughts, and emotions currently in practice, and development of redeployment strategies.
5. Completion of formal and informal assessments, and identification of the possible ones that will be chosen from.
6. Assessment of patterns that persistently interfere with developmentally appropriate functioning, regarding times they are used more often than normal, or not at all.

Poor Service Delivery Methods

Many organizations have a lack of sensitivity about the process of developing service delivery goals, with a heightened focus on the removal or reduction of behaviors or thoughts deemed problematic. It is not unusual for organizations to put demands for logic and reason on the patient/client when they start service delivery that can add extra stress to an already aroused system. Below are some examples of service delivery methods to avoid:

1. Soliciting a life-role goal at the very beginning of service delivery planning may seem like a great idea—but that is if you are dealing with a rational, regulated individual. Most patients and clients initiating service delivery are not operating from the logical mind, but the reactive and chaotic brain of survival and reactivity.

2. Pushing to identify a specific goal is a process that will require collaboration, and in early service delivery, trust and safety have not been developed adequately to engage in this. When done prematurely, the helper ends up suggesting possibility after possibility to the patient/client, until the patient/client picks one. This is overly directive and not truly collaborative.

3. Having too many goals may feel overwhelming to the patient/client, and may make the service delivery plan overly complicated and unwieldy. Using a set of basic goals allows you to assure the patient/client that by the time they get to Stage Two, they will be adequately prepared to not only choose a goal, but succeed in obtaining it.

Stage Two: Psychoeducation and Self-Regulation

Goals:

1. Create an understanding that behavior is congruent with aroused physiology.
2. Normalize problem behaviors as being reasonable when a patient/client or family are in a state of sympathetic nervous system dominance (SD).
3. Relate everyday interactions to SD and help patients/clients connect their thinking, behaviors, and perceptions in daily life to SD.
4. Increase motivation to engage in the service delivery process.
5. Increase patient/client belief in the effectiveness of service delivery.

Objectives:

1. Teaching the mechanics of the threat-response system.
2. Creating a common language to enhance ease of discussion and relational connection.
3. Teaching the impact of environment on behavior, thinking, and perception.
4. Converting discussions of anger, sadness, fear, etc., to physiological dysregulation of SD.
5. Normalizing internal negative messages.
6. Normalizing perceptions of self, significant relationships, and worldview.

Transitioning from Stage One to Stage Two:

Patients and clients who have experienced traumatic stress often enter service in crisis, feeling overwhelmed and demoralized. After years and sometimes generations of failed attempts to manage their symptoms, they express despair that their pain will never be alleviated.

Creating predictability and increasing safety is established by explaining the therapeutic process through Stage One, when a key element is the prioritization of self-regulation. We will begin by modeling it, and referring back to the orientation phase as a reference point. We will then identify our own body's response to stress, and express the process of transitioning to a more relaxed body. This includes elaborating on how our thinking is changing, and how feelings of being grounded increase. After modeling the benefits of our own emotional regulation, the patient/client will have an example of how to move through transitioning from a stressed to a relaxed body, increasing their hope that it is possible to do so. Once the patient/client has moved through Stage One with repeated modeling, they develop preparedness for instruction and have trust in the benefits of that instruction.

Minimum Criteria Required for Transition to Stage Two of Treatment:

What is the minimal standard of safety necessary to begin Stage Two of treatment? While this question has not yet been addressed in the literature (much less resolved), we propose the following criteria:

1. Resolution of impending environmental and physical danger (i.e., ambient, interpersonal, and intrapersonal). The safety factor in Stage One must be achieved. Traumatic memories will not resolve if the patient/client is in *active* danger, and we must use cognitive and behavioral strategies to assist them in removing themselves from harm's way (see "am safe" versus "feel safe" discussion below).

2. Ability to distinguish between "am safe" and "feel safe." Many trauma survivors feel as if danger lurks around every corner, at all times. In fact, the symptom cluster of "arousal" is mostly about this phenomenon. We need to confront this distortion and help the patient/client to distinguish, objectively, between "outside danger" and "inside danger." Outside danger, or a "real" environmental threat, must be met with behavioral interventions designed to help the survivor remove or protect themselves from this danger. Inside danger, or the fear resultant from intrusive symptoms of past traumatic experiences, must be met with interventions designed to lower arousal and develop awareness and insight into the source (memory) of the fear (see Figure 4 in Chapter Two).

3. Development of a battery of self-soothing, grounding, containment, and expression strategies and the ability to utilize them for self-rescue from intrusions. We will teach these techniques during the early sessions prior to beginning Stage Two of treatment. At a minimum, patients/clients should learn the following skills:

· 3-2-1 sensory grounding and containment technique.

· Visualization of a "safe place."

· Progressive relaxation (and/or other anxiety reduction skills).

· Development of self-soothing discipline (i.e., working out, music, art, gardening, etc.).

· Containment strategies.

· Expression strategies.

4. Ability to practice/demonstrate self-regulation and self-rescue. It is useful to ask the patient/client to begin to narrate their traumatic experiences, and when they start to experience fight-or-flight activation/intensification from those memories, we will challenge them to implement the skills above to demonstrate their ability to self-rescue from a full-blown flashback. This successful experience can then be utilized later in treatment to empower the patient/client to extricate themselves from overwhelming traumatic memories. It is also a testament to the patient/client that they are being empowered with *choice* to continue treatment and confront trauma memories. A useful metaphor we can refer to is that of the novice sailor learning the procedures of the boat prior to casting off, so that during rough seas they can assist with management of the ship instead of becoming a liability.

5. Positive prognosis and contract to address traumatic material. The final important ingredient to complete in the first stage of the structure is negotiating a contract with the patient/client to move forward to Stage Two (when they will work through the trauma).

We will remember the importance of mutual goals in the creation and maintenance of the therapeutic alliance, and will harness that power in the patient/client's willful intention to resolve the trauma memories before moving forward. An acknowledgment of the patient/client's successful completion of Stage One of treatment, coupled with an empowering statement of positive prognosis, will most likely be helpful here (i.e., "I've watched you develop some very good skills to keep yourself safe and stable in the face of these horrible memories. Judging from how well you've done this, I expect the same kind of success as we begin to work toward resolving these traumatic memories. What do you need before we begin to resolve them?").

It is not necessary that the patient/client meet *all* the objective criteria before moving to Stage Two, however, we should be able to interpret any shortcomings to ensure that there is no danger in moving ahead with treatment. "Red flags" or concerns about dissociative symptoms or potential regression should alert us that movement forward might be premature. These warning signs may indicate that: 1) the patient/client needs more work toward the development of stabilization skills; and/or 2) the patient/client is experiencing a dissociative regression.

Motivation Statements to Begin with in Stage Two:

We motivate based on what we have learned about the patient/client or family in Stage One. Example motivation statements are as follows:

1. "The hard part of your life is over. You survived! The rest of this is just cleaning it up. Service isn't difficult compared to what you've already accomplished." *We use subtext to build capacity and believability, to validate the patient/client's efforts, and consolidate their choices, saying, "You remember how you felt when you were struggling to decide to come into service delivery? What's the first positive difference you see between that 'struggling you' and this you sitting here today?"*

2. "Healing trauma is simple. It's not always easy, but it's simple. You only have to complete two things to resolve your symptoms. The first is to learn to get the muscles in your body relaxed and to keep them relaxed. Once you've developed this skill, then you'll work on sharing the stories of your trauma to me while keeping a relaxed body." *We use subtext to build capacity and strengthen their belief in a future without the problem.*

3. "You're in the top ten percent of resilient people on this planet. I know that because you're here! You're not dead. You're not in jail. You're not actively drug-addicted." *Again, this builds capacity and strengthens a belief in a future without the problem.*

4. “The absolute hardest part of recovery from trauma is the stopping of avoidance and trying to run away from it. Look at you sitting here in my office, ready to confront one of the most frightening things of your life.” *We can ask, “What was the first thing you learned about yourself that allowed you to choose to recover from suffering?”*

5. “Throughout this service process, I promise I’ll do my best to keep a pace that allows for identification and exploration of skills. You’ll be able to lessen your symptoms to a point of comfort, and find a new way to live that isn’t ruled by fear once skills are brought to awareness and mastered through practice.”

Teaching the Mechanics of the Threat-Response System:

Below is a “script” of the type of conversation we will have with a patient/client at this stage in regards to their overactivated autonomic nervous system:

“You are a normal person, having normal reactions to a traumatic past. You are perfectly adapted to the historical traumas of your life. The problem is that your adaptations have remained at the same level that was necessary to survive in your past, and you no longer need that level of sensitivity and vigilance. You aren’t sick, but rather ‘over-adapted’ for a life where there are not as many demands upon you as there once were.”

We will share the following to support the above statement:

1. Autonomic nervous system functioning and its purpose.

2. Primary components of the autonomic nervous system (the parasympathetic nervous system is “cool,” while the sympathetic nervous system is “hot”).

3. The fact that trauma is usually related to a state of sympathetic dominance (SD): “Symptoms of traumatic stress are evidence of a system that’s attempting to heal itself from a wound—in this case, your trauma. With the fear you’ve lived in since the traumas of your past, you’ve prevented your system from completing healing. What we’re going to do is help you manage your physiological fear response and allow this process to complete.”

Next we will discuss:

1. What the body experiences during SD.

2. The overwhelming and accumulative harmful effects of trauma on the body.

3. The normal behaviors that emerge when the body is in a state of sympathetic dominance.

4. How behavior results from the body system in charge.

We will have the individual or family come up with personalized names for the scientific materials that we have just explained—this allows for us to talk about it through a verbally unique bond that strengthens the relationship.

We will then ask, "What would any normal/healthy/rational person with your history likely believe about themselves, their world, and nature relationships?"

1. We will give multiple examples of what would be common everyday reactions to being in a state of SD.

2. We will go back through their own history, picking small events from the client's past and helping them to see that in those moments of SD, they behaved irrationally and reactively.

3. We will tie as many personal life examples as possible to each point before moving on to the next example. This effectively normalizes behavior, removes stigma, and reduces shame.

4. As it relates to self-image, relationships, and worldview, we will suggest that they identify differences that they have experienced when they were in SD and when they were not, and define their behavior—while sometimes unfortunate—as completely congruent with the system they were dominated by in that moment.

We will explain to the patient/client that any time a human being has a painful learning experience, a precedent is set for what to expect the next time they encounter a situation that is in any way similar to the previous learning experience.

Up until this point, we will have been modeling self-regulation for the patient/client. Now that they are ready to learn how to regulate themselves, we will identify the benefits we have been receiving by self-regulating during sessions. "With a relaxed body, I am stronger, faster, and smarter."

We will begin practicing "relaxed vigilance" instead of reactive hypervigilance with patients and clients, and teach stabilizing skills such as sensory grounding, envelope containment, postural grounding, motivational interviewing and positive expectancy, Thought Field Therapy (TFT), Emotional Freedom Techniques (EFT), and more.

Creating a Common Language to Enhance Ease of Discussion and Relational Connection:

Building a common language with the patient/client or family helps empower quicker and more thorough understanding of concepts, increases utilization of concepts, and improves communication in general throughout the service process. Also, this common language lends functionality implementation to strategies for intervention.

The principle of developing a common language among members of any community to empower effective communication is well established. Examples can be seen in all walks of life, including healthcare, manufacturing, entertainment, sports, religion, politics, and military or police forces. Similarly, our development of a common language with individual patients/clients that is not stigmatizing or pejorative is essential for effective communication.

We can also develop self-regulation references based on the language of the family. For instance, instead of saying we are going to "be calm," we might say, "We're defeating that sneaky rage monster."

Teaching the Impact of Environment on Behavior, Thinking and Perception:

We will relate common, everyday behavior to the environment. An example might be, "Have you ever walked into a room and felt tension there? Where in your body did you notice it first, second, and third? Did this shift require any conscious or intentional action on your part?" We could also say, "When have you received a careless comment from someone, and even though you knew it wasn't their intention to be rude, found your emotions firing off?"

It is suggested that if you are working with an individual, you draw out six to eight examples of how the environment affects the body, emotions, thinking, and reactions. If you are with a family, then two to three per member should be sufficient.

Our environments can exert influence on our physical and mental health in very complex ways. Some of these may be modulated by our genetic makeup, psychological factors, and by our perceptions of the risks that they present. We will use examples like being in a location that is so loud that a headache develops, or how mothers who smoked during pregnancy gave birth to babies with lower birth weights.

Identifying the environment as a provocative agent increases normalization and empowerment, while reducing shame and stigma. The patient/client is not an awful person—the environment was in some way activating their autonomic nervous system. We will share that they will be learning regulation skills to help them manage themselves when in a provocative environment.

Building Capacity by Reframing Emotions to Physiological Dysregulation:

Many of the problem behaviors that bring people into service delivery are congruent with the system that is in charge at the time, which has become habituated and sometimes dominant through life experience.

Poor behavior reduces automatically when the body is not in a state of SD, so when an expression of anger or frustration emerges from the patient/client, this is our opportunity to tie it back to what we have discussed about physiology. This highlights to our patients and clients their need for self-regulation, even when it is a foreign concept to them and their history. This is a place where the instruction of self-regulation skills for the body can easily be plugged into the discussion with the patient/client.

Normalizing Internal Negative Messages:

The critical inner voice is a well-used pattern of destructive thoughts that have been built into our systems as we each experience a history of adversity. The nagging "voices" or thoughts that make up this internalized dialogue are at the root of much of our self-destructive and maladaptive behavior. We will normalize how this is an SD response set, relating this idea back to the point of activation discussion where worrisome fantasies were discussed.

We will use examples of when the patient/client and/or family experienced their inner critic, helping them see it as part of the activation sequence of becoming SD. We will then teach the patient/client and/or family how to regulate themselves when the inner critic is speaking to them or through them.

Normalizing Perceptions of Self, Significant Relationships, and Worldview:

Questions we will ask the patient/client when normalizing their perceptions include:

1. "What would any reasonable, rational human being come to believe about themselves (intellectually, emotionally, spiritually, psychologically, physically, socially, and academically) from having these things occur in their life? How has your personal history of SD contributed to this view of yourself?"

2. "What would any reasonable, rational human being come to believe about important relationships (intellectually, emotionally, spiritually, psychologically, physically, and socially) from having these things occur in their life? How has your personal history of SD contributed to this view of your relationships?"

3. "What would any reasonable, rational human being come to believe about the world at large from having these things occur in their life? How has your personal history of SD contributed to this view of the world?"

Next we will teach self-regulation as it would relate to balancing the views of self, relationships, and the world. These views are likely quite binary, but through self-regulation can be broadened a bit. We will relate back to the collapsed categories of the overactivated anterior cingulate cortex (ACC) to support our instruction.

Reviewing Patient/Client's Daily Experiences and Tying in Self-Regulation:

We will go through the common and daily experiences of the patient/client, tying them in to the activation of the SD and practicing self-regulation imaginally during those activating moments. It is suggested that this be done throughout most of one session, or that we give the patient/client at least eight to ten opportunities to regulate while recalling an aversive experience. If the patient/client struggles to be successful at the degree of activation in their SD, we will have them correct, and see that maybe more practice is needed.

Bringing in the Timeline:

This is a great place to bring the timeline into discussion, and begin working on it:

1. We will explain to the patient/client that now that they have a better capacity to regulate themselves, we would like to have a fuller understanding of their timeline to help them prepare for service delivery in Stage Three more effectively.

2. We will detail that the timeline is a list of positives and negatives that have happened to each person in the family.

3. We will give examples of both positive and negative things that might be on a timeline, demonstrating how we would summarize them in small three- to four-word statements.

4. We will start with the oldest and end with the youngest.

5. We will remind them of the first rule.

6. We will ask them to begin with the safe items.

Foster parents or adoptive parents also need to create a timeline that we can compare to the child's, looking for any similarities or differences and exploring what that might lead us to. When we go through the timeline, we are using subtext to consolidate the gains in self-regulation.

Thirty-Day Video Stabilization Program for Adjunctive Online Trauma Therapy

From a therapeutic standpoint, very few of us have the opportunity to work daily with our patients and clients to keep them moving in the right direction every moment that a trauma trigger occurs. As a result of increased access to online therapeutic devices, materials, and learning tools, trauma-informed professionals have a variety of mechanisms to guide our patients and clients with daily instructions and strategies to keep them on track.

The Traumatology Institute's thirty-day video stabilization program was developed to assist patients and clients in their daily focus on stabilization, helping them to build the foundation and hardiness required to move into Stage Two (working through their trauma). Each video focuses on a unique skillset or knowledge base with the goal of establishing a concrete sense of stabilization, along with a commitment to required daily practice. We believe that daily practice forms a foundation that allows for improved trauma recovery.

The video stabilization program is part of the larger Trauma Treatment Online Program, which offers complex adjunctive therapy for patients and clients to aid them in their recovery. Information can be found at: **www.whatisptsd.com/trauma-care-online**, and the first ten days can be accessed at no charge on request. For details or to register, go to: **www.whatisptsd.com/10-days-absolutely-free/**.

Stage Three: Integration and Desensitization

As paraprofessionals, you likely will not be moving people into the mental health interventions that comprise the primary functions of Stage Three. Therefore, this section will only highlight components of this stage. (You will, however, have plenty of opportunities to move people into Stage Four.) As an overview to understand the process of Stage Three, here are a few key highlights:

· Sharing exposure and relaxation/trauma resolution techniques such as Prolonged Exposure (PE), Cognitive Processing Therapy (CPT), EMDR, and others.

· Sharing the "Telling Story + Relaxed Body" concept.

· Creating narratives that can be expanded as needed, and in the process, lessening reactivity to the event/events.

· Normalizing difficulties, unwanted emotions, thoughts, behaviors, and beliefs.

· Focusing on discovering and highlighting strengths and patient/client's capacity.

· Helping the patient/client to mourn and/or work through grief.

Stage Four: Post-Traumatic Growth and Resilience

There are three domains of change in the post-traumatic growth component of Stage Four:

1. Consolidate/change the perception of self.
2. Consolidate/change interpersonal relationships.
3. Consolidate/change philosophy of life.

There are also five core factors in post-traumatic growth:

1. Relating to others.
2. New possibilities.
3. Personal strength.
4. Spiritual change and maturity.
5. Appreciation of life.

Skills that patients and clients can use to recover their sense of personal safety include multiple techniques for self-regulation and anxiety reduction, such as interoception, mindfulness and "bodyfulness," diaphragmatic breathing, guided visualization, peripheral vision, and core relaxation.

Additionally, psychoeducational and cognitive restructuring tools empower trauma survivors to catalyze their natural resilience by overcoming their "victim mythology." Shifting clients' focus from an external to an internal locus of control enables them to regain a sense of self-efficacy, and to concentrate on solutions rather than problems.

Learning how trauma is more accurately understood as an injury rather than an illness and why the underlying biological and neurological mechanisms must be addressed before proceeding to service delivery using cognitive and behavioral techniques is revelatory for the patient/client. Throughout the Empowerment and Resiliency Structure, practitioners and patients/clients jointly explore the nature and function of the human threat-detection system, the Polyvagal response, and the roles these systems play in the development and maintenance of post-traumatic symptoms and adaptations (i.e., addiction).

A suggested resource to master the four stages of this trauma assessment and treatment structure can be found here: **www.ashlandmhrb.org/upload/mastering_the_four_stages_of_trauma_assessment**.

Teaching Patients and Clients Ways to Build Resilience:

There are a variety of ways we will teach our patients and clients how to build resilience, but here are a few suggestions for getting them started:

- Make connections.
- Avoid seeing crises as insurmountable problems.
- Accept that change is a part of living.
- Move toward your goals.
- Take decisive actions.
- Look for opportunities for self-discovery.
- Nurture a positive view of yourself.
- Keep things in perspective.
- Maintain a hopeful outlook.
- Take care of yourself.

Chapter Summary

The importance of safety, transparency, and caregiver/client collaboration in trauma treatment has been demonstrated throughout many empirical studies and personal caregiver experiences over the decades. These principles can be enhanced in treatment through the use of a clinical pathway of service delivery, which provides a general framework of design applicable to any model of treatment.

Benefits of clinical pathway structures include improved care, outcomes, governance, competence, and supervision, a reduction in costs and variability in treatment, and the ability to measure improvement through specific criteria. The Empowerment and Resiliency Structure is one such clinical pathway for trauma service delivery, and is comprised of four stages of treatment that include preparation and relationship building, psychoeducation and self-regulation, integration and desensitization, and post-traumatic growth and resilience. Each stage can enrich and improve the quality of care for those seeking help, and when paired with adjunctive online trauma therapy material that supports stabilization and patient/client capacity, healing is that much more achievable.

Chapter Eight

Safety and Stabilization in Crisis Work

Focus Questions:

- How can I use the principles of trauma-informed care to deescalate a crisis situation?
- What skills can I apply from the C-A-S-E-R Model to stabilize a crisis situation and maximize recovery thereafter?

In this chapter you will learn more about:

- How to articulate the application of trauma-informed care to a crisis situation.
- The powerful negative effects that chronic stress has in a volatile environment.
- Developing skills for deescalating a crisis situation and ongoing self-regulation.
- A five-step protocol called the C-A-S-E-R Model for helping clients to maximize their recovery and minimize the negative effects after the crisis.

No social stability without individual stability.

– Aldous Huxley

When working with any vulnerable population, measures should always be taken to ensure the safety and welfare of patients and clients. Survivors of trauma can certainly be identified as a vulnerable population, since they have a heightened vulnerability for adverse outcomes. In addition, specific acutely injured trauma survivors "may be at high risk for later psychiatric morbidity" (Seedat et al., 2004, p. 263). These adverse outcomes can be contributed to the overwhelming flooding of negative emotions invoked by implicit traumatic memories that may force victims to relive a traumatic event, and as a result, dysregulate homeostatic activity in the brain and autonomic nervous system.

As trauma support specialists, it is vital that you learn skills to augment your ability to manage and navigate through high-demand crisis situations, including: 1) helping to prevent a situation from escalating into danger or violence; and 2) knowing how to quickly, efficiently, and professionally manage those situations where there is little danger but upset individuals, or additionally, during the aftermath of violence. You will learn to use the principles of trauma-informed care to rapidly stabilize a crisis situation so that violence can be avoided. These skills are drawn from research and development among first responders and crisis workers in disaster contexts, so they apply equally to many crisis situations.

Trauma-Focused Care in Crisis Stabilization

In its most basic form, trauma-informed care is a paradoxical shift from pathology ("what's wrong with you") to one of caring and understanding. Trauma-informed care focuses on: 1) what happened to the victim; 2) who experienced the traumatic event; and 3) how that post-traumatic stress carries on in the survivor's life and impacts their everyday functionality.

This type of sensitive, understanding care is a good start to liberating healing from the technician and placing it firmly in the hands of those who put the therapeutic relationship before models of treatment and highly ritualized protocols. As explained in Chapter Three on the foundations of trauma-informed care, the National Center for Trauma-Informed Care (NCTIC) and the Substance Abuse and Mental Health Services Administration (SAMHSA) have formulated their list of six principles or philosophical stances that are integral to delivering trauma-sensitive treatment, especially in the event of a crisis situation. Let us revisit them now:

1. Safety.
2. Trustworthiness and Transparency.
3. Peer Support and Mutual Self-Help.

4. Collaboration and Mutuality.

5. Empowerment, Voice, and Choice.

6. Cultural, Historical, and Gender Issues.

These markers of being trauma-informed are solid clinical practices anytime, but especially for stabilization during or immediately after a crisis. Keep them in mind as we detail the protocols for offering crisis-specific trauma treatment, and how they can be employed during interactions with survivors.

Safety in Crisis Stabilization

The effects of trauma reverberate through time and across a wide spectrum of life activities. Depending on the circumstances, these effects can result in debilitating behaviors meant to alleviate anxiety that are often less than healthy and less than useful to that purpose. Survivors may withdraw from their social life, use alcohol or drugs, or develop personality habits that are self-defeating, and can actually continue to place themselves in situations that are chaotic and anxiety-provoking because they lack the skills and emotional stability to make better choices.

To accomplish the task of trauma symptom reduction, the patient/client must be able to create a state of relaxation—and with a chaotic life and self-soothing methods that are less than useful, creating this state is next to impossible. This section is devoted to providing techniques by which the caregiver can assist their patients and clients in creating the environment of safety necessary for trauma work post-crisis, and addresses the elements of body, cognition, behavior, emotions, and relationships essential to recovery.

In 1996, while completing a fellowship in Psychotraumatology at West Virginia University, Dr. Gentry wrote an article on creating and maintaining safety with trauma survivors that provided a protocol for assessment and development of stabilization. In it, Dr. Gentry attempted to define and "operationalize" the concept of safety into three levels relative to the treatment of trauma survivors. These three levels of safety are:

1. Resolution of impending environmental physical danger (ambient, interpersonal, and intrapersonal), including:

· Removal from "war zone" (i.e., domestic violence, combat, abuse).

· Behavioral interventions to provide maximum safety.

· Addressing and resolving self-harm.

2. Amelioration of self-destructive thoughts and behaviors (i.e., suicidal and/or homicidal ideation and/or behavior, eating disorders, persecutory alters/ego-states, addictions, trauma-bonding, risk-taking behaviors, isolation).

3. Restructuring victim mentality into a proactive survivor identity by development and habituation of life-affirming self-care skills (i.e., daily routines, relaxation skills, grounding/containment skills, assertiveness, secure provision of basic needs, self-parenting).

One of the most difficult questions that a clinician must answer is: "What's the adequate level of stability necessary for a patient/client to safely transition to Stage Two of treatment?"

We are taught from the first days of our clinical training to "above all do no harm" (*primum non nocere*), which makes it logical to assume that the more safety and stability that we as clinicians can affect in the lives of our patients and clients, the better for their treatment—right?

The answer to this question can be a double-edged sword. For example, Dr. Gentry has stated that early in his career as a trauma therapist, he spent many therapy hours working with clients to establish safety and stability. Upon closer inspection, he saw that this delay was his own anxiety about approaching the traumatic material that actually "escalated the crises of his clients." The safety issue was as much about his own emotional safety as that of the trauma survivors.

A commonly held hypothesis among trauma therapists is that the most important tool for the effective establishment of stabilization and even treatment outcomes is the warm confidence of the clinician. A non-anxious presence, along with an unwavering optimism for the patient/client's prognosis, is probably the most powerful intervention you can provide toward the development of their stabilization. However, you will find that destabilization and lack of safety are often precipitated by patient/client behaviors and thoughts in response to the bombardment of intrusive symptoms (i.e., nightmares, flashbacks, psychological and physiological reactivity).

A protracted period of attempting to overdevelop safety for these patients and clients is not helpful—an approach is needed that develops the minimum ("good enough") level of safety and stabilization, and then addresses and resolves the intrusive symptoms by enabling a narrative of the traumatic experience. This is counterintuitive, and almost always produces anxiety for the clinician initially—but resolving the patient/client's intrusive symptoms allows them to more easily change self-destructive patterns (i.e., addictions, eating disorders, abusive relationships), because they have better access to the faculties needed for intervention.

So how safe does your patient/client have to be, and how do you get them there? There are no hard-and-fast rules for safety, but we will discuss various techniques for helping to establish safety and stabilization, and discuss reference points that can be useful to help you decide which to use.

The C-A-S-E-R Model

The C-A-S-E-R Model was originally developed in 2002 to be used as a method of service delivery for peer-driven community crisis support teams in Hillsborough County, Tampa, Florida. Due to the model's common confusion with the International Critical Incident Stress Foundation's "defusing" group discussion intervention (Mitchell, 1995), and because Young and Ford's model fails to address many of the important aspects of initial intervention, we have created our own intervention model entitled the Initial Trauma Intervention (ITI).

The ITI combines elements from several different individual debriefing and defusing models (Mitchell, 1995; Lerner and Shelton, 2001), current research (Bisson and Deahl, 1994), publications (World Health Organization, 2017; The National Institute of Mental Health, 2002) and field experience from experts in the area of disaster traumatology.

The ITI is designed to be utilized with survivors and/or witnesses of a recent traumatic event. Ideally, the survivor will have already received triage services from an emergency medical service professional, and has been cleared of any possible injuries requiring emergency medical attention. However, the trauma interventionist should constantly assess for any physical injury or ailments that may have been missed by EMS and *immediately* refer the survivor for further medical follow-up.

An ITI may be conducted onsite at a disaster or emergency, although it is more likely that this and other crisis support services will be provided at a staging area near the site, a hospital, shelter, or some other location. There is often very little need for mental health/crisis support services onsite in the immediate aftermath of a disaster. This is because first responders are busy controlling the perimeter, triaging survivors/victims, and providing rescue and recovery functions. Unnecessary personnel such as mental health professionals and crisis support workers could easily be in the way at the disaster site, inadvertently thwarting crucial efforts of immediate rescue.

It is imperative that the trauma intervention worker follow the direction of their Team Leader, who is under the direction of the Incident Commander (the Incident Command System will be covered in day five of this training). Under no circumstances can the intervention worker engage in unauthorized solicitation or service delivery with survivors or witnesses. It is also imperative that the helper does not engage the survivor where there is any environmental threat or presence of danger. The helper should assist the survivor to a place that has been declared safe by the Incident Command.

Previous to meeting with the survivor, the interventionist should take a moment to develop their non-anxious presence and be prepared to monitor and self-regulate so that this important condition can be maintained throughout their work with survivors. Achieving and maintaining this desired state is crucial for work with survivors for three reasons:

1. A non-anxious presence will allow you optimal cognitive and motor functioning during your work with survivors. The areas of the brain associated with these functions can become diminished with high levels of anxiety (Sapolsky, 1996).

2. Your calmness will model and assist the survivor in quickly developing stabilization and control. Conversely, an anxious caregiver can potentially exacerbate the anxiety of the survivor.

3. A non-anxious presence may heighten your resiliency to secondary traumatic stress and other possible deleterious effects associated with helping trauma survivors.

For these reasons, this book includes several exercises designed to teach training participants and future interventionists the skills for developing and maintaining a non-anxious presence.

The Five Phases of the Initial Trauma Intervention (C-A-S-E-R)

The ITI is conducted in five phases: **C**ontact, **A**ssessment, **S**tabilization, **E**ducation, and **R**eferral. They are usually conducted in chronological order until all are completed, but an ITI may also include any of these phases in any order depending on the needs and presentation of the survivor.

Phase One: Contact

The first phase of the ITI is arguably its most important. In making first contact with the survivor after a traumatic event, it is crucial that the helper exudes a sense of warmth, calmness, and authenticity, as this first contact will establish the tone for future interventions and service utilization/effectiveness. It is well demonstrated that the relationship between the caregiver and patient/client is the number one predictor of positive outcomes in helping contexts (Bergin and Garfield, 1994). Although it has yet to be demonstrated by empirical research, we expect the same to be true for helping survivors—better relationships established rapidly with survivors will likely yield better results in terms of rapid stabilization, symptoms being lessened, and future utilization of services. Again, the importance of the non-anxious presence is emphasized to facilitate this positive relationship. In addition to the non-anxious presence, qualities such as warmth, caring, unconditional positive regard, active listening, eye contact, open body posture (with open hands in sight), soothing but clear voice tones, and the communication of positive expectations of a normal recovery are also important ingredients to building a positive short-term helping relationship.

The survivor should be greeted with a warm introduction: "My name is ________, and I am helping here today," followed by the offer of a handshake. Offering a bottle of water and/or a small snack can also be helpful in developing contact with the survivor.

The handshake should be the first and only time that touch with the survivor is initiated by the helper. The helper should refrain from hugs, hand-holding, or other forms of touch unless they are initiated or requested by the survivor. Even then, touch should be used most judiciously and carefully. It is easy to quickly foster a sense of dependence with survivors, which is one of the possible unintended negative consequences of immediate or near-immediate post-trauma assistance. The responder should make every effort to engage the survivor's resiliency and self-soothing skills to restore self-efficacy. Connecting the survivor with their preexisting support systems for this comfort is one of the goals of the ITI, and can occur at any time during the interaction with the survivor ("Who can I call to come be with you?").

Phase Two: Assessment/Triage

In emergency and disaster contexts, activities and services are often chaotic. Survivors with significant physical injuries and/or deep psychological wounds can slip through the cracks of on-scene service delivery. For this reason, it is crucial that the early intervention specialist develop competency with rudimentary assessment and triage skills.

All the survivors with whom we work will most likely have been evaluated, triaged, and served by some emergency medical services personnel beforehand. If a person has survived a traumatic event during which people were injured or killed, then all survivors of that experience should, as a matter of routine, be evaluated by Emergency Medical Services (EMS). If the EMS professional has pronounced the survivor as ambulatory and not in need of immediate services, only then is it appropriate to begin early trauma intervention. It is possible, however, for an early intervention specialist to come in contact with a survivor with injuries that have not yet been evaluated by EMS, or whose injuries escaped detection. It is imperative that the early intervention specialist remains vigilant throughout their contact with survivors for the possibility of physical injury. If the helper identifies an injured survivor or suspects that a survivor has untreated injuries, then the helper should immediately contact an EMS professional for evaluation and consultation.

The majority of survivors experience normal stress reactions, but some may require immediate crisis intervention to help manage intense feelings of panic or grief. Signs of panic include trembling, agitation, rambling speech, and erratic behavior, while signs of intense grief may present as loud wailing, rage, or catatonia. In such cases, attempt to quickly establish therapeutic rapport, ensure the survivor's safety, acknowledge and validate the survivor's experience, and offer empathy. Interventions designed to rapidly stabilize the survivor's thinking and emotions may be indicated (see the third phase of Stabilization). Medication may be appropriate and necessary, if available.

Early trauma interventionists should remember that the needs of individual members of a community may vary greatly. The following early intervention strategies can yield good results:

1. Providing direct services as soon as is feasible after the event may require temporarily bringing in outside experts. It is of the *greatest importance* that needs assessment, planning, and service delivery be done in full coordination and with explicit knowledge of local providers. Outside help should at no time be imposed; respectful, coordinated interfacing with local resources, however limited these may be, is essential.

2. Empowering local care providers to assume ever-greater responsibilities for delivering services in their community. This can be achieved by providing in-field training from the start of an intervention, which increases professional self-esteem and helps local resources expand quickly. We cannot forget that care providers from within a community may themselves be overwhelmed and/or traumatized, and need to ensure that comprehensive professional support and supervision are available for them to attend to their own mental health needs.

An algorithm for initial trauma assessment with survivors of recent traumatic events is provided below. Assessment with the survivor should be recursive and continuous throughout the duration of contact:

Assessment/Triage

Is the helper safe?

· If no, discontinue help immediately and seek safety.

· If yes, then…

Is the survivor…

· Injured, unconscious, or suspected of some physiological anomaly?

· Yes – Immediate EMS response.

· No – Continue with ITI.

· In imminent danger from immediate threat?

· Yes – Contact EMS or Incident Command.

· No – Continue with ITI.

· Engaging in threatening or dangerous behavior and/or talking of harming self or others? (If survivor is combative or threatening to helper, contact EMS.)

· Yes – Contact EMS or Team Leader.

· No – Continue with ITI.

· Experiencing overwhelming trauma reaction?

· Yes – What kind?

- · Shock, unresponsive, inability to focus, inability to speak – If already seen and released by EMS, seek a second consultation. If released a second time, continue with ITI.
- · Intense affect (fear, terror, grief, elation, rage) – Demonstrate non-anxious presence and attempt stabilization. If survivor becomes stabilized (ten to fifteen minutes), then continue with ITI. If not, seek EMS or acute psychiatric intervention.
- · Racing, uncontrollable thoughts – Demonstrate non-anxious presence and attempt stabilization. If survivor becomes stabilized (ten to fifteen minutes), then continue with ITI. If not, seek EMS or licensed mental health professional for evaluation.

· No – Continue with ITI.

· Able to remain oriented to helper and situation?

· Yes – Continue with ITI (contact family member/support person, education, referral/follow-up). Do not leave survivor alone. Connect with family member, support person, or stay with survivor until support can be located.

· No – Demonstrate non-anxious presence and attempt stabilization. If survivor becomes stabilized (ten to fifteen minutes), then continue with ITI (contact family member/support person, education, and referral/follow-up). If not, seek EMS or acute psychiatric intervention.

Phase Three: Stabilization

As with assessment, this phase of the ITI is ubiquitous throughout the contact with the survivor. The stabilization phase of the ITI serves two functions:

1. To help the overwhelmed survivor rapidly regain self-regulation and self-efficacy.
2. To help the survivor develop skills for the management of potential traumatic stress following the event.

For survivors who are safe and uninjured but are experiencing overwhelming uncontrollable feelings, thoughts, intrusive images, or other post-traumatic phenomena, offering some simple grounding, stabilization, and stress management skills can be very beneficial. Additionally, teaching the survivor self-help anxiety management skills to cope with potential stressors that may follow can also be useful. The helper should always get permission from the survivor before attempting to intervene with these skills ("I know some things that might be helpful for you to get back in control. Would you like to try them?" or "would you like to learn some techniques that might be helpful for lowering stress after this is over?").

Included below are some grounding, stabilization, and anxiety techniques drawn from *Trauma Practice: Tools for Stabilization and Recovery – A Cognitive Behavioral Approach* (Baranowsky, Gentry, and Schultz, in press) that can be utilized with a survivor on-scene during the ITI:

3-2-1 Sensory Grounding and Containment Technique

Time required: Five minutes.

Materials required: None.

Indications for use: Use when the primary need is to enhance physical and emotional coping skills in this safety and stabilization stage of trauma recovery.

Counter-indications: None.

This technique assists the trauma survivor in developing the capacity to "self-rescue" from the obsessive, hypnotic, and numinous power of the traumatic intrusions/flashbacks. It is based on the assumption that the survivor is able to break their internal attention on the traumatic images, thoughts, and feelings by instead focusing on and connecting with their current external surroundings through their senses (the "here and now") so that the accompanying fight/flight arousal will diminish.

This technique will assist the survivor in understanding that they are perfectly safe in their present context and the value of using their sensory skills (sight, touch, smell, hearing, and even taste) to "ground" them to this safety in their present empirical reality. The 3-2-1 sensory grounding and containment technique is delivered as follows:

1. Begin by asking the patient/client to tell part of their trauma narrative, allowing them to begin to experience some affect (reddening of eyes, psychomotor agitation, constricted posture).

2. When they have begun to experience some affect (~ 5 on a Subjective Units of Distress Scale/SUDS), ask them, "Would you like some help out of those uncomfortable images, thoughts, and feelings?"

3. If they answer "yes," ask them to describe, out loud, three objects they can see in the room that are above eye level. (Make certain they are physical, not imaginal, objects).

4. Ask them to identify, out loud, three "real world" sounds they can currently hear sitting there in the room (the sounds can be from beyond the room, but make certain they are empirical and not from the traumatic material).

5. Hand them any item (a pen, notebook, tissue), and ask them to really feel it and to describe, out loud, the texture of this object. Repeat this with two additional objects.

6. Start the round over again with sight, this time asking the patient/client to identify two objects above eye level. Follow that with the identification of two sounds. When you get to touch, ask the patient/client to reach out and touch two objects of their choosing, describing their texture to you.

7. Complete one final round of sight, sound, and touch with one object each.

8. Once all three rounds are completed, ask the patient/client, "What happened with the traumatic material?" Most of the time your patient/client will describe a significant lessening of negative feelings, thoughts, and images associated with it.

For many survivors, this technique will mark the first time they have been able to "rescue" themselves from a flashback/traumatic material. It is often an experience of tremendous empowerment because it can represent the "beginning of the end of victimization" for the survivor. The clinician may want to allow ample opportunity to explore this process and utilize the "teachable moment" inherent in it.

Diaphragmatic Breathing

Time required: Five minutes.

Materials required: None.

Indications for use: Use when the primary need is to enhance physical coping skills in the safety and stabilization stage of trauma recovery.

Counter-indications: Any respiratory complications.

If we watch an infant sleep, we will see the rhythmical movement of deep belly breathing. This is the ideal breathing for relaxation and the nourishing of the body with breath.

When we feel upset or anxious about something, our breathing is often the first thing to change. It is likely to become shallow, rapid and jagged, or raspy. If we were to instead practice intentional diaphragmatic breathing, we would be better able to consciously regulate our breathing when we became upset. The delivery of this approach is as follows:

Find a comfortable, unrestricted position to sit or lie in. Place your hands on your belly as a guide to the breath. Begin to consciously slow and smooth out the breath, just noticing the rhythm through the inhalation and exhalation. Is it smooth, deep, and full, or jagged, shallow, and slight? Now focus on bringing a deeper breath into the belly. Let a full breath be released on the exhalation. Inhale fully, not holding the breath at any time. On the exhalation, release completely and pause, counting to three after the exhalation is complete. Then inhale slowly once more, full and deep. Continue to focus in this manner on the breath.

Dr. Gentry suggests placing your clasped hands behind your neck, which opens the chest through the lifting and spreading of the elbows. As this occurs, breath moves more freely deep into the belly. This procedure is an excellent alternative to placing your hands on the belly for those just learning deep breathing exercises.

At first the individual is taught to deep breathe in sets of five. Then this is increased to ten inhalations and exhalations. Finally, an instruction is given to practice two times each day, for five minutes per day. In this way, the individual is learning to relax through deep breathing.

<u>Progressive Relaxation</u>

Time required: Five to thirty minutes depending on script.

Materials required: None.

Indications for use: Use when the primary need is to enhance physical coping skills in the safety and stabilization stage of trauma recovery.

Counter-indications: Actively dissociating or dissociates during exercise.

Ehrenreich (1999) provides a simple script for progressive relaxation that can be expanded upon with minimal effort:

> Begin this exercise by instructing the individual to focus on lengthening and deepening the breath. Focus on the inhalation and exhalation, making the breath smooth and deep.
>
> "Now tighten both fists, and tighten your forearms and biceps...hold the tension for five or six seconds...now relax the muscles. When you relax the tension, do it suddenly, as if you're turning off a light. Concentrate on the feelings of relaxation in your arms for fifteen or twenty seconds. Now tense the muscles of your face and tense your jaw...hold it for five or six seconds...now relax, and concentrate on the relaxation for fifteen or twenty seconds. Now arch your back and press out your stomach as you take a deep breath...hold it...and relax. Now tense your thighs and calves and buttocks...hold...and now relax. Concentrate on the feelings of relaxation throughout your body, breathing slowly and deeply." (Ehrenreich, 1999)

From the brief description above, the clinician can encourage tightness and relaxation throughout the patient/client's body, resulting in a progressive release of tension from top to bottom.

Phase Four: Education

This phase of the ITI is utilized to help survivors make sense of the symptoms they experience or may experience resulting from the trauma. Helping the survivor to understand that they are a "normal person having normal responses to an abnormal event" can have a powerful ameliorative effect upon their anxiety about being sick or damaged from the traumatic event. Most survivors can and do recover from traumatic events with the help of their families and indigenous support, and we want to provide them with information and education designed to assist and accelerate this natural healing.

Remember that educational material and psychoeducational interventions should be conversational, in lay language, and only supplied at the invitation of the survivor and only after the survivor is stabilized. Thrusting material and information upon an already overwhelmed survivor is not helpful.

Phase Five: Referral

This is the final phase of the ITI. As the helper and survivor arrive at this phase, hopefully the survivor will have become stabilized, learned stress management skills, developed a rudimentary understanding of traumatic stress, have made significant contact with the helper, and have a support person on their way to meet them.

In addition, the early intervention specialist should have a resource handout they can give survivors that contains contact information for indigenous health and mental health professionals that the survivor can contact if they later find they are in need of services. This sheet should also have professional (not personal) contact information for the early intervention specialist.

The early intervention team may also offer additional services following a traumatic event such as group debriefing, family groups, individual brief psychotherapy, and grief support groups. All of these available services can be offered to the survivor during this phase of the intervention.

We concur with the National Institute of Mental Health's (NIMH) recommendation of the need for follow-up services with survivors of recent traumatic events (2002). It is recommended that the early intervention specialist maintain a logbook of the contacts they have made and the ITIs they have completed for each day of work on crisis scenes. Contact information should be voluntarily elicited from the survivor and recorded. ("Is it okay if I take your name, address, and telephone number? I'd like to check in on you within the next couple of days to see how you're doing and ask whether you might need anything.") Team Leaders or other designees of the Incident Command should compile this contact information along with the provisions available for systematic follow-up for survivors. This component has been identified by the experts from the NIMH publication (2002) as one of the most important aspects of facilitating and accelerating individual and community healing following a traumatic event.

Chapter Summary

The six principles of trauma-focused care are applicable to any trauma situation, but can be especially useful during or immediately following a crisis. Safety must be established immediately, and is crucial to deescalating a crisis situation and maximizing recovery thereafter. A trauma interventionist should begin stabilization by following three protocols: 1) resolving the potential for any physical threat or danger to the survivor (i.e., removal from war zone, abusive relationship, etc.); 2) ameliorating potential for self-destructive thoughts or behaviors; and 3) working to restructure the individual's mentality from that of a victim to one of proactive healing.

The C-A-S-E-R Model was created as a peer-driven service delivery approach for communities following a crisis, and provided the foundation for the Initial Trauma Intervention (ITI) created by the authors of this book. Designed to be used on or near a crisis site immediately following a traumatic event, the ITI is comprised of five phases: Contact, Assessment/Triage, Stabilization, Education, and Referral. These phases are typically followed chronologically, but can be executed in any order in accordance with the situation and survivor's needs. The ITI includes several stabilization and relaxation techniques for the survivor's "self-rescue" following the traumatic event, such as the 3-2-1 sensory grounding and containment technique, diaphragmatic breathing, and progressive relaxation. These methods can be taught quickly and efficiently, and provide the individual with empowerment over the traumatic material.

Chapter Nine

Integrated Care: Trauma-Specific Services in Primary Care Settings

Focus Questions:

- Why is it important for a trauma-focused caregiver to consider comorbid medical conditions?
- What are the calmative adverse effects to traumatic exposure?

In this chapter you will learn more about:

- Understanding how comorbid medical conditions influence the treatment outcomes of one another.
- The prevalence of traumatic stress and medical conditions.
- Understanding the mechanisms of pain, its relation to traumatic stress, and its treatment.

An ounce of prevention is worth a pound of cure.

– Benjamin Franklin

Take care of the patient and everything else will follow.

– Thomas F. Frist Jr., MD

Comorbidity in Medical and Mental Health Conditions

Many caregivers, including psychotherapists, frequently encounter patients/clients who are suffering from comorbid medical conditions. If not addressed professionally, several medical conditions (i.e., diabetes, chronic physical pain, respiratory issues, fibromyalgia, HIV/AIDS, cancer, Alzheimer's disease, accident-related injuries, etc.) can result in poor mental health treatment outcomes. Similarly, a patient suffering from a mental health disorder or battling the symptoms of traumatic stress can result in poor medical treatment outcomes if their mental health concerns are not addressed adequately. Thus, the trauma-focused caregiver should have a basic reference of understanding about how mental health or traumatic stress and medical conditions are interconnected, and learn the importance of working in an integrated multidisciplinary treatment team to enhance treatment outcomes.

The management of type 2 diabetes mellitus, for example, requires the lifelong active role of maintaining a new lifestyle, with long to-do lists that lack any immediate rewards. Now imagine how strenuous and daunting it would be for an individual to manage type 2 diabetes—through medication compliance, insulin therapy, blood thinners and/or statins, exercise five days a week for twenty to thirty minutes, and a diabetic diet—when they are battling the symptoms associated with traumatic stress (i.e., depression, anxiety, isolation, mistrust, etc.). Conversely, it becomes a futile task for a trauma-focused caregiver to help create a sense of safety when patients/clients are suffering from severe medical conditions that are life-threatening without proper medical care. It is evident, therefore, that the treatment of comorbid medical and mental health conditions, including traumatic stress, requires a multidisciplinary integrative care approach from the perspective of providing better patient outcomes and even incurring the benefits of a medical cost offset.

In many instances, either the medical or the mental health conditions are etiological factors of the other condition (i.e., psychosocial stress as a major factor in triggering physical illness), or they exacerbate one another. The National Association of State Mental Health Program Directors (NASMHPD) recognizes associated links with comorbid medical and mental health conditions. For example, collective data show that sixty percent of premature deaths among individuals diagnosed with schizophrenia are due to medical conditions, such as cardiovascular, respiratory, and infectious disease, or diabetes (2006, p. 12). Other reports indicate that particular psychotropic medication (i.e., second-generation antipsychotic drugs) were associated with weight gain (leading to obesity/being overweight), insulin resistance, diabetes, dyslipidemia, high cholesterol, and metabolic syndrome (p. 39). Alarmingly, research data indicate a growing need for mental health services, yet quality treatment and good outcomes are lacking according to a "systematic review of the peer-reviewed literature" on mental disorders and medical comorbidity, which approximates that "sixty-eight percent of adults with mental disorders have at least one medical condition" (Goodell, Druss, and Walker, 2011, p. 4).

SAMHSA reports that 9.8 million U.S. adults aged eighteen and older have a serious mental illness (2017, para. 1). In addition, they published a national survey in 2013 that estimated 40 to 50 million individuals could have benefited from mental health services but never received them (U.S. Department of Health and Human Services, 2014).

Besides the U.S. adult population, approximately thirteen percent of children ages eight to fifteen suffer from a severe mental illness (Merikangas et al., 2010). One out of five adolescents between thirteen and eighteen suffers from a diagnosable mental disorder (Schwarz, 2009). One in six children has a developmental disability, and one in sixty-eight children are identified with an autism spectrum disorder with a high prevalence of comorbid conditions, such as chronic diarrhea or colitis, anxiety, severe headaches, depression, epilepsy, gastrointestinal problems, sleeping disturbances, etc. (Schieve et al., 2012). These statistics point to the importance of trauma-focused caregivers understanding how to support individuals who suffer from comorbid medical and mental health conditions. At the same time, it appears that U.S. adults suffering from mental health conditions also have a high prevalence of traumatic exposure, which can exacerbate both the medical and mental health conditions.

In many cases, individuals suffering from a mental disorder have been exposed to some form of trauma. In a Western Norway study (n = 139), approximately ninety-one percent of psychiatric patients reported at least one traumatic exposure, and sixty-nine percent reported being "repeatedly exposed to trauma for longer periods of time" (Floen and Elklit, 2007, p. 12).

Similar results were found in another study in Concord and Manchester, New Hampshire, and the city of Baltimore in Maryland. In this study of 275 patients with severe mental illness, ninety-eight percent of patients reported being exposed to at least one traumatic event (Mueser et al., 1998). Another study of women (n = 204) who had incurred injuries and sexual violence during human trafficking found that "sexual violence was associated with higher levels of PTSD" and the duration "in trafficking was associated with higher levels" of mood disorders and anxiety (Hossain et al., 2010). Other studies also showed an association and prevalence of exposure to trauma with various mental health diagnoses (i.e., mood disorders, anxiety disorders, substance-related disorders, cluster B personality disorders or traits, etc.) (van Zyl et al., 2017; Breslau, Davis, and Schultz, 2003; Neria et al., 2002). Of course, these are correlational studies that do not prove causality or that one factor causes the other, and further research needs to be conducted in this area to prove any causality (or lack of). However, research does seem to point to growing concerns of exposure to traumatic events not only resulting in mental health conditions, but comorbid medical conditions as well.

In the case of traumatic exposure, there seems to be a significantly increased likelihood of chronic medical conditions with individuals diagnosed with PTSD compared to non-traumatized patients. Research such as the landmark Adverse Childhood Experiences (ACE) study and data collected from the National Comorbidity Survey-Replication (NCS-R) suggest that "multiple traumas have a cumulative [adverse] effect on physical health," and are linked to chronic health conditions (Sledjeski, Speisman, and Dierker, 2008, p. 341; Felitti et al., 1998). This includes a two-to-four-fold increased risk of heart disease, chronic lung disease, severe obesity, cancer, emphysema, stroke, diabetes, and a shortened lifespan (Anda and Felitti, 2003; Middlebrooks and Audage, 2008; World Health Organization, 2006).

There are a number of research survey studies indicating that more than half of U.S. adults are survivors of at least one major traumatic incident (Elliott, 1997; Kessler et al., 1995; Norris, 1992). Keep in mind that these studies more than likely focused solely on exposure to "big T" traumatic events, while not taking into account the cumulative effects of "little t" traumatic exposure. This is alarming to say the least, since these findings suggest that over half of American adults have an increased risk of developing a chronic medical condition. Further research is required to account for those Americans who have been exposed to "little t" traumas and may also be more susceptible to the development of chronic physical illnesses.

Unfortunately, it appears that our children are also at an increased risk for developing a chronic medical condition at some point in their lifespan. According to the U.S. Department of Health and Human Services (HHS, 2015), Child Protective Services (CPS) received 4 million referrals and 3,358,000 children were recipients of some form of service in 2015. Of these referrals, a rounded figure of 683,000 children were substantiated to be victims of abuse and neglect, which is a slight increase compared to the two previous years (in 2013 it was an estimated 658,000, and in 2014 an estimated 676,000). This is an alarming number of children each year who are being exposed to the effects of trauma. These figures, however, do not account for the unreported traumatic incidents.

Results from the National Survey of Adolescents discovered that thirty-nine percent of children ages twelve to seventeen had witnessed a violent incident, seventeen percent reported being physically assaulted, and eight percent reported being sexually assaulted (Kilpatrick and Saunders, 1997). In another survey conducted at 536 elementary and middle schools, approximately thirty percent of the children had witnessed a stabbing, and twenty-five percent had observed a shooting (Bell and Jenkins, 1993). According to retrospective child abuse studies, approximately ten to twenty percent of men and twenty-five to thirty-five percent of women reported being sexually abused as a child (Briere and Elliott, 2003; Finkelhor et al., 1990). These findings are troubling since the environment of those children is having a cumulative adverse effect on their physical health, and increasing their risk of developing a chronic medical condition. Thus, it is imperative that professional caregivers in healthcare be trained in trauma-informed services, so that they can address both the medical and mental health needs of children and adults while finding preventive ways to reduce the adverse risks associated with traumatic stress.

Many medical and mental health disorders are complex and multifaceted, and treatment should be offered in a collaborative approach with various healthcare professionals. Clinical observations highlight the importance of good coordination of care, but the aforementioned studies draw attention to the need for behavioral health integration in the primary care setting. Keep in mind that many survivors of traumatic events will first seek help from their primary care provider instead of a mental health provider, so primary care settings are frequently encountering patients dealing with mental disorders or suffering from traumatic stress. Most primary care settings are unprepared to handle and provide adequate and quality services for these issues; as a result, those seeking help are not able to truly ameliorate their symptoms.

In the pediatric medical care setting, many children who have been exposed to emotionally traumatic events have never been adequately evaluated and treated for traumatic stress. This is alarming since "exposure to traumatic events is prevalent in children who are treated in the pediatric medical care setting," and is believed to be on the rise, partly due to intrusive medical procedures (Shemesh et al., 2005, p. 582). The pediatric setting may encounter families seeking help for a child displaying unwanted adaptive or mitigating behaviors (i.e., aggression, impulsivity, withdrawing or isolating, avoidant behaviors, sleeping difficulties, inattentiveness, hyperactivity or hypervigilance, etc.) resulting from a variety of traumatic exogenous experiences. Many pediatricians lack training in evaluating and providing less intrusive—but effective—treatments for traumatic stress. This can consequently result in undesirable forms of treatments (i.e., psychotropic medication) or other interventions that create additional stress on the child and their family, incurring a greater risk for later comorbid psychological and medical difficulties.

Effective treatment for this age range is crucial, since most children have a higher vulnerability to traumatic events compared to adults due to their developing neurobiology. Implementation of screening and assessment tools for trauma can help improve overall identification of traumatic stress symptoms, and trauma-focused treatment in the pediatric setting reduces the need for intrusive medical treatments. These pediatric findings are equally applicable to adult medical care.

Until behavioral integrated healthcare (a multidisciplinary team of mental health and medical practitioners working collaboratively in an integrated way for the provisional care of the patient) becomes a common practice in the primary care setting, the trauma healer can help improve the patient/client's quality of life by advocating and providing better coordination of care with both medical and mental health services.

Psychotropic Treatment in Children

The prevalence of psychotropic medication used among children has been increasing, as evidenced in this publication from the HHS: "There's been a steady rise in the use of medication to address children's emotional and behavioral problems over the last decade, even among preschoolers" (2012, p. 2). Although traumatic stress in children and adolescents has an exogenous etiology, many times children suffering from behavioral and mood symptoms caused by an overly charged autonomic nervous system are only being prescribed medication as treatment.

While psychopharmacological agents may be indicated for severe and debilitating behavioral and mood symptoms, there is a dire need to empirically evaluate psychopharmacological interventions for children suffering from traumatic stress. For example, "no controlled studies have been reported in pediatric post-traumatic stress disorder" for children who have been prescribed a psychopharmacological agent for treatment (Kaminer, Seedat, and Stein, 2005, p. 124). Additionally, Kaminer, Seedat, and Stein (2005) reported that "there are almost no controlled studies to guide the use of very early medication interventions in traumatized children" (p. 124), while the U.S. Food and Drug Administration (FDA) states on their website that recent studies reveal only around twenty percent of medications prescribed to children have actually been *tested* on children (2016).

Contrary to the lack of empirical data to support psychopharmacological interventions with traumatized children, Trauma-Focused Cognitive Behavioral Therapy (TF-CBT) has demonstrated, through rigorous controlled studies, evidence that supports its efficacy in treating traumatized children with behavioral problems that arose after exposure to a traumatic event (King et al., 2000; Cohen et al., 2004).

Primary care professionals (PCPs) might argue that hiring a trauma-informed professional caregiver to assess and help mitigate the symptoms of traumatic stress in the pediatric setting is not cost-effective. The provision of prompted therapeutic treatment, however, can result in the offsetting of medical costs by reducing medical utilization in lieu of effective trauma-informed therapeutic work. One study found that the provision of psychotherapy services could provide cost savings that ranged from "nine percent to twenty-four percent" (Cummings and Sayama, 1995, p. 25). Thus, we hope to see a rise in professional trauma-focused caregivers in the primary care setting.

Integrating Trauma-Focused Healthcare in the Primary Care Setting

The trauma-focused caregiver is in a position to help patients both with their mental or behavioral health symptoms as well as comorbid medical conditions. Trauma-focused medical professionals can recognize when an individual is displaying adaptive or mitigating behaviors from traumatic stress in the emergency room or primary care setting, and diagnose it as an activated sympathetic nervous system or dorsal vagal system (refer to Figure 4 in the fourth chapter for examples of these behaviors).

As a trauma-focused caregiver, you now understand that treating the behaviors or asking the survivor to stop engaging in them is futile, since they are the result of a charged and overactive neurobiological system. The key to effective treatment requires that the survivor be able to self-regulate and "deactivate" the survival response first. It is important, therefore, to create a climate that allows the body to return to a state of homeostasis before further treatment is administered.

Over the years, stress reduction has become an increasingly important component in the treatment of many medical conditions, including interventions for a healthy pregnancy (i.e., the Lamaze method, stress management, etc.). These treatments may have been influenced by a burgeoning literature suggesting stress can manifest itself in a number of physical ailments, interfering with pregnancy through direct hormonal effects or presenting medical conditions (Parker and Douglas, 2010).

Many of the behavioral treatments used in the primary and/or behavioral care setting have generalized protocols for the treatment of chronic stress (i.e., meditation, exercises, and medication management), but can fail to adequately and comprehensively address the etiology of patients suffering from traumatic stress. Relying on these treatments as a primary means of therapy is comparable to covering a gas leak with duct tape. Although these methods may act as a bandage for the issue at hand by providing useful individual stress reduction tools, they overlook the evidence-based components of traumatic stress treatment. This can result in a reduction of treatment efficacy, while failing to address the underlying systemic problems associated with the individual's symptoms.

In response, we are proposing the implementation of protocols for the treatment of compassion fatigue found in Chapter Two in the primary care setting. This will help patients and staff members to recover from the wounds of traumatic stress and burnout in their everyday lives, while assisting them to build the antibodies (resiliency) needed to combat the effects of future stress.

Adverse Childhood Experiences Study

For caregivers currently working or planning to work in a pediatric setting, it is a good idea to take a look at one of the largest epidemiological studies available, which shows the association between ten types of childhood trauma and adult health and social problems (Anda and Felitti, 2003). Known as the Adverse Childhood Experiences (ACE) study, this evaluation of over 17,000 participants headed by Dr. Robert Anda of the Center for Disease Control (CDC) and Dr. Vincent Felitti was revelatory in understanding the risk factors for adult chronic health and mental health concerns, lifespan, and actuarial predictions of early death. Felitti (2002) expressed the following:

> The ACE study reveals a powerful relationship between our emotional experiences as children and our physical and mental health as adults, as well as the major causes of adult mortality in the United States. It documents the conversion of traumatic emotional experiences in childhood into organic disease later in life. (p. 360)

Felitti and Anda's findings showed a direct link from trauma in childhood to an increased risk of chronic disease in adulthood, including cardiovascular disease, diabetes, cancer, early death, and addiction (Huffhines, Noser, and Patton, 2016; Pretty et al., 2013; Wade, 2013; Felitti, 2004).

The research compared ten factors of adversity in childhood against health and mental health outcomes decades later, all of which are listed below from the ACE questionnaire:

Prior to your eighteenth birthday…

1. Physical abuse. Did a parent or other adult in the household often or very often push, grab, slap, or throw something at you?

2. Sexual abuse. Did an adult or person at least five years older than you ever touch or fondle you, or have you touch their body in a sexual way?

3. Neglect. Did you often or very often feel that you didn't have enough to eat, had to wear dirty clothes, or had no one to protect you?

4. Emotional abuse. Did a parent or other adult in the household often or very often swear at you, insult you, put you down, or humiliate you?

5. Feeling unloved. Did you often or very often feel that no one in your family loved you or thought you were important or special?

6. Domestic abuse. Was your mother or stepmother ever repeatedly hit over at least a few minutes or threatened with a gun or a knife?

7. Parental separation or divorce. Were your parents ever separated or divorced?

8. Parental mental illness. Was a household member depressed or mentally ill or did a household member attempt suicide?

9. Substance abuse in the family. Did you live with anyone who was a problem drinker or alcoholic, or who used street drugs?

10. Incarceration of a parent. Did a household member go to prison?

Felitti and Anda evaluated whether a stressful event had *happened*, not the frequency, intensity, or duration—and what they discovered was alarming and profound. The research showed that there was a tipping point of impact for the participants who partook in the study; first, that when four of the above were present in the history of adversity—any four—there existed a correlated health risk even five to six decades later. Additionally, the more items present in an individual's history, the higher the risk for adverse effects to their physical and mental health, longevity, and social, relational, and economic functioning.

Table 5 below represents the effects of an ACE score of four. As a paraprofessional, many of the predictable outcomes of a person's ACE score set the stage for our involvement, as we are often working to address the consequences of these scores.

Table 5. Effects of an ACE Score of 4

Alcoholism/heavy drinking	21.3 percent
Cardiovascular disease	25.5 percent
Cancer	24.3 percent
Separation or divorce	32.9 percent
Life dissatisfaction	67.2 percent
Mental health condition(s). Disturbed 14+ days of work/activity	61.4 percent
Hopelessness	42.5 percent
Mental health medical treatment of psychopharmacology	42.7 percent
Anxiety	55.7 percent
High risk for HIV	58.9 percent

The ACE study is an important piece of research because it initiated a focus of attention on a very simple fact: that a history of adversity often has lifelong consequences for an individual. These early adverse experiences create changes in emotion, thinking, behavior, and health, and increase the likelihood of adults having multiple health problems as well as relational and social challenges.

Oftentimes the public misses the importance of understanding and endeavoring to reduce ACE scores in their community and/or families. An example of the impact of experiencing interpersonal adversity in early life was found in a longitudinal birth cohort study (Enlow et al., 2012), when researchers concluded that interpersonal trauma exposure was significantly associated with decreased cognitive scores (a.k.a. intelligence quotient/IQ) at twenty-four, sixty-four, and ninety-six months of age, even after controlling other influential variables (i.e., socioeconomic status, gender, race/ethnicity, birth weight, birth complications, maternal IQ, and even cognitive stimulation in the home).

One of the things that must be acknowledged by the professional caregiver in relation to working with people is that an ACE score increases their vulnerability and likelihood of needing multiple levels of services and support. These levels can be medical, educational, legal/judicial, and/or related to detox and substance abuse treatment, family protection, and domestic violence.

Researchers have expressed concern about the long-term impacts of a high ACE score: "The timing, intensity, and cumulative burden of adversities, especially in the relative absence of protective factors, can affect gene expression, the conditioning of stress responses, and the development of immune system function" (Szilagyi and Halfon, 2015, p. 457). How often are people put on a pathway of reduced functioning, health, learning, and mental health in addition to an increased risk of legal involvement primarily due to the ACE score they carry in their personal history of adversity?

Dr. Bonnie Kerker and her associates claimed in a 2015 publication that:

· 98.1 percent of children were reported to have had an ACE of at least 1 in their lifetime; the average number of ACEs was 3.6.

· There was a 32 percent increase in the likelihood of having chronic mental health issues with each additional ACE score.

· There was a 21 percent increase in the chances of having a chronic medical condition with each additional ACE score.

· There was a 77 percent increase in the possibility of a socialization/relational problem with each additional ACE score.

Adverse childhood experiences are one of many significant social and relational determinants that detract from one's health and quality of life, starting in childhood and creating a trajectory that increases risk and failure throughout the lifespan. The World Health Organization (WHO) has been actively pursuing improvements in what they call the social determinants of health (SDOH), making it clear that society and community impact health and well-being. The areas being focused on by the WHO include:

1. Income and social status. Higher income and social status are linked to better health. A greater gap between high- and low-income status correlates with an increased disparity in health. The ACE study did not look at income or social status, but the question of how deprivation in income or social status might impact the likelihood of an ACE score can be clearly understood and seems reasonable.

2. Education. Low education levels are linked with poor health, more stress, and lower self-confidence. The ACE study did not look at education as a factor either, but it seems logical that a lack of education would impact an individual's confidence, abilities to access resources like healthcare, and abilities to engage in healthy, stress-relieving activities.

3. Physical environment. Safe water and clean air, healthy workplaces, safe houses, communities, and roads all contribute to good health. People who are employed are healthier, particularly those who have more control over their working conditions. The ACE study is principally a study of the environment, looking at the safety and security of it as well as the stability of those adults raising children.

4. Social support networks. Greater support from families, friends, and communities is linked to better health. Culture, customs, traditions, and the beliefs of the family and community all affect health. The ACE study is highly concerned with the family, caregiving, and supportive adults in a child's life.

A tremendous amount can be said about the results of the ACE study, and trauma-focused caregivers take into account the considerable influence an ACE score can have on those they are serving. This knowledge can direct interactions in a forward trajectory for more effective treatment and resolution of symptoms.

As caregivers working with survivors of trauma, there is a likely chance we will encounter individuals contending with considerable physical pain. Let us now examine the mechanics of pain, and how they can be linked to trauma.

The Mechanics of Pain

There is a clear link of co-occurring chronic physical pain and PTSD after the survival of a traumatic stressor (Asmundson et al., 1998; Beckham et al., 1997; Benedikt and Kolb, 1986; Hickling et al., 1992; Chibnall and Duckro, 1994). It may also be more likely that a survivor of trauma seeks professional help for physical pain rather than emotional distress, so trauma-focused professionals should have a comprehensive understanding of the physiological mechanisms of pain for their work with patients and clients.

Pain is not entirely or solely a physical or psychological problem—it is a complex issue that interacts with biological, psychological, and social factors. Unfortunately, many believe that pain is only related to some form of injury or disease. The problem with believing that pain is exclusively related to an injury or disease is that it fails to account for various types of pain. There are specific forms of pain that consist of physical abnormalities (i.e., an injury or disease), however, other forms of pain can have minimal or no evidence for nociceptive pain (no observable physical cause). An example of chronic pain that is disconnected from nociceptors (nerves that sense and respond to bodily injury) is the phenomenon called "phantom pain." This type of pain sometimes happens when an individual has undergone amputation of a limb. Even though the limb is no longer there, the individual still experiences pain in the area of the removed extremity.

This does not mean that phantom pain or any type of pain is "made up," or that the person is lying. Specific brain activity can be seen and measured when someone is in pain, even if there are no physical causes. Essentially, *pain is in the brain*. This is obvious when an athlete or a soldier in battle is injured, but only feels the pain of that injury when they have noticed the seriousness of it. Why is the pain not felt immediately? Because the intensely focused soldier or athlete is pumped full of epinephrine (adrenaline) and otherwise mentally occupied; therefore, the signal of pain in the nervous system is overridden by other incoming and outgoing messages to and from the brain.

Pain should not be completely eliminated from our lives; in the case of the soldier and athlete, they *needed* to know they were in pain to seek medical assistance. The issue arises when the brain is no longer able to interpret and regulate pain signals correctly, and is being controlled by other psychological, social, and emotional factors.

The influence of psychological and social factors on pain can be observed when individuals suffering from chronic pain report their pain to be heightened, more intense, or unbearable when they are feeling depressed, anxious, or under the duress of traumatic stress (both "little t" and "Big T" exposures). Medical research has developed a new paradigm that includes non-physical contributable factors to explain pain. In this model there are biological mechanisms, analogous to a gate, "between the location of physical injury and the brain" (Hunter et al., 2009, p. 174). This gate regulates the flow of pain signals that ascend and descend along the spinal cord, and the brain will register chemical-type messages (i.e., prostaglandins) of pain when the gate is wide open. If the gate is closed slightly, the perception of pain is minimized because the signals are blocked and cannot deliver the message to the brain.

The skills and tools shared throughout this book have been proven to influence the opening or closing of this gate, which means you have learned powerful skills that you can teach your patients and clients to overcome factors contributing to their "pain gate" remaining wide open.

Remember that negative emotions such as anger, sadness or depression, anxiety, and feeling stressed or overwhelmed seem to increase or intensify the perception of pain. This chronic pain then contributes to more negative emotions, in turn leaving the gates wide open and resulting in pain exacerbation. The cycle can create an endless spiraling loop, leading to additional mental and medical health complications.

Exercising with Chronic Pain

As we master the art of self-care to teach others, we will inevitably begin working with a patient/client who suffers from chronic pain. Due to this chronic pain, they will naturally restrict their physical movement to avoid aggravating their pain. As we mentioned in Chapter Two, exercise is a vital part of self-care and revitalization to overcome traumatic stress. Thus, this section will explore how to support the exercise regimen of a patient/client with chronic pain. *Note: Before beginning any exercise program with a patient/client, make sure they have consulted with their primary care provider to ensure the program is safe for them.*

Physical pain is the body's alarm system telling us when something is wrong. For example, the sensation of a sprained ankle would likely discontinue someone's act of running or walking, as that may aggravate the injury. Individuals experiencing chronic pain may have an overactive alarm system that is no longer functioning adequately, and their frequent feeling of pain is not a reliable source to distinguish between harm and suffering. Instead of the person's brain being warned about an actual injury or disease, it is receiving neurological pain signals that represent the sum total of mental, emotional, and social *suffering* they are experiencing, but not physical harm.

As a result, individuals with chronic pain tend to stop doing everything and remain inactive, sitting or lying for extended periods. This can be counterproductive, since an inactive lifestyle can open the gate for pain signals to overflood the pathways to the brain. In addition, the lack of involvement in pleasurable and enjoyable activities can contribute to frustration, boredom, and depression that *also* floods the brain with pain signals. Individuals might try to compensate for these feelings and/or make up for lost time during moments when the pain is low by becoming overly active or engaging in activities that are infeasible during high levels of pain. The result of overexertion can trigger and increase pain, creating a vicious cycle that ends up with more inactivity in an attempt to avoid further discomfort.

Pacing Activities

In order to break this pattern, individuals simply need to learn how to pace out their activities. This involves setting a reasonable standard or goal (i.e., amount of time or level of pain) that is appropriate for engaging in an activity before resting or taking a break. An excellent way to determine a reasonable amount of time to pace each activity is to instruct the patient/client on how to use a ten-point rating scale to monitor the level of pain when they are active. For example, if their pain level increases by two points above the normal level during an activity, it is time to take a break (Hunter, McDougall, and Keefe, 2009). At that point, the patient/client knows to stop the activity and engage in some form of relaxation exercise, or to remain mostly sedentary until the pain drops to its original place. After their pain has dropped back to its original level (a decrease of two points), they can resume their activity and continue this cycle of starting, then taking a rest, and so on.

Let us say, for instance, that your patient/client says their pain is at a five on the ten-point scale when they begin to vacuum. After about five minutes of them engaging in the activity, they notice that the pain has increased by two points, to a seven on the scale. At that point they should sit down and do something relaxing (i.e., read a book, listen to music, watch TV, perform a body scan and relax their muscles, etc.). As they rest, they notice that fifteen minutes later their pain has returned to a five, so they can resume vacuuming. This cycle will then continue, with the pattern being five minutes of activity and fifteen minutes of rest. The rate will need to be adjusted for various activities since each type may stress the body differently, but pacing them out will help to improve the patient/client's level of functioning and their overall sense of satisfaction.

Chapter Summary

The issue of comorbidity between medical and mental health conditions is supported by a large body of research, including the revolutionary ACE study. This 17,000-participant study uncovered a correlation between ten types of childhood trauma and lifelong consequences in adults that spanned from medical issues (i.e., cancer, cardiovascular disease, higher risk of HIV, etc.) and mental health struggles (i.e., anxiety, hopelessness, overall life dissatisfaction, etc.) to high alcohol use and separation/divorce. The WHO also explored other determining factors of an individual's overall health, finding that income and social status, education, safety of the physical environment, and social support all impact a person's well-being.

The mechanics of pain are necessary for a trauma-focused caregiver to know, as many survivors experience chronic pain and/or seek assistance for physical ailments over psychological symptoms. Pain is a construct of the brain, meant to be a warning for human beings to cease a damaging activity and possibly seek medical care if the discomfort is great enough. Comprised of biological, psychological, and social factors, an individual's pain receptors and brain-body messaging system can become dysregulated through changes in these factors brought on by trauma.

For sufferers of chronic pain, exercise and daily activity can be a useful strategy for self-care. By teaching patients and clients how to pace out their activities with a simple ten-point pain level scale, they can better understand their capabilities while improving their resilience, sense of accomplishment, and physical health.

Chapter Ten

Ethical Considerations

Focus Questions:

- What is my identity as a trauma-focused caregiver?
- How am I displaying that every day in my professional environment?
- Why do I want to be identified this way, and what are the personal and professional payoffs I am expecting?

In this chapter you will learn more about:

- What living by the principles of trauma-informed care looks like.
- What you will have to change about yourself and your work to maintain those changes.
- Ethical considerations you will be faced with throughout your caregiving career, and how to address them with integrity and professionalism while following legal stipulations and protecting human life.

Have the courage to say no. Have the courage to face the truth. Do the right thing because it is right. These are the magic keys to living your life with integrity.

– W. Clement Stone

Ethics in Trauma-Focused Caregiving

Anytime professional caregivers are engaged in the process of providing support to another person, it is essential that they understand and attune to the ethical parameters required of the helping professional. "The ancient Greek philosopher Plato maintains a virtue-based eudaemonistic conception of ethics. That is to say, happiness or well-being (*eudaimonia*) is the highest aim of moral thought and conduct, and the virtues (arête: 'excellence') are the requisite skills and dispositions needed to attain it" (Frede, 2013, para. 1).

Platonian ethics are not a passive set of intellectual thoughts, but suggest a rigorous process of self-appraisal, self-reflection, and intentional growth toward excellence. In the pursuit of this excellence all human beings are strengthened, and the community of man is improved. The Platonian idea is a very different philosophy to embrace than some, because its success or failure has nothing to do with what is going on in the world. Instead, the Platonian focus is on the quality of the caregiver's character as a helper/healer and how they are actively increasing their adequacy, competence, and excellence in their chosen profession.

Similarly, in modern times we have various ethical standards in clinical practice that govern the practitioner and organizations directly or indirectly providing clinical services to people. At the organizational level, there are accrediting boards, such as the Joint Commission on Accreditation of Healthcare Organization/Joint Commission for Consistency (JCAHO) and the Commission on Accreditation of Rehabilitation Facilities (CARF) that attempt to promote quality services at a systemic level. In order to ensure quality care to survivors, however, trauma-focused caregivers also need to consider a personal and professional code of ethics.

Caregivers, including professional medical and mental health practitioners, should take time to develop a set code of ethics to protect against and prevent exploitation, and ensure quality service and safety for those seeking their help. At the practitioner's level there are many well-established professional codes of ethics, which include but are not limited to:

1. American Case Management Association: Code of Conduct (ACMA).
2. American Association for Marriage and Family Therapy: Code of Ethics (AAMFT).
3. American Counseling Association: Code of Ethics (ACA).
4. National Association of Social Workers: Code of Ethics (NASW).
5. National Certification Commission for Addiction Professionals: Code of Ethics (NAADAC).
6. American Psychological Association: Ethical Principles of Psychologists and Code of

Conduct (APA).

7. Behavior Analyst Certification Board: Professional and Ethical Compliance Code for Behavior Analysts (BACB).

8. American Nurses Association: Code of Ethics for Nurses (ANA).

Whether a practitioner is abiding by their professional code of ethics or state statute laws, most codes emphasize several common values or principles. This chapter will consider the following ethics: confidentiality, duty to warn, mandated reporting, beneficence and non-maleficence, scope of practice, practicing with compassion, and boundaries.

Confidentiality

Confidentiality is a central principle for building the trust between those offering to provide help and support and those who are receiving that help and support. Trauma-focused caregivers know that confidentiality is both an ethical principle and a legal right of the person seeking their professional help. Therefore, it is imperative for those operating in a support role to have a clear understanding of their responsibility to keep things confidential. Patients and clients who cannot rely on the caregiver's ability to maintain confidentiality are exposed to greater difficulty in feeling safe during services. Disclosing or sharing information appropriately is indispensable to creating and providing safe, effective care, and caregivers can help build trust with transparency of confidentiality. An example of this would be in reference to collegial sharing; it is wise for the caregiver to ask the survivor for permission before staffing or sharing protected health information with colleagues who have specialized knowledge that can contribute or benefit the survivor.

Caregivers should take all precautions to avoid unintentional disclosure, even ensuring that peers/colleagues cannot overhear any consultations with their patients/clients. Occasionally with severe or complicated cases, it might be tempting to share the dilemma of a patient or client in casual conversation. Though this seems safe, it may prove not to be so. An example of this is when a case manager was overheard speaking negatively about one of his clients by the family members of that client, who had been eating in the booth beside him. This violation resulted in the case manager losing employment at a job he enjoyed, and to some extent hindered his future employment opportunities.

When disclosing information, professionals should ensure that the disclosure is within the correct setting, proportional to the needs of the patient/client, and conveys the minimum level of detailed information necessary. In fact, most states prohibit the release of information regarding an individual's HIV/AIDS status unless the individual seeking help signed a separate and specific document giving the permission to release that information. If the person has not given written consent, it is the caregiver's responsibility to delete all references to the HIV/AIDS status of the individual.

Ultimately, the trauma-focused caregiver is responsible for keeping patient/client information secure and protected against inappropriate disclosure at all times. This is not just in reference to significant medical or health-related information, but *all* information that is held in trust by the caregiver. When in doubt, always consult with your supervisor before releasing information.

Duty to Warn

As professional caregivers, we have an ethical obligation to our patients and clients to ensure confidentiality—but there are times we are required by law to break it. Many caregiving professionals (i.e., psychiatrists, psychologists, counselors/therapist, nurses, case managers, etc.) have some form of duty to warn built into the legal status and even policies and procedures at their place of employment. Duty to warn is an ethical demand to protect the patient/client and the public from harm and death. In some states protection from crime is also included, but that would be an individual state difference that an organization makes clear to their staff.

Duty to warn commonly refers to the responsibility of a caregiver to notify someone else of the harming intentions of the patient or client. The obvious receiver of these reports is often the legal authorities. For example, if a patient/client shares that they are going to hurt, injure, or kill themselves or another person, there is a duty to act in the best interest of the public. Most organizations offer training about how to know if a report must be made, but the basic tenet is uniformly the protection of people.

All professional organizations have a specific ethical architecture that they expect members to follow. Ethical architecture guides the professional on when it is appropriate or legally required to violate confidentiality and disseminate a patient/client's information.

Some of the other common instances when information can be shared include when receiving consultations from other professionals, to obtain payment for services, and to protect oneself, the patient/client, or a third party from a potential threat. These situations require that information be revealed to someone who is capable of taking action to reduce the threat.

Mandated Reporting

All U.S. states require that social services professionals report *any and all* abuse, neglect, or exploitation of a child. Some states also mandate the reporting of abuse, neglect, or exploitation of a vulnerable adult (i.e., the elderly). Professional caregivers must conform to state laws that require mandated reporting, since refraining from reporting the suspected abuse, neglect, or exploitation of a child or vulnerable adult can be a criminal offense.

It is not the responsibility of a mandated reporter to investigate or determine the validity or accuracy of suspected abuse, neglect, or exploitation—it is a legal responsibility to always report any reasonable cause to suspect abuse, neglect, or exploitation of a child or vulnerable adult. In states that do not have a statute for the mandated reporting of elderly abuse, as professional caregivers we still have an ethical responsibility to notify protective organizations (i.e., National Adult Protective Services Association/NAPSA).

Beneficence and Non-Maleficence

The concept of beneficence was born out of research ethics. In its basic form, the caregiver practices and provides care with the welfare and the good of the survivor in mind. In other words, the trauma-focused caregiver's actions are intended to promote the good or benefit of those seeking their professional help.

This ethical concept parallels the ethical duties of caregivers to practice non-maleficence. Caregivers who practice non-maleficence take extra caution to practice the Hippocratic Oath, or the so-called physicians' guided maxim, "First, do no harm" (Sokol, 2013, p. 347).

Keep in mind that just as with the Tanzanian folktale of the monkeys "saving" the fish by putting them on dry land in Chapter One, the practice of beneficence does not prevent unintentional maleficence or accidentally doing harm. Thus, in order to practice beneficence and non-maleficence, the caregiver must develop sound ethical decision-making skills and cultural competency when considering the care of those seeking their help.

This type of wisdom requires both knowledge and the application of this knowledge in life experiences. We must consistently work within our scope of practice and competency, use evidence-based standards of care, and seek out professional growth for as long as we are practicing in this field. We have provided you with that knowledge in this book, but knowledge is only as powerful as its use and requires ongoing, continual professional growth.

Scope of Practice

As professional caregivers, we need to acknowledge the importance of working within our scope of practice and competency. This is a process that organizations are constantly fine-tuning, in part due to the growing changes in understanding, science, and standards within any work environment.

The organizations that hire people to provide support and care for others are usually tasked with defining the individual performance needs of employees based on company needs, charter, or purpose. The skills necessary to perform within the expectations and scope of a business are usually broadly defined in job descriptions, but what is less clear is how the company might evaluate or measure effectiveness or compliance within roles and duties. It is often challenging for employers to define knowledge, skills, and judgment necessary to perform a job effectively, so the weight of that understanding may end up on the shoulders of the worker.

When beginning a new career or employment, it is critical to learn the expected competencies and how they are defined and evaluated in a way that is unique to that organization. One cannot assume that the same words or even very similar descriptions are conveying the same intent by various companies. Once one understands the competency or scope of the role and practice, then the active living and practicing in accord with that scope is part of the professional's daily work responsibility.

Practicing with Compassion

The entire premise of this book has been to train professionals in trauma-focused caregiving. As trauma-focused caregivers, you have been given a new pair of lenses to view trauma differently: *with compassion.*

We have highlighted some of the pitfalls of caring for a survivor based on a disease-focused or deficiency-based model, and how our ability to facilitate healing increases when we address trauma as an overly charged automatic nervous system (biology) and hypervigilant threat-response system (neurology), both of which are functioning adequately in response to painful past experiences. From this viewpoint, it would be non-beneficent for a caregiver to continue creating more pain in the survivor's life by inaccurately judging their behaviors when they are a natural, functional biological process. The caregiver's expectation or insistence that survivors stop these biological processes, without adequate tools or training, is not only unreasonable—it is unethical.

As professional caregivers, we are to be intentional in our care for trauma survivors. We understand that this is a vulnerable population that requires compassion and understanding to create a therapeutic environment that is conducive to healing. Just like a father teaching his daughter to ride a bicycle and beginning with training wheels, the caregiver is intentional and careful not to ask survivors to do things when they are not ready. In accordance with the stabilization protocol we introduced in Chapter Six, we are to: regulate ourselves, create an environment of safety, help the survivor regulate in our presence, and show them how to regulate *without* our presence. This is a gradual process, meant to empower the survivor while making us obsolete.

There are times, however, when either the survivor or others attempt to dictate the type of treatment or the speed and progress of healing. These parties or individuals insist that the survivor start a particular treatment or stage in the healing process they are not yet ready to begin. In these times, the professional caregiver must advocate for the trauma survivor with their best interest and welfare in mind. This may result in making an appropriate referral—while avoiding abandonment—to someone who can provide the type of services being sought, since they would not follow the healing philosophy of the trauma-focused caregiver.

Boundaries

Oftentimes boundary issues reflect immaturity on the part of those providing services, in that the caregiver is endeavoring to meet some personal need through the relationship with the patient/client while justifying their actions as beneficial. It is always a reasonable and responsible act to search out support and supervision from leadership related to the issues of boundaries and dual relationships.

There is a value base or professional morality involved with defining and living by a set of standards that can be called professional boundaries or ethical behavior. The challenge to each individual is that as human beings, there is a naturally occurring, multiple overlapping of our relationships. Outside of the services we are providing, this overlapping is generally conceptualized as being part of a community. In providing support for trauma, however, there exists a naturally counterintuitive process for boundaries that is largely meant for the protection of vulnerable people. The Australian Association of Social Workers (AASW) details their ethical code of conduct for professional boundaries and dual relationships in detail, which can be found at: **www.aasw.asn.au/document/item/2354**.

Additional Ethical Considerations

We want to once again re-familiarize you with SAMHSA's six principles of trauma-informed care, before going into how they can act as guidelines for ethical considerations in trauma-sensitive practice:

1. Safety: Throughout the organization, staff and the people they serve feel physically and psychologically safe.

2. Trustworthiness and Transparency: Organizational operations and decisions are conducted with transparency and the goal of building and maintaining trust among staff, patients/clients, and family members of those receiving services.

3. Peer Support and Mutual Self-Help: These are integral to the organizational and service delivery approach, and are understood as key vehicles for building trust, establishing safety, and promoting empowerment.

4. Collaboration and Mutuality: There is true partnering and leveling of power differences between staff and patients/clients, and among organizational staff from direct care staff to administrators. There is recognition that healing happens in relationships, and in the meaningful sharing of power and decision-making. The organization recognizes that everyone has a role to play in a trauma-informed approach—one does not have to be a therapist to be therapeutic.

5. Empowerment, Voice, and Choice: Throughout the organization and among the patients and clients served, individuals' strengths are recognized, built upon, and validated while new skills are developed as necessary. The organization aims to strengthen the staff's, patients/clients', and their family members' experience of choice, and recognizes that every person's experience is unique and requires an individualized approach. This includes a belief in resilience, and in the ability of individuals, organizations, and communities to heal and promote recovery from trauma. This builds on what patients/clients, staff, and communities have to offer, rather than responding to perceived deficits.

6. Cultural, Historical, and Gender Issues: The organization actively moves past cultural stereotypes and biases (i.e., based on race, ethnicity, sexual orientation, age, geography, etc.), offers gender-responsive services, leverages the healing value of traditional cultural connections, and recognizes and addresses historical trauma.

Safety in Ethics

If the well-being of the patient/client is of the highest value, the question then becomes, "What does it require for the healer to develop personal and professional excellence in producing safety? What is necessary from the caregiver to behave ethically around safety?"

1. The healer should actively be thinking about the process, policy, and procedures related to their work, with a focus on stability, predictability, transparency, engagement, and keeping the patient/client calm and regulated while traversing the continuum of care. In other words, it is ethical to be intentional and deliberate in delivering well-thought-through services from the perspective of those being helped. That ability to think clearly through the process of service delivery and adapt/change oneself to be increasingly better and more emotionally and psychologically effective is essentially the primary ethic of creating safety for the patient/client.

2. The healer should constantly look for ways to explain concepts and ideas in more useful and appealing ways, and engage patients and clients in a manner that builds their competence and increases their hope for an improved future.

Cummings and Sayama (1995) spoke about the importance of creating safety with a patient contract, one that makes an ethical promise for a collaborative partnership:

> I shall never abandon you as long as you need me, and I shall never ask you to do anything until you're ready. In turn for this, you'll be joining me in a partnership to make me obsolete as soon as possible. (p. 1)

Trustworthiness and Transparency in Ethics

Ethically, the starting point for a caregiver in treatment is an honest and fair self-appraisal of their reasoning and drive for wanting to provide help and support. If that "reason" betokens a personal agenda, then it is likely the patient/client will see efforts to help as manipulative.

1. The first ethical practice related to trustworthiness and transparency is the *why* behind the helper's actions. There is a significant difference in how the helped will comprehend the actions of the helper who is working from an agenda or personal mission, versus one with deep compassion and affection for others. One must come to a clear understanding of who they are as a caregiver, and what they expect to obtain from doing the work of a helper. Another aspect of this ethical practice is a constant increase in the helper's ability to keep themselves in a relaxed body, practicing self-regulation of their own emotions, thinking, and behavior. Being a helper requires unrelenting growth and maturation, coupled with self-evaluation.

2. The next ethical step in the creation of trustworthiness and transparency is understanding the process you are inviting others to share in. A caregiver should be able to explain the process in detail, providing clear, concise descriptions. Additionally, one should be able to convey what the typical experience is going to be like, so the patient/client has a sense of hope and a personal belief that this activity will be powerful and useful. This requires that the helper has thoroughly thought out each interaction that they normally have with patients and clients, discovering and implementing ways to be more descriptive and build increased faith in the process for those seeking help.

Do not ever obfuscate the truth of how things run or operate, but boldly declare the truth. Do not tolerate peers or those who may report to you to be deceptive, because sometimes conversations can be difficult and challenging.

3. Do not fake knowledge about something, as this is disrespecting the relationship and the patient/client's trust in you. Focus on what you do know, and freely admit you may need to do more research if a particular issue arises that you are unfamiliar with.

4. Be timely about responding to requests, following up with a phone call or other form of correspondence.

Peer Support and Mutual Self-Help in Ethics

Helpers constantly focus on relationships that are ethically fundamental for healing to occur. They actively build relationships with those they serve, and in many circumstances endeavor to connect peers in a community to provide concurrent and post-service support.

It is vital that those who are struggling with significant histories of adversity or trauma have supportive relationships for healing and regulating themselves. Peer support programs can provide an opportunity for traumatized individuals who have found significant relief to mentor and assist others. Oftentimes peers can have a relationship that the helper and peer cannot, thus making it increasingly possible for the helped to gain improvements.

The primary ethical question in this section is not "should one suggest or encourage peer support participation?" but *when* it is suggested. If the suggestion is made too early in the helping process, it can be perceived as an attempt by the helper to slough off something they do not want to bother with, or may be seen as the undervaluing of the patient/client's distress or pain. Use discretion when recommending this step in a patient/client's recovery, and seek council from a supervisor if needed.

Collaboration and Mutuality in Ethics

The ethics related to collaboration and mutuality are interesting, as most organizations are not truly designed to collaborate on care issues. Often each person in the collaborative care team possesses a unique and often organizational-centric view of what needs to take place. True collaboration then is only possible if the helper strives to develop a *sharing of perspective*, goals, and outcomes in regards to the patient/client's care. An ethical trauma-focused helper will possess or develop the skills to navigate and connect highly diverse, differentially opinionated individuals, directing systemic demands in such a way as to create unity and a shared purpose.

Empowerment, Voice, and Choice in Ethics

Ethically striving to increase empowerment, voice, and choice is a practical process that starts with the healer possessing a true belief that people can live a better life, no matter what kind of history or past experiences might suggest. Please be clear in the meaning of this—one does not have to be oblivious to the realities of life, but *should* possess a fundamental belief that all people, regardless of their history, can make improvements and live more self-reflective and regulated lives.

To practice this principle ethically requires a significant amount of thought and planning around issues such as:

1. How patients and clients can be given a choice in each situation.
2. Deciding what is necessary to engage patients and clients in advocating for themselves.
3. How helpers can patiently and encouragingly listen to the patient/client's ideas, finding strength and competency in their thinking and efforts.
4. What should be done if the first choice fails?

Additionally, the ethics of empowerment, voice, and choice may require the healer to sometimes be at odds with the organization they work with. This happens when the organization only allows a limited array of possibilities, and the path your patient/client chose is not included in their business plan of services. You will then need to navigate your role and duty in this situation, with management possibly not being in favor of your decision. Choosing to take right action in situations like these is a challenge to ethics and personal integrity alike.

Cultural, Historical, and Gender Issues in Ethics

As a trauma-focused healer who embraces the idea of human well-being as the highest aim of moral thought and conduct, it is quite natural that the consideration of patients/clients' diversity in beliefs, culture, history, religion, and gender would occur. There is a growing need for the designing of services and programs that first take the time to understand the culture of others, before stepping forward to implement and utilize the inherent strengths and socioemotional capital of that culture to support change and healing.

Interacting with an individual who has a history of adversity means that a necessary awareness of their culture, personal and family history, and concepts of gender and family roles be shown at all times. Ethical practice requires a constant curiosity about others, and respect for them and their beliefs. Respect means that as an outside party, the helper never acts as a critical observer, nor do they bring judgments or demands to their work with patients and clients.

The goal for this ethical principle is to improve the quality of services to ethnic and culturally diverse populations. There is a lot of diversity in the United States, and this is likely to continue. This increase means that the ethical practice of being a helper is to welcome and constantly expect complex sets of values, beliefs, and cultural expectations in all of the major domains of the patient/client's life.

The National Organization for Human Services (NOHS) highlights their ethical standards for human service professionals here: **www.nationalhumanservices.org/ethical-standards-for-hs-professionals**. It discusses the fundamental values of our profession, among them being to respect the dignity and welfare of all people, promote self-determination, honor cultural diversity, advocate for social justice, and always act with integrity, honesty, genuineness, and objectivity.

Chapter Summary

Ethics in trauma-focused care date back to the eudaemonistic concept started by Greek philosopher Plato that denotes happiness or well-being as the highest goal of moral thought and conduct by caregivers. This pursuit to comply with and uphold ethical standards in trauma treatment for individuals with a history of adversity is evident in the many codes of conduct and ethics upheld by a variety of mental health and medical organizations across the globe.

Ethics to be followed by the trauma-focused caregiver include confidentiality, duty to warn, mandated reporting, beneficence and non-maleficence, scope of practice, practicing with compassion, and maintaining appropriate boundaries with patients and clients.

Additionally, the six principles of trauma-focused care outlined by SAMHSA can be applied to and expanded upon for treatment in order to enhance and nurture healing in the trauma survivor.

Appendix I: Self-Care Tips

Self-Care Things to Try

1. Physical exercise alternated with relaxation will alleviate some of your physical reactions.
2. Structure your time and keep busy. Some people find lists helpful, even if they do not normally use them.
3. Set aside time for your spiritual practice.
4. You are normal and experiencing normal reactions; do not label yourself as crazy, weak, or paranoid.
5. Talk to people—talk is the most healing medicine.
6. Be aware of numbing the pain with overuse of drugs or alcohol. You do not need to complicate the issue with a substance abuse problem. In addition, alcohol, caffeine, and some drugs interfere with normal sleep patterns and can leave you feeling more exhausted the next morning.
7. Reach out; people do care.
8. Reconnect with support groups (i.e., spiritual support groups, school clubs, etc.).
9. Maintain as normal a schedule as possible.
10. Spend time with others and do not isolate yourself.
11. Take part in community observance.
12. Help your coworkers as much as possible by sharing feelings and checking out how they are doing.
13. Give yourself permission to feel rotten and share your feelings with others.
14. Keep a journal; write your way through those sleepless hours.
15. Do things that feel good to you.
16. Realize that those around you are under stress.
17. Do not make any big life changes.
18. Do make as many daily decisions as possible that will give you a feeling of control over your life (i.e., if someone asks you what you want to eat, make a choice, even if you are not sure).
19. Get plenty of rest.
20. Reoccurring thoughts, dreams, or flashbacks are normal, so do not try to fight them. They will decrease over time and become less painful.

21. Eat well-balanced and regular meals (even if you do not feel like it).
22. Find a safe setting to explore the effects of the trauma on your life.
23. Help others who have suffered from traumatic stress.
24. Reassure them that they are safe.
25. Help them with everyday tasks like cleaning, cooking, caring for the family, minding children, etc.
26. Give them private time.
27. Take the time to listen.
28. Do not tell them that they are "lucky it wasn't worse"—traumatized people are not consoled by those statements. Instead, tell them you are sorry such an event occurred, and that you want to understand and assist them.
29. Do not take anger or other feelings personally.
30. Take care of your own needs. Do not be drawn into a position of providing all the support for a traumatized person. Set limits and boundaries and keep them.
31. Get help for yourself if you feel overwhelmed. Secondary trauma is more common than people are aware. If you are close to a person who has been severely traumatized, you will need to get more information and support for yourself as well.
32. Seek professional help. If intrusive thoughts and avoidance of the reminders of the trauma continue for more than a few weeks, seek help from counselors and therapists.

Appendix II: Certified Trauma Support Specialist (CTSS)

The material outlined in this book in conjunction with an approved college, university course, or workshop satisfies the educational and certification structure requirement for the *Certified Trauma Support Specialist* through Trauma Institute International:

- Section I: Introduction to the Trauma-Informed Caregiver
- Section II: Professional Resilience and Compassion Fatigue Prevention
- Section III: Foundations of Trauma-Informed Care
- Section IV: Trauma and Traumagenesis
- Section V: The History of Traumatic Care and Current Trends
- Section VI: Working with Trauma Survivors
- Section VII: Empowerment and Resiliency Structure
- Section VIII: Safety and Stabilization in Crisis Work
- Section IX: Integrated Care: Trauma-Specific Services in Primary Care Settings
- Section X: Ethical Considerations

The *Certified Trauma Support Specialist* course is designed to use evidence-based, cutting edge interventions and protocols that caregivers can immediately implement to augment their work in supporting survivors of trauma. Qualified participants who successfully complete the course, competency examination, and application are eligible for the *Certified Trauma Support Specialist* designation available through the Trauma Institute International. This knowledge-based certification is an attestation, through the Trauma Institute International, that the student has met the educational requirements of the *Certified Trauma Support Specialist.* Participants completing this certification may use the CTSS designation to indicate to peers and potential clients that they have acquired this knowledge and offer their services to survivors of trauma. Completing this certification is a demonstration of the caregiver's dedication to achieving and maintaining a professional knowledge base. For more information, visit the Trauma Institute International website at: **www.traumainstituteinternational.com**.

References

Achor, S. (2010). *The happiness advantage: The seven principles of positive psychology that fuel success and performance at work.* New York, NY: Crown Business.

Achor, S. (2011). 5 ways to turn happiness into an advantage. *Psychology Today*. Retrieved from http://www.psychologytoday.com/blog/the-happiness-advantage/201108/5-ways-turn-happiness-advantage

Adams, F. (1856). *The extant works of Aretaeus, the Cappadocian*. London, UK: Sydenham Society.

Adams, R. E., Boscarino, J. A., and Figley, C. R. (2006). Compassion fatigue and psychological distress among social workers: A validation study. *American Journal of Orthopsychiatry, 76*(1), 103-108.

Adams, S. A., and Riggs, S. A. (2008). An exploratory study of vicarious trauma among therapist trainees. *Training and Education in Professional Psychology, 2*(1), 26-34.

Ai, A., Park, C., Huang, B., Rodgers, W., and Tice, T. (2007). Psychosocial mediation of religious coping styles: A study of short-term psychological distress following cardiac surgery. *Personality and Social Psychology Bulletin, 33*(6), 867-882.

Ai, A., Tice, T., Peterson, C., and Huang, B. (2005). Prayers, spiritual support, and positive attitudes in coping with the September 11 national crisis. *Journal of Personality, 73*(3), 763-791.

Ager, A. (1997). Balancing skills transmission and indigenous understanding: A conceptual framework for planning support for trauma recovery. In D. Ajdukovic (Ed.). *Trauma recovery training: Lessons learned* (pp. 73-81). Zagreb, Croatia: Society for Psychological Assistance.

American Psychiatric Association. (1980). *Diagnostic and Statistical Manual of Mental Disorders, Third Edition.* Washington, D.C.: American Psychiatric Publishing.

American Psychiatric Association. (2013). *Diagnostic and Statistical Manual of Mental Disorders, Fifth Edition.* Arlington, VA: American Psychiatric Publishing.

American Psychiatric Association. (2017, January). *What is Posttraumatic Stress Disorder?* Retrieved from https://www.psychiatry.org/patients-families/ptsd/what-is-ptsd

Anda, R. F., and Felitti, V. J. (April 2003). *Origins and essence of the study*. ACE Reporter. Retrieved from http://www.acestudy.org/yahoo_site_admin/assets/docs/ARV1N1.127150541.pdf

Ano, G. G., and Vasconcelles, E. B. (2005). Religious coping and psychological adjustment to stress: A meta-analysis. *Journal of Clinical Psychology, 61*, 461–480.

Arden, B., and Linford, L. (2009). *Brain-based therapy with adults: Evidence-based treatment for everyday practice.* Hoboken, NJ: John Wiley and Sons.

Aristotle. (1893). *The Nichomachean Ethics of Aristotle* (5th ed.). (F. H. Peters, Trans.). London: Kegan Paul, Trench, Truebner, and Co. (Original work published 350 B.C.E.)

Aslan, R. (2013). *Zealot: The life and times of Jesus of Nazareth.* New York, NY: Random House.

Asmundson, G. J., Norton, G. R., Allerdings, M. D., Norton, P. J., and Larsen, D. K. (1998). Posttraumatic stress disorder and work-related injury. *Journal of Anxiety Disorders. 12*(1), 57–69.

Australian Geographic. (2011, March 16). *The 10 most destructive tsunamis in history.* Retrieved from http://www.australiangeographic.com.au/topics/science-environment/2011/03/the-10-most-destructive-tsunamis-in-history/

Baranowsky, A. B., and Gentry, J. E. (1998a). *Compassion satisfaction manual.* Toronto: Psych Ink Resources.

Baranowsky, A. B., and Gentry, J. E. (1998b). *Workbook/Journal for a compassion fatigue specialist.* Toronto: Psych Ink Resources.

Baranowsky, A., Gentry, E., and Baggerly, J. (2005). Accelerated recovery program: Training-as-treatment. *Canadian Association of Rehabilitation Professionals, 22 (18 -29).*

Bauer, J. J., and Bonanno, G. A. (2001). Doing and being well (for the most part): Adaptive patterns of narrative self-evaluation during bereavement. *Journal of Personality*, 69.

BBC News. (2011, May 17). *Rwanda: How the genocide happened.* Retrieved from http://www.bbc.com/news/world-africa-13431486

Beauchaine, T., Gatzke-Kopp, L., and Mead, H. (2007). Polyvagal Theory and developmental psychopathology: Emotion dysregulation and conduct problems from preschool to adolescence. *Biological Psychology, 74*, p. 3.

Beckham, J., C., Crawford, A., L., Feldman, M., E., Kirby, A., C., Hertzberg, M., A., Davidson, J., T., … and Moore, S., D. (1997). Chronic posttraumatic stress disorder and chronic pain in Vietnam combat veterans. *Journal of Psychosomatic Research. 43*(4), 379-389.

Bellamy, C., Schmutte, T., and Davidson, L. (2017). An update on the growing evidence base for peer support. *Mental Health and Social Inclusion, 21*(3), 161-167.

Benedikt, R. A., and Kolb, L. C. (1986). Preliminary findings on chronic pain and posttraumatic stress disorder. *American Journal of Psychiatry. 14*(3), 908-910.

Berceli, D. (2007). *Evaluating the effects of stress reduction exercises* (Doctoral dissertation). Arizona State University, Tempe, AZ.

Bercelli, D. (2007). *A bodily approach to trauma recovery*. Retrieved from http://www.traumaprevention.com/index. php?nid=article&article_id=67

Bergin, A. E., and Garfield, S. L. (1994). The effectiveness of psychotherapy. In A. E. Garfield and S. L. Bergin (Eds.), *Handbook of psychotherapy and behavior change* (pp. 143-189). New York, NY: J. Wiley.

Bisson, J. I., and Deahl, M. P. (1995). Psychological debriefing and prevention of Post-Traumatic stress: More research is needed. *The British Journal of Psychiatry, 165*(6), 717-720.

Bisson, J., Roberts, N., Andrew, M., Cooper, R., and Lewis, C. (2013). Psychological therapies for chronic post-traumatic stress disorder (PTSD) in adults. *Cochrane Database of Systematic Reviews,* (12). http://doi.org/10.1002/14651858.CD003388.pub4

Bleakley, A. (2014.) *Patient-centred medicine in transition: The heart of the matter*. Cham, Switzerland: Springer International Publishing.

Bradley, R., Greene, J., Russ, E., Dutra, L., and Westen, D. (2005). A multidimensional meta-analysis of psychotherapy for PTSD. *American Journal of Psychiatry, 162*, 214-227.

Breslau, N., Davis, C., and Schultz, R. (2003). Posttraumatic stress disorder and the incidence of nicotine, alcohol, and other drug disorder in persons who have experienced trauma. *Archives of General Psychiatry, 60*(3), 289-294.

Brethour. P. (2001, November 14). *The Globe and Mail.* Toronto, Canada.

Briere, J., and Elliot, D. (2003). Prevalence and psychological sequelae of self-reported childhood physical and sexual abuse in a general population sample of men and women. *Child Abuse and Neglect, 27*(10), 1205-1222.

Britton, P. J. (n.d.) *Teaching tip sheet: Counselor attitude bias*. Retrieved from http://www.apa.org/pi/aids/resources/education/counselor-bias.aspx

Brown, S., Baker, C., and Wilcox, P. (2012). Risking connection trauma training: A pathway toward trauma-informed care in child congregate care settings. *Psychological Trauma: Theory, Research, Practice, and Policy, 4*(5), 507-515.

Bryant-Davis, T., Ullman, E., and Tsong, Y. (2012). Surviving the storm: The role of social support and religious coping in sexual assault recovery of African American women. *Violence Against Women, 17*(12), 1601-1618.

Buber, M. (1958). *I and Thou*. (R. G. Smith, Trans.). New York, NY: Charles Scribner's Sons. (Original work published 1929)

Burgess, A., and Holmstrom, L. (1974). Rape trauma syndrome. *American Journal of Psychiatry, 131*(9), 981-986.

Burns, D. (1980). *Feeling good: The new mood therapy*. New York, NY: Morrow.

Carrere, S., and Gottman, J. (1999). Predicting divorce among newlyweds for the first three minutes of a marital conflict discussion. *Family Process, 38*(3), 293-301.

Carrier, L. M., Rosen, L. D., Cheever, N. A., and Lim, A. F. (2015). Causes, effects, and practicalities of everyday multitasking. *Developmental Review, 35*, 64-78.

Catherall, D. (1995). Coping with secondary traumatic stress: The importance of the therapist's professional peer group. In B. Stamm (Ed.), *Secondary traumatic stress: Self-care issues for clinicians, researchers, and educators* (pp. 80-92). Lutherville, MD: Sidran Press.

Center for Disease Control. (2015, May 14). *Injury prevention and control: Division of violence prevention*. Retrieved April 20, 2015, from http://www.cdc.gov/violence prevention/acestudy/

Cherniss, C. (1980). *Professional burnout in human service organizations*. New York, NY: Praeger.

Chibnall, J. T., and Duckro, P. N. (1994). Post-traumatic stress disorder in chronic post-traumatic headache patients. *Headache. 34*(6), 357–361

Chödrön, Pema. (2016.) *Transforming the heart of the suffering*. Retrieved from https://www.lionsroar.com/transforming-the-heart-of-suffering/

Cohen, J., Deblinger, E., Mannarino, A., and Steer, R. (2004). A multisite randomized controlled trial for children with sexual abuse-related PTSD symptoms. *Journal of the American Academy of Child and Adolescent Psychiatry, 43*, 393-402.

Cohen, J., Mannarino, A., and Knudsen, K. (2004). Treating childhood traumatic grief: A pilot study. *Journal of the American Academy of Child and Adolescent Psychiatry, 43*, 1225-1233.

Cohen, J., Mannarino A., and Knudsen, K. (2005). Treating sexually abused children: 1 year follow-up of a randomized controlled trial. *Child Abuse Neglect, 29*, 135-145.

Cohen, J., Mannarino, A., and Staron, V. (2006). A pilot study of modified Cognitive Behavioral Therapy for childhood traumatic grief. *Journal of the American Academy of Child and Adolescent Psychiatry, 45*, 1465-1473.

Cohen, J., Mannarino, A., and Deblinger, E. (2008). How to implement Trauma-Focused Cognitive Behavioral Therapy (TF-CBT). *National Child Trauma Stress Network,* 1-68.

Cohen, J., Mannarino, A., and Iyengar, S. (2011). Community treatment of PTSD for children exposed to intimate partner violence: A randomized controlled trial. *Archives of Pediatrics and Adolescent Medline, 165*, 16-21.

Cohn, M. A., Fredrickson, B. L., Brown, S. L., Mikels, J. A., and Conway, A. M. (2009). Happiness unpacked: Positive emotions increase life satisfaction by building resilience. *Emotion, 9*(3), 361-368.

Chow, D., Miller, S., Seidel, J., Kane, R., Thornton, J., and Andrews, W. (2015). The role of deliberate practices in the development of highly effective psychotherapist. *Psychotherapy, 52*(3), 337-347.

Cox, C. L. (1992). Perceived threat as a cognitive component of state anxiety and confidence. *Perception and Motor Skills, 75*(3:2), 1092-1094.

Cozolino, L. (2016.) *Why therapy works: Using our minds to change our brains.* New York, NY: W.W. Norton and Company.

Craigie, M., Slatyer, S., Hegney, D., Osseiran-Moisson, R., Gentry, E., Davis, S., and Rees, C. (2016). A pilot evaluation of a Mindful Self-Care and Resiliency (MSCR) intervention for nurses. *Mindfulness, 7*(3), 764-774.

Critchley, D., Mathias, J., Josephs, O., O'Doherty, J., Zanini, S., Dewar, K., … and Dolan, R. (2003). Human cingulate cortex and autonomic control: Converging neuroimaging and clinical evidence. *Brain: A Journal of Neurology, 126*(10), 2139-2152.

Critchley, H., Melmed, R., Featherstone, E., Mathias, C., and Dolan, R. (2001). Brain activity during biofeedback relaxation: A functional neuroimaging investigation. *Brain, 124*(5), 1003-1012.

Crowley, C. F. (2011, September 28). *If you're stressed so is your kid: Canadian doctor says many developmental problems in kids tied to parents' stress*. Retrieved from http://www.timesunion.com/local/article/If-you-re-stressed-so-is-your-kid-2192120.php

Csikszentmihalyi, M. (1997). *Finding flow: The psychology of engagement with everyday life.* New York, NY: Basic Books.

Culture. (n.d.) *Merriam-Webster*. Retrieved from https://www.merriam-webster.com/dictionary/culture

Cummings, N. and Sayama, M. (1995). *Focused psychotherapy. A casebook of brief, intermittent psychotherapy throughout the life cycle*. New York, NY: Routledge.

Danieli, Y. (1982). Psychotherapists' participation in the conspiracy of silence about the Holocaust. *Psychoanalytic Psychology*, *1*(1), 23-46.

Davidson, P. R., and Parker, K. C. (2001). Eye movement desensitization and reprocessing (EMDR): A meta-analysis. *Journal of Consulting and Clinical Psychology, 69*, 305-316.

Deblinger, E., Stauffer, L., and Steer, R. (2001). Comparative efficacies of supportive and cognitive behavioral group therapies for young children who have been sexually abused and their non-offending mothers. *Child maltreatment, 6*, 332-343.

Deblinger, E., Mannarino, A., Cohen, J., Runyon, M., and Steer, R. (2011). Trauma-focused CBT for children: Impact of the trauma narrative and treatment length. *Depression and Anxiety, 28*, 67-75.

De Champlain, J., Karas, M., Toal, C., Nadeau, R., and Larochelle, P. (1999). Effects of antihypertensive therapies on the sympathetic nervous system. *The Canadian Journal of Cardiology, 15*, 8A.

Dedovic, K., Slavich, G., Muscatell, K., Irwin, M., and Eisenberger, N. (2016). Dorsal anterior cingulate cortex response to repeated social evaluative feedback in young women with and without a history of depression. *Frontiers in Behavioral Neuroscience, 20,* 64.

De Leon, G. (1994). The therapeutic community: Toward a general theory and model. *National Institute on Drug Abuse Research Monograph Series, 144*(144), 16-53.

De Leon, G. (1997). *Community as method: Therapeutic community for special populations and special settings*. Westport, CT: Greenwood Publishing Group.

Dezelic, M., Ghanoum, G., and Neale, A. (2016.) *Trauma treatment: Healing the whole person.* Miami, FL: Presence Press International.

Diamond, D., Campbell, A., Park, C., Halonen, J., and Zoladz, P. (2007). The temporal dynamics model of emotional memory processing: A synthesis on the neurobiological basis of stress-induced amnesia, flashbulb and traumatic memories, and the Yerkes-Dodson law. *Neural Plasticity, 2007*, (2090-5904), 60803.

Dindar, M., and Akbulut, Y. (2016). Effects of multitasking on retention and topic interest. *Learning and Instruction, 41*, 94-105.

Dovan, M. L. (2013). *Examining the effects of anxiety on running efficiency in a cognitive-motor dual-task* (Unpublished doctoral dissertation). Concordia University, Montreal, Canada.

Druss, G. B., and Walker, R. E. (2011). Mental disorders and medical comorbidity. *Research Synthesis Report, 22*, p. 1-26.

Dyer, W. (2004). *The power of intention: Change the way you look at things and the things you look at will change*. London, UK: Hay House.

Ehrenreich, J. H. (1999). *Coping with disaster: A guidebook to psychosocial intervention.* Retrieved from http://www.mhwwb.org/contents.htm

Eisenberger, N. I., and Lieberman, M. D. (2004). Why rejection hurts: A common neural alarm system for physical and social pain. *Trends in Cognitive Sciences, 8*, 294-300.

Elliott, D. M. (1997). Traumatic events: Prevalence and delayed recall in the general population. *Journal of Consulting and Clinical Psychology, 65*, 811-820.

Enlow, M., Egeland, B., Blood, E., Wright, R. O, and Wright, R. J. (2012). Interpersonal trauma exposure and cognitive development in children to age 8 years: A longitudinal study. *Journal of Epidemiology and Community Health, 66*(11), 1005-1010.

Escribà-Agüir, V., and Pérez-Hoyos, S. (2007). Psychological well-being and psychosocial work environment characteristics among emergency medical and nursing staff. *Stress Health, 23*(3), 153-160.

Fallot, R., and Harris, M. (2008). Trauma-informed approaches to systems of care. *Trauma Psychology, 3*(1), 6-7.

Farber, B. A. (1983). Introduction: A critical perspective on burnout. In B. A. Farber (Ed.), *Stress and burnout in the human service professions* (pp. 1-20). New York, NY: Pergamon Press.

Felitti, V. J. (2002). The relation between adverse childhood experiences and adult health: Turning gold into lead. *The Permanente Journal, 6*(1), 44-47.

Felitti, V., Anda, R., Nordenberg, D., Williamson, D., Spitz, A., Edwards, V., Koss M., and Marks, J. (1998). Relationship of childhood abuse and household dysfunction to many of the leading causes of death in adults. The Adverse Childhood Experiences (ACE) Study. *American Journal of Preventative Medicine, 14*(4), 245-258.

Figley, C. R. (1983). Catastrophe: An overview of family reactions. In C. R. Figley and H.I. McCubbin (Eds.), *Stress and the family, volume II: Coping with catastrophe*. New York, NY: Brunnel/Mazel.

Figley, C. R. (1988). Toward a field of traumatic stress. *Journal of Traumatic Stress, 1*(1), 3-16.

Figley, C. R. (1995). *Compassion fatigue: Coping with secondary traumatic stress disorder in those who treat the traumatized.* New York, NY: Bruner/Mazel.

Figley, C. R. (1995). Beyond the "victim": Secondary traumatic stress. In R. F. Kleber (Ed.), *Beyond trauma: Cultural and societal dynamics* (p. 75-98). New York, NY: Pelham Press.

Figley, C. R., and Stamm, B. H. (1996). Psychometric review of Compassion Fatigue Self-Test. In B. H. Stamm (Ed.), *Measurement of stress, trauma and adaptation* (pp. 127-130). Lutherville, MD: Sidran Press.

Figley, C., Bride, B., and Mazza, N. (1997). *Death and trauma: The traumatology of grieving.* Washington, D.C.: Taylor and Francis.

Finklehor, D., Hotaling, G., Lewis, I., and Smith, C. (1990). Sexual abuse in a national survey of adult men and women: prevalence, characteristics, and risk factors. *Child Abuse and Neglect, 14*(1),19-28.

Flarity, K., Gentry, E., and Mesnikoff, N. (2013). The effectiveness of an educational program on preventing and treating compassion fatigue in emergency nurses. *Advanced Emergency Nursing Journal, 35*(3), 247-258.

Flarity, K., Nash, K., Jones, W., and Steinbruner, D. (2016). Intervening to improve compassion fatigue resiliency in forensic nurses. *Advanced Emergency Nursing Journal, 38*(2), 147-156.

Floen, S., and Elklit, A. (2007). Psychiatric diagnoses, trauma, and suicidiality. *Annals of General Psychiatry, 6*, 12.

Foa, E. B., Dancu, C. V., Hembree, E. A., Jaycox, L. A., Meadows, E. A., and Street, G. P. (1999). The efficacy of exposure therapy, stress inoculation training and their combination in ameliorating PTSD for female victims of assault. *Journal of Consulting and Clinical Psychology, 67*, 194-200.

Foa, E., Davidson, J., and Frances, A. (1999). The expert consensus guideline series: treatment of posttraumatic stress disorder. *The Journal of Clinical Psychiatry,* 60.

Foa, E. B., and Meadows, E. A. (1997). Psychosocial treatments for posttraumatic stress disorder: A critical review. *Annual Review of Psychology, 48*, 449-480.

Follette, V. M., Ruzek, J. I., and Abueg, F. R. (1998). *Cognitive behavioral therapies for trauma.* New York, NY: Guilford Press.

Frankl, V. E. (1963). *Man's search for meaning: An introduction to logotherapy*. Boston, MA: Beacon Press.

Frede, D. (July, 2013). *Stanford Encyclopedia of Philosophy: Plato's ethics: An overview. The Metaphysics Research Lab*. Retrieved from https://plato.stanford.edu/entries/plato-ethics/

Fredrickson, B. L. (2000). Cultivating positive emotions to optimize health and well-being. *Prevention and Treatment, 3*. Retrieved from http://journals.apa.org/prevention

French, G., and Harris, C. (1998). *Traumatic incident reduction (TIR)*. Boca Raton, FL: CRC Press.

Freudenberger, H. (1974). Staff burn-out. *Journal of Social Issues, 30*, 159-165.

Friedman, M. J. (2013, November 7). PTSD from Armistice Day to DSM-5. U.S. Department of Veterans Affairs. Retrieved from http://www.blogs.va.gov/VAntage/10827/ptsd-from-armistice-day-to-dsm-5/

Garfield, A. E., and Bergin S. L. (1994). *Handbook of psychotherapy and behavior change* (Eds.). New York, NY: J. Wiley.

Gentry, J. E. (1999). *The trauma recovery scale (TRS): An outcome measure*. Poster presentation at the meeting of the International Society for Traumatic Stress Studies, Miami, FL.

Gentry, J. E. (2000). *Certified compassion fatigue specialist training: Training-as-treatment* (Unpublished dissertation). Florida State University, Tallahassee, FL.

Gentry, J. E. (2001). *Traumatology 1002: Brief treatments*. Tampa, FL: International Traumatology Institute.

Gentry, J. E. (2002). Compassion fatigue: A Crucible of transformation. *Journal of Trauma Practice, 1*(3/4) 37-61.

Gentry, J., Baggerly, J., and Baranowsky, A. (2004). Training-as-treatment: The effectiveness of the Certified Compassion Fatigue Specialist Training. *International Journal of Emergency Mental Health, 6*(3), 147-155.

Gentry, J. E., and Baranowsky, A. B. (1998). *Treatment manual for the Accelerated Recovery Program: Set II*. Toronto, Canada: Psych Ink.

Gentry, J. E., and Baranowsky, A. B. (1999a). *Accelerated recovery program for compassion fatigue.* Pre-conference workshop presented at the 15th annual meeting of the International Society for Traumatic Stress Studies, Miami, FL.

Gentry, J. E., and Baranowsky, A. B. (1999b). *Compassion satisfaction manual: 1-day group workshop, set III-B.* Toronto, Canada: Psych Ink.

Gentry, J. E., and Baranowsky, A. B. (1999c). *Compassion satisfaction manual: 2-day group retreat, set III-C.* Toronto, Canada: Psych Ink.

Gentry, J., Baranowsky, A., and Dunning, K. (1997, November). *Accelerated recovery program for compassion fatigue.* Paper presented at the meeting of the International Society for Traumatic Stress Studies, Montreal, QB, Canada.

Gentry, J., Baranowsky, A., and Dunning, K. (in press). The accelerated recovery program for compassion fatigue. In C. R. Figley (Ed.), *Compassion fatigue II: Treating compassion fatigue*. New York, NY: Brunner/Mazel.

Gilman, L., King, H., Porter, R., Rousseau, G., and Showalter, E. (1993). *Hysteria beyond Freud.* Los Angeles, CA: University of California Press.

Gold, S., and Faust, J. (2001). The future of trauma practice: Visions and aspirations. *Journal of Trauma Practice, 1*(1), 1-15.

Goldberg, E. (2001). *The executive brain: Frontal lobes and the civilized mind.* New York, NY: Oxford Press.

Goldberg, A., Moore, J., Houck, C., Kaplan, D., and Barron, C. (2017). Domestic minor sex trafficking patients: A retrospective analysis of medical presentation. *Journal of Pediatric and Adolescent Gynecology, 30*(1), 109-115.

Goodell, A. M., Druss, G. B., and Walker, R. E. (2011). Mental disorders and medical comorbidity. *Robert Wood Johnson Foundation, 21*, 1-26.

Gottman, J. M. (1999). *The marriage clinic: A scientifically-based marital therapy.* New York, NY: W.W. Norton and Company.

Gottman, J., and Silver, N. (1999). "How I predict divorce," in *The seven principles for making marriages work* (chapter two, 25-46). New York, NY: Three Rivers Press-Random House, Inc.

Gottman, J. M., Gottman, J. S., and DeClaire, J. (2006). *10 lessons to transform your marriage: America's love lab experts share their strategies for strengthening your relationships.* New York, NY: Three Rivers Press-Random House, Inc.

Grant, R. (1999). Spirituality and trauma: An essay. *Traumatology, 5*(1), 8-10.

Gratton, L., and Erickson, T. (2007). 8 ways to build collaborative teams. *Harvard Business Review, 85*(11), 100-9, 153.

Grosch, W. N., and Olsen, D. C. (1994). Therapist burnout: A self psychology and systems perspective. In W. N. Grosch and D. C. Olsen (Eds.), *When helping starts to hurt: A new look at burnout among psychotherapists* (pp. 439-454). New York, NY: W.W. Norton and Company.

Gilligan, L. A. (2011). Massachusetts Trauma Sensitive. *News Archive, 13*, 2011.

Haley, S. (1974). When the patient reports atrocities. *Archives of General Psychiatry, 39*, 191-196.

Hamarat, E., Thompson, D., Zabrucky, K., Steele, D., Matheny, K., and Aysan, F. (2001). Perceived stress and coping resource availability as predictors of life satisfaction in young, middle-aged, and older adults. *Experimental Aging Research, 27*(2), 181-196.

Hanson, R. (2013). *Hardwiring happiness: The new brain science of contentment, calm, and confidence*. New York, NY: Harmony.

Happiness. (n.d.) *Merriam-Webster*. Retrieved from https://www.merriam-webster.com/dictionary/happiness

Hayden, B. Y., and Platt, M. L. (2009). Cingulate cortex. In L.R. Squire (Ed.), *Encyclopedia of neuroscience, volume 2* (pp. 887-892). Oxford, UK: Academic Press.

Heim, C., Ehlert, U., Hanker, J., and Hellhammer, D. (1998). Abuse-related posttraumatic stress disorder and alterations of the hypothalamic-pituitary-adrenal axis in women with chronic pelvic pain. *Psychosomatic Medicine, 60*(3), 309-31.

Hensel, J., Ruiz, C., Finney, C., and Dewa, C. (2015). Meta-analysis of risk factors for secondary traumatic stress in therapeutic work with trauma victims. *Journal of Traumatic Stress, 28*(2), 83-91.

Herman, J. L. (1992). *Trauma and recovery*. New York, NY: Basic Books.

Hickling, E. J., and Blanchard, E. B. (1992). Post-traumatic stress disorder and motor vehicle accidents. *Journal of Anxiety Disorder, 6*, 285-291.

Hickling, E. J., Blanchard, E. B, Silverman, D. J., and Schwarz, S. P. (1992). Motor vehicle accidents, headaches and post-traumatic stress disorder: Assessment findings in a consecutive series. *Headache, 32*(3), 147-51.

History. (n.d.) In *The Free Dictionary by Farlex*. Retrieved from https://www.thefreedictionary.com/history

Holmes, D., and Tinnin, L. (1995). The problem of auditory hallucinations in combat PTSD. *Traumatology, 1*(2).

Hook, J., David D., Owen, J., Worthington, E., and Utsey, S. (2013). Cultural humility: Measuring openness to culturally diverse clients. *Journal of counseling psychology, 60*(3), 353-366.

Hooper, C., Craig, J., Janvrin, D., Wetsel, M., and Reimels, E. (2010). Compassion satisfaction, burnout, and compassion fatigue among emergency nurses compared with nurses in other selected inpatient specialties. *Journal of Emergency Nursing, 36*(5), 420-427.

Hossain, M., Zimmerman, C., Abas, M., Light, M., and Watts., C. (2010). The relationship of trauma to mental disorders among trafficked and sexual exploited girls and women. *American Journal of Public Health, 100*(12), 2442-2449.

Hubble, M. A., Duncan, B. L., and Miller, S. D. (1999). *The heart and soul of change.* Washington, D.C.: American Psychological Association.

Huffhines, L., Noser, A., and Patton, R. (2016). The link between adverse childhood experience and diabetes. *Current Diabetes Reports, 16*(6), 54.

Hunter, D. J., McDougall, J. J., and Keefe, F. J. (2009). The symptoms of osteoarthritis and the genesis of pain. *Medical Clinics of North America, 93*(1), 83-100.

International Labour Office. (2012). ILO global estimate of forced labour: Results and methodology. International Labour Organization. Retrieved from http://www.ilo.org/wcmsp5/groups/public/---ed_norm/---declaration/documents/publication/wcms_182004.pdf

Jacobson, E. (1938). *Progressive relaxation* (2nd ed.). Oxford, UK: University of Chicago Press.

Jamison, J. (1999). Stress: The chiropractic patients' self-perceptions. *Journal of Manipulative and Physiological Therapeutics, 22*(6), 395-398.

Jung, C. G. (1960). The psychology of dementia praecox. In G. Adler, and H. Read (Eds.), *The collected works of C. G. Jung, volume 3: Psychogenesis of mental disease.* Princeton, N.J.: Princeton University Press. (Original work published 1907)

Kabat-Zinn, J. (1994). *Wherever you go, there you are: Mindfulness meditation for everyday life.* New York, NY: Hyperion.

Kagan, R., and Spinazzolla, J. (2013). Real life heroes in residential treatment: Implementation of an integrated model of trauma and resiliency-focused treatment for children and adolescents with complex PTSD. *Journal of Family Violence 28*(7), 705-715.

Kaminer, D., Seedat, S., and Stein, D. (2005). Post-traumatic stress disorder in children. *World Psychiatry, 4*(2), 121-125.

Karakashian, M. (1994). Countertransference issues in crisis work with natural disaster victims. *Psychotherapy, 31*(2), 334-341.

Kardiner, A. (1941). *The traumatic neuroses of war*. Washington, D.C.: National Research Council.

Katz, C., and Yehuda, R. (2006). Neurobiology of trauma. In J. Rose, H. Spitz, L. Schein, G. Burlingame, and P. Muskin (Eds.), *Psychological effects of catastrophic disasters: Group approaches to treatment* (pp. 61-81). New York, NY: Haworth Press.

Kerker, B., Zhang, J., Nadeem, E., Stein, R., Hurlburt, M., Heneghan, A., … and McCue Horwitz, S. (2015). Adverse childhood experiences and mental health, chronic medical conditions, and development in young children. *Academic Pediatrics, 15*(5), 510-517.

Kessler, R., Sonnega, A., Bromet, E., Hughes, M., and Nelson, C. (1995). Posttraumatic stress disorder in the national comorbidity survey. *Archives of General Psychiatry, 52*, 1048-1060.

Kilpatrick, D., and Saunders, B. (1997). *Prevalence and consequences of child victimization: Results from the National Survey of Adolescents Final Report*. Charleston, SC: Medical University of South Carolina, Department of Psychiatry and Behavioral Sciences.

King, N., Tonge, B., Mullen, P., Myerson, N., Heyne, D., Rollings, S., Martin, R., and Ollendick, T. (2000). Treating sexually abused children with posttraumatic stress symptoms: A randomized clinical trial. *Journal of the American Academy of Child and Adolescent Psychiatry, 39*, 1347-1355.

Kinsman, L. (2004). Clinical pathway compliance and quality improvement. *Nursing standard: official newspaper of the Royal College of Nursing, 18*(18), 33-35.

Klumpp, H., Angstadt, M., and Phan, K. (2011). Insula reactivity and connectivity to anterior cingulate cortex when processing threat in generalized social anxiety disorder. *Biological Psychology, 89*(1), 273-276.

Krost, B. (2007). Understanding and releasing the psoas muscle. Retrieved from http://www.naturalreflexes.com/pages/psoas.html

Landes, S. J., Garovoy, N. D., and Burkman, K. M. (2013). Treating complex trauma among veterans: Three stage-based treatment models. *The Journal of Clinical Psychiatry, 69*(5), 523-533.

LeDoux, J. E. (1996). *The emotional brain: The mysterious underpinnings of the emotional life.* New York, NY: Simon and Schuster.

Lee, C., and Cuijpers, P. (2013). A meta-analysis of the contribution of eye movements in processing emotional memories. *Journal of Behavior Therapy and Experimental Psychiatry, 44*, 231-239.

Leiter, P., and Maslach, C. (2009). Nurse turnover: The mediating role of burnout. *Journal of Nursing Management, 17*(3), 331-339.

Lerias, D., and Byrne, K. (2003). Vicarious traumatization: Symptoms and predictors. *Stress and Health, 19(*3), 129-138.

Lerner, M. D., and Shelton, R. D. (2005). *Comprehensive acute traumatic stress management-CATSM.* Commack, NY: American Academy of Experts in Traumatic Stress.

Lin, C. S., Wu, S. Y., and Wu, L. T. (2015). The anterior insula and anterior cingulate cortex are associated with avoidance of dental treatment based on prior experience of treatment in healthy adults. *BMC Neuroscience, 16*, 88.

Lindy, J. D. (1988). *Vietnam: A casebook*. New York, NY: Brunner/Mazel.

Lopes, P., Macedo, F., Coutinho, F., Figueira, I., and Ventura, R. (2014). Systematic review of the efficacy of cognitive-behavior therapy related treatments for victims of natural disasters: A worldwide problem. *PloS One, 9*(10), e109013.

Lowel, S., and Singer, W. (1992). Selection of intrinsic horizontal connections in the visual cortex by correlated neuronal activity. *Science, 255*(5041), 209-212.

Luu, P., and Posner, I. (2003). Anterior cingulate cortex regulation of sympathetic activity. *Brain: A Journal of Neurology, 126*(10), 2119-2120.

Mandl, K. D., Kohane, I. S., and Brandt, A. M. (1998). Electronic patient-physician communication: Problems and promise. *Annals of Internal Medicine, 129*(6), 495-500.

Marmar, C. R., Weiss, D. S., Metzler, T. J., Delucchi, K. L., Best, S. R., and Wentworth, K. A. (1999). Longitudinal course and predictors of continuing distress following critical incident exposure in emergency services personnel. *Journal of Nervous and Mental Disease, 187*(1), 15-22.

Maslach, C. (1976). Burnout. *Human Behavior, 5*, 16-22.

Maslach, C., and Goldberg, J. (1998). Prevention of burnout: New perspectives. *Applied and Preventive Psychology, 7*, 63-74.

Mathews, C. S., Paulus, P. M., Simmons, N. A., Neleson, A. R., and Dimsdale, E. J. (2004). Functional subdivisions within anterior cingulate cortex and their relationship to automatic nervous system function. *NeuroImage, 22*(3), 1151-1156.

Matsakis, A. (1994). *Vietnam wives: Facing the challenges of life with veterans suffering post-traumatic stress.* New York, NY: Basic Books.

Mello, G. P., Silva, R. G., Donat, C. J., and Dristensen, C. H. (2013). An update on the efficacy of cognitive-behavioral therapy, cognitive therapy, and exposure therapy for posttraumatic stress disorder. *The International Journal of Psychiatry in Medicine, 46*(4), 339-357.

McCann, I. L., and Pearlman, L. A. (1990). Vicarious traumatization: A framework for understanding the psychological effects of working with victims. *Journal of Traumatic Stress, 3*(1), 131-149.

McMullen, J., O'Callaghan, P., Richards, J., Eakin, J., and Rafferty, H. (2012). Screening for traumatic exposure and psychological distress among war-affected adolescents in post-conflict northern Uganda. *Social Psychiatry and Psychiatric Epidemiology, 47*(9), 1489-1498.

McNally, V. (November, 1998). Training of FBI employee assistance professionals and chaplains at FBI headquarters. Washington, D.C.

McNaughton, N. (1997). Cognitive dysfunction resulting from hippocampal hyperactivity—A possible cause of anxiety disorder? *Pharmacology Biochemistry and Behavior, 56*(4), 603–611.

Merikangas, K., He, J., Burstein, M., Swanson, S., Avenevoli, S., Cui, L., … and Swendsen, J. (2010). Lifetime prevalence of mental disorders in U.S. adolescents: Results from the National Comorbidity Survey Replication--Adolescent Supplement (NCS-A). *Journal of the American Academy of Child and Adolescent Psychiatry, 49*(10), 980-989.

Middlebrooks, J. S., and Audage, N. C. (2008). *The effects of childhood stress on health across the lifespan.* Atlanta, Georgia: Centers for Disease Control and Prevention, National Center for Injury Prevention and Control.

Miller, S. D., and Hubble, M. A. (2011). The road to mastery. *The Psychotherapy Network, 35*(2), 22-31, 60.

Miller, S., Hubble, M., and Duncan, B. (2007). Supershrinks: Learning from the field's most effective practitioners. *Psychotherapy Network, 31*(6), 26-35, 56.

Milad, R., Quirk, J., Pitman, K., Orr, P., Fischl, B., and Rauch, L. (2007). A role for the human dorsal anterior cingulate cortex in fear expression. *Biological Psychiatry, 62*(10), 1191-1194.

Mitchell, J. (1995). The critical incident stress debriefing (CISD) and the prevention of work-related traumatic stress among high risk occupational groups. In G. Everly (Ed.), *Psychotraumatology: Key papers and core concepts in post-traumatic stress* (267-280). New York, NY: Plenum Press.

Mueser, K., Goodman, L., Trumbetta, S., Rosenberg, S., Osher, F., Vidaver, R., … and Foy, D. (1998). Trauma and posttraumatic stress disorder in severe mental illness. *Journal of Consulting and Clinical Psychology, 66*(3), 493-499.

National Association of State Mental Health Program Directors. (2006). *NASMHPD medical directors council technical report: Morbidity and mortality in people with serious mental illness*. Alexandria, VA: NASMHPD.

National Child Traumatic Stress Network. *Creating trauma-informed systems*. Retrieved from http://www.nctsn.org/resources/topics/creating-trauma-informed-systems

National Institute of Mental Health. (2002). *Mental health and mass violence: Evidence-based early psychological intervention for victims/survivors of mass violence. A workshop to reach consensus on best practices.* NIH Publication No. 02-5138, Washington, D.C.: U.S. Government Printing Office.

Neria, Y., Bromet, E., Sievers, S., Lavelle, J., and Fochtmann, L. (2002). Trauma exposure and posttraumatic stress disorder in psychosis: Findings from a first-admission cohort. *Journal of Consulting and Clinical Psychology, 70*(1), 246-251.

New World Bible Translation Committee. (2013). *New world translation of the Holy Scriptures.* New York, NY: Watch Tower Bible and Tract Society of Pennsylvania.

Norman, J. (2001). The brain, the bucket, and the schwoop. In E. Gentry (Ed.), *Traumatology 1001: Field traumatology training manual* (pp. 34-37). Tampa, FL: International Traumatology Institute.

Norris, F. H. (1992). Epidemiology of trauma. Frequency and impact of different potentially traumatic events on different demographic groups. *Journal of Consulting and Clinical Psychology, 60*, 409-218.

Panella, M., Marchisio, S., and Di Stanislao, F. (2003). Reducing clinical variations with clinical pathways: do pathways work? *International Journal for Quality in Health Care, 15*(6), 509-521.

Parker, V. J., and Douglas, A. J. (2010). Stress in early pregnancy: Maternal neuro-endocrine-immune responses and effects. *American Journal of Reproductive Immunology, 85*(1), 86-92.

Pearlman, L. A., and Saakvitne, K. W. (1995). *Trauma and the therapist: Countertransference and vicarious traumatization in psychotherapy with incest survivors*. New York: W.W. Norton and Company.

Pembrey, M., Saffery, R., and Bygren, L. (2014). Human transgenerational responses to early-life experience: potential impact on development, health and biomedical research. *Journal of Medical Genetics, 51*(9), 563-572.

Pennebaker, J. W. (1997). Writing about emotional experiences as a therapeutic process. *Psychological Science, 8*(3), 162-166.

Perry, B. D. (2007). Self-regulation: The second core strength. Retrieved from http://teacher.scholastic.com/professional/bruceperry/self_regulation.htm#bio

Perry, B., and Szalavitz, M. (2006). *The boy who was raised as a dog: And other stories from a child psychiatrist's notebook—What traumatized children can teach us about love, loss, and healing.* New York, NY: Basic Books.

Pole, N., Best, S., Weiss, D., Metzler, T., Liberman, A., Fagan, J., and Marmar, C. (2001). Effects of gender and ethnicity on duty-related posttraumatic stress symptoms among urban police officers. *Journal of Nervous and Mental Disease, 189*(7), 442-448.

Popoli, M., Yan, Z., McEwen, B., and Sanacora, G. (2011). The stressed synapse: The impact of stress and glucocorticoids on glutamate transmission. *Natures Review Neuroscience, 13*(1), 22-37.

Porges, S. W. (1992). Vagal tone: A physiologic marker of stress vulnerability. *Pediatrics*, *90*(3), 498-504.

Porges, S. W. (2001). The Polyvagal Theory: phylogenetic substrates of a social nervous system. *International Journal of Psychophysiology, 42*, 123-146.

Porges, S. W. (2011). *The Polyvagal Theory: Neurophysiological foundations of emotions, attachment, communication, and self-regulation.* New York, NY: W. W. Norton and Company.

Potter, P., Deshields, T., Divanbeigi, J., Berger, J., Cipriano, D., Norris, L., and Olsen, S. (2010). Compassion fatigue and burnout: Prevalence among oncology nurses. *Clinical Journal of Oncology Nursing, 14*(5), 56-62.

Potter, P., Deshields, T., and Rodriguez, S. (2013). Developing a systemic program for compassion fatigue. *Nursing Administration Quarterly, 37*(4), 326-332.

Potter, P., Pion, S., and Gentry, J. E. (2015). Compassion fatigue resiliency training: The experience of facilitators. *Journal of Continuing Education in Nursing, 46*(10), 1-6.

Pretty, C., O'Leary, D., Cairney, J., and Wade, T. (2013). Adverse childhood experiences and the cardiovascular health of children: a cross-sectional study. *BMC Pediatrics, 13*, 208.

Ranabir, S., and Reetu, K. (2011). Stress and hormones. *Indian Journal of Endocrinology and Metabolism, 15(*1), 18-22.

Repper, J., and Carter, T. (2011). A review of the literature on peer support in mental health services. *Journal of Mental Health, 20*(4), 392-411.

Resick, P., Jordan, C., Girelli, S., Hutter, C., and Marhoefer-Dvorak, S. (1988). A comparative outcome study of behavioral group therapy for sexual assault victims. *Behavior Therapy, 19*(3), 385-401.

Resick, P. A., and Schnicke, M. K. (1993). *Cognitive Processing Therapy for rape victims: A treatment manual*. Newbury Park, CA: Sage Publications, Inc.

Rojo Aubrey, T. E. (2016). *Cognitive-behavioral self-management program*. Manuscript submitted for publication. 1-35.

Rojo Aubrey, T. E. (2015). Breathing exercises for stress management. *The Connection: Maricopa County Community College District, 12*(1), 6.

Rojo Aubrey, T. E. (2015). *Medical hypnosis and cognitive-behavioral treatment for pregnancy related lumbago* (Unpublished doctoral dissertation). Arizona State University, Tempe, AZ.

Rojo Aubrey, T. E., and Gentry, J. E. (2019). *Unlocking the code to human resiliency*: Building immunity against traumatic stress, burnout and compassion fatigue. Ann Arbor, MI: XanEdu.

Rosenbaum, P. R. (2001). Stability in the absence of treatment. *Journal of American Statistical Association, 96*(453), 210-219.

Rothbaum, B., Meadows, E., Resick, P., and Foy, D. (2000). Cognitive-Behavioral Therapy. In E. B. Foa, T.M. Keane, and M. J. Friedman (Eds.), *Effective treatments for PTSD* (pp. 60-83). New York, NY: The Guilford Press.

Rotter, T., Kinsman, L., James, E., Machotta, A., and Steyerberg E. (2012). The quality of the evidence base for clinical pathway effectiveness: Room for improvement in the design of evaluation trials. *BMC Medical Research Methodology, 12*, 80.

Rothschild, B. (2000). *The body remembers: The psychophysiology of trauma and trauma treatment.* New York, NY: W.W. Norton and Company.

Rubenking, B. (2017). Boring is bad: Effects of emotional content and multitasking on enjoyment and memory. *Computers in Human Behavior, 72*, 488-495.

Sadigh, M. R., and Montero, R. P. (2013). *Autogenic training: A mind-body approach to the treatment of fibromyalgia and chronic pain syndrome*. New York, NY: CRC Press.

Salston, M. G. (2000). *Secondary traumatic stress: a study exploring empathy and the exposure to the traumatic material of survivors of community violence* (Unpublished doctoral dissertation). Florida State University, Tallahassee, FL.

Substance Abuse and Mental Health Services Administration. (September, 2017). Mental and Substance Use Disorders. Retrieved from https://www.samhsa.gov/disorders

Sapolsky, R. M. (1996). Why stress is bad for your brain. *Science, 273*(5276), 749-750.

Scaer, R. C. (2005). *The trauma spectrum: Hidden wounds and human resiliency*. New York, NY: W.W. Norton and Company.

Schaefer, C. F., Blazer, G. D., and Koenig, G. H. (2009). Religious and spiritual factors and the consequences of trauma: A review and model of the interrelationship. *The International Journal of Psychiatry in Medicine, 38*(4).

Schneider, K. J. (2010). Toward a humanistic positive psychology: Why can't we just get along? *Psychology Today*. Retrieved from https://www.psychologytoday.com/blog/awakening-awe/201011/toward-humanistic-positive-psychology-why-cant-we-just-get-along

Schieve, L., Gonzalez, V., Boulet, S., Visser, S., Rice, C., Van Naarden Braun, K., and Boyle, C. (2012). Concurrent medical conditions and health care use and needs among children with learning and behavioral developmental disabilities, National Health Interview Survey, 2006-2010. *Research in Developmental Disabilities, 33*(2), 467-476.

Schwarz, S. W. (2009). Adolescent mental health in the United States. *National Center for Children in Poverty*. Retrieved from http://www.nccp.org/publications/pub_878.html.

Sedgewick, D. (1995). *Countertransference from a Jungian perspective (transcript of a lecture given at Grand Rounds to the Department of Psychiatric Medicine, University of Virginia).* Retrieved from http://www.cgjung.com/articles/roundsx.html

Seedat, S., Pienaar, P., Williams, D., and Stein, J. (2004). Ethics of research survivors of trauma. *Current Psychiatry Reports, 6*, 262-267.

Seidler, G. H., and Wagner, F. E. (2006). Comparing the efficacy of EMDR and Trauma-Focused Cognitive-Behavioral Therapy in the treatment of PTSD: a meta-analytic study. *Psychological Medicine, 36*, 1515-1522.

Seidmahmoodi, J., Rahimi, C., and Mohamadi, N. (2011). Resiliency and religious orientation: Factors contributing to posttraumatic growth in Iranian subjects. *Iran Journal of Psychiatry, 6*(4), 145-150.

Seligman, M. E. (1972). Learned helplessness. *Annual Review of Medicine, 23*(1), 407–412.

Sexton, L. (1999). Vicarious traumatization of counselors and effects on their workplaces. *British Journal of Guidance and Counseling, 27*(3), 393-403.

Shachar-Dadon, A., Schulkin, J., and Leshem, M. (2009). Adversity before conception will affect adult progeny in rats. *Developmental Psychology, 45*(1), 9-16.

Shalev, A., Bonne, O., and Eth, S. (1996). Treatment of posttraumatic stress disorder: A review. *Psychosomatic Medicine, 58*(2), 165-182.

Shanafelt, T., Hasan, O., Dyrbye, L., Sinsky, C., Satele, D., Sloan, J., and West, C. (2015). Changes in burnout and satisfaction with work-life balance in physicians and the general US working population between 2011 and 2014. *Mayo Clinic Proceedings, 90*(12),1600-1613.

Shapiro, F. (1989). Efficacy of the eye movement desensitization procedure: A new treatment for post-traumatic stress disorder. *Journal of Traumatic Stress, 2*(2), 199-223.

Shapiro, F. (1995). *Eye movement desensitization and reprocessing: Basic principles, protocols, and procedures.* New York, NY: Guilford Press.

Shapiro, F., and Forrest, M. (1997). *EMDR: The Breakthrough Therapy for Overcoming Anxiety, Stress, and Trauma.* New York: Basic Books.

Shemesh, E., Newcorn, J., Rockmore, L., Shneider, B., Emre, S., Gelb, B., … and Yehuda, R. (2005). Comparison of parent and child reports of emotional trauma symptoms in pediatric outpatient settings. *Pediatrics, 115*(5).

Sheppard, K. (2015). Compassion fatigue among registered nurses: Connecting theory and research. *Applied Nursing Research. 28*(1), 57-59

Shenhav, A., Cohen, J., and Botvinick, M. (2016). Doral anterior cingulate cortex and the value of control. *Nature Neuroscience, 19*(10), 1286-12891.

Sherin, J., and Nemeroff, C. (2011). Post-traumatic stress disorder: The neurobiological impact of psychological trauma. *Dialogues in Clinical Neuroscience, 13*(3), 263-278.

Sherman, J. (2012, June 13). *Counselor bias: A dumb reason we think we're smart (staying calm in good times and hard times are whole different ball games).* Retrieved from https://www.psychologytoday.com/blog/ambigamy/201206/counselor-bias-dumb-reason-we-think-were-smart

Shusterman, V., and Barnea, O. (2005). Sympathetic nervous system activity in stress and biofeedback relaxation. *IEEE Engineering in Medicine and Biology Magazine, 24*(2), 52-57.

Siegel, J. D. (May, 2008). *The neurobiology of "we": How relationships, the mind, and the brain interact to shape who we are.* Unabridged: Sounds True.

Sinclair, S., Raffin-Bouchal, S., Venturato, L., Mijovic-Kondejewski, J., and Smith-MacDonald, L. (2017). Compassion fatigue: A meta-narrative review of the healthcare literature. *International Journal of Nursing Studies, 69*, 9-24.

Sledjeski, E., Speisman, B., and Dierker, L. (2008). Does number of lifetime traumas explain the relationship between PTSD and chronic medical conditions? Answers from the National Comorbidity Survey-Replication (NCS-R). *Journal of Behavioral Medicine, 31*(4), 341-349.

Sokol, D. K. (2013). "First do no harm" revised. *British Medical Journal, 347*, f6426.

Sorenson, C., Bolick, B., Wright, K. and Hamilton, R. (2016). Understanding compassion fatigue in healthcare providers: A review of current literature. *Journal of Nursing Scholarship, 48*(5), 456-465.

Spunt, R. P., Lieberman, M. D., Cohen, J. R., and Eisenberger, N. I. (2012). The phenomenology of error processing: The dorsal ACC response to stop-signal errors tracks reports of negative affect. *Journal of Cognitive Neuroscience, 24*(8), 1753-1765.

Stamm, B. H. (1995). *Secondary traumatic stress: Self-care issues for clinicians, researchers, and educators.* Lutherville, MD: Sidran Press.

Staugaard-Jones, J. A. (2012). *The vital psoas muscle: Connecting physical, emotional, and spiritual well-being*. Berkeley, CA: North Atlantic Books.

Sussell, A. (2010, October 22). *School of education works to eliminate bias from counseling sessions*. Retrieved from http://www.themaneater.com/stories/2010/10/22/school-education-works-eliminate-bias-counseling-s/

Sussman, M. (1992). *A curious calling: Unconscious motivations for practicing psychotherapy.* Northvale, NJ: Jason Aronson.

Szilagyi, M., and Halfon, N. (2015). Pediatric adverse childhood experiences: implications for life course health trajectories. *Academic Pediatrics, 15*(5), 467-468.

The Human Rights Watch. (2014). *Women's rights*. Retrieved from https://www.hrw.org/topic/womens-rights

The National Child Traumatic Stress Network. (April, 2012). *TF-CBT: Trauma-informed interventions: General information.* Retrieved from http://nctsn.org/sites/all/modules/pubdlcnt/pubdlcnt.php?file=/sites/default/files/assets/pdfs/tfcbt_ general.pdfandnid=1718

Takahashi, T., Ikeda, K., Ishikawa, M., Kitamura, N., Tsukasaki, T., Nakama, D., and Kameda, T. (2005). Anxiety, reactivity, and social stress-induced cortisol elevation in humans. *Neuroendocrinology Letters, 4*(26), 351-354.

Taylor, A. H. (2012). *Assessing the effects of stress resilience training on visual discrimination skills: Implications for perceptual resilience in US warfighters* (Unpublished doctoral dissertation). Virginia Commonwealth University, Richmond, VA.

Tervalon, M., and Murry-Garcia, J. (1998). Cultural humility versus cultural competence: A critical distinction in defining physician training outcomes in multicultural education, *Journal of Health for the Poor and Underserved, 9*(2), 117-125.

Tinnin, L. (1994). *Time-Limited Trauma Therapy: A treatment manual*. Bruceton Mills, WV: Gargoyle Press.

U. S. Department of Health and Human Services, Administration for Children and Families, Children's Bureau. (2017). *Child maltreatment 2015*. Retrieved from https://www.acf.hhs.gov/cb/resource/child-maltreatment-2015

U.S. Department of Veterans Affairs. (n.d.). *PTSD: National Center for PTSD*. Retrieved from https://www.ptsd.va.gov/public/PTSD-overview/basics/history-of-ptsd-vets.asp

U.S. Food and Drug Administration. (2016.) *Drug research and children.* Retrieved from https://www.fda.gov/Drugs/ResourcesForYou/Consumers/ucm143565.htm

USA Today. (2017, October 7). *How police zeroed in on the Las Vegas gunman*. Retrieved from https://www.usatoday.com/story/news/2017/10/07/how-police-zeroed-las-vegas-gunman/737178001/

van der Kolk, B. A. (1996a). The black hole of trauma. In B. A. van der Kolk and A. C. McFarlane (Eds.), *Traumatic stress: The effects of overwhelming experience on mind, body, and society* (pp. 3-23). New York, NY: Guilford Press.

van Zyl, L., Nel, C., du Toit, M., and Joubert, G. (2017). Reported exposure to trauma among adults patients referred for psychological services at the Free State Psychiatric Complex, Bloemfontein. *Health SA Gesondheid, 22*, 235-240.

Vincent, J. F. (2004). *The origins of addictions: Evidence from the Adverse Childhood Experiences Study*. San Diego, California: Kaiser Permanente Medical Care. Retrieved from http://www.nijc.org/pdfs/Subject%20Matter%20Articles/Drugs%20and%20Alc/ACE%20Study%20-%20OriginsofAddiction.pdf

Vogel, D., and Wei, M. (2005). Adult attachment and help-seeking intent: The mediating roles of psychological distress and perceived social support. *Journal of Counseling Psychology, 52*(3), 347-357.

Wampold, B. E., and Imel, Z. E. (2015.) *The great psychotherapy debate: The evidence for what makes psychotherapy work* (2nd ed.). New York, NY: Routledge.

Weiner, D., Schneider, A., and Lyons, J. (2009). Evidence-based treatments for trauma among culturally diverse foster care youth: Treatment retention and outcomes. *Children and Youth Services Review, 31*, 1199-1205.

Williams, R. (2011, May 1). *The duty to address personal bias*. Retrieved from https://www.schoolcounselor.org/magazine/blogs/may-june-2011/the-duty-to-address-personal-bias

Wilson, C., Pence, D., and Conradi, L. (2013). *Trauma-informed care*. National Association of Social Workers Press and Oxford University Press. Retrieved from http://socialwork.oxfordre.com/view/10.1093/acrefore/9780199975839.001.0001/acrefore-9780199975839-e-1063

Wilson, J., and Lindy, J. (1994). *Countertransference in the treatment of PTSD*. New York, NY: Guilford Press.

Wiseman, T. (1996). A concept analysis of empathy. *Journal of Advanced Nursing, 23*, 1162-1167.

World Health Organization. (2014). *Social determinants of mental health*. Retrieved from http://apps.who.int/iris/bitstream/10665/112828/1/9789241506809_eng.pdf?ua=1

World Health Organization. (2017). *Health impact assessment: The determinants of health*. Retrieved from http://www.who.int/hia/en/

World Health Organization and International Society for Prevention of Child Abuse and Neglect. (2006). *Preventing child maltreatment: A guide to taking action and generating evidence*. Geneva, Switzerland: WHO Press. Retrieved from http://apps.who.int/iris/bitstream/10665/43499/1/9241594365_eng.pdf

Yerkes, R. M., and Dodson, J. D. (1908). The relation of strength of stimulus to rapidity of habit-formation. *Journal of Comparative Neurology, 18*(5), 459-482.

Yartz, A. R., and Hawk, A. W. (2001). Psychophysiological assessment of anxiety: Tales from the heart. In M. Antony, S. Orsillo, and L. Roemer (Eds.), *Practitioner's guide to empirically based measures of anxiety*. New York, NY: Springer.

Index

About the Authors

Dr. Robert Rhoton, PsyD, is the CEO of the Arizona Trauma Institute and possesses a rich history of experience in the mental health field. Dr. Rhoton has supervised multiple outpatient clinics, juvenile justice programs, and intensive outpatient substance abuse programs for adolescents, day treatment programs for children and youth, adult offender programs, and child and family therapeutic services. Additionally, Dr. Rhoton has advanced training in child and adolescent trauma treatment, family therapy, and family trauma. Dr. Rhoton served as president of the Arizona Trauma Therapy Network from 2010 to 2012. Dr. Rhoton was a professor at Ottawa University in the Behavioral Sciences and Counseling Department, whose primary interests were training counselors to work with traumagenic family dynamics, child and family trauma, and non-egoic models of treatment. Dr. Rhoton is a trainer for the International Association of Trauma Professionals in Trauma and Compassion Fatigue, serves as an editor for the International Journal of Trauma Practice and Research, and is an internationally certified Expert Trauma Therapist by the International Association of Trauma Professionals (IATP). Dr. Rhoton is a Diplomate of the American Academy of Experts in Traumatic Stress, and collaborates and consults with numerous Arizona agencies to fine-tune their understanding of trauma and the impact of developmental trauma on the individual and family. Dr. Rhoton also serves on the Arizona Department of Health Services Trauma-Informed Care (TIC) taskforce as a community member.

Email Contact: robert.rhoton@aztrauma.org

Dr. Thomas E. Rojo Aubrey, DBH, is the Director of the Behavioral Health Sciences and Counseling faculty at Glendale Community College in Glendale, Arizona. He serves on the advisory boards for both the Arizona Trauma Institute and the Cummings Graduate Institute for Behavioral Health Studies. Dr. Rojo Aubrey has over fifteen years of diverse experience in behavioral healthcare, including trauma treatment, crisis stabilization, marital counseling, career and academic counseling, and integrated behavioral medicine for the treatment of comorbid behavioral and medical conditions. He is a Certified Clinical Trauma Professional and Certified Family Trauma Professional with the International Association of Trauma Professionals (IATP). He is trained in Trauma Focused-Cognitive Behavioral Therapy (TF-CBT), Eye Movement Desensitization and Reprocessing (EMDR), Dialectical Behavioral Therapy (DBT), Medical Hypnosis, Pivotal Response Treatment, Positive Behavioral Support-Applied Behavior Analysis, Emotionally Focused Therapy (EFT), and the Gottman Method Couples Therapy. Dr. Rojo Aubrey also has a strong background in crisis work and is a certified trainer in Nonviolent Crisis Intervention, and is trained in Applied Suicide Intervention Skills Training (ASIST), Critical Incident Stress Management (CISM), and Crisis De-escalation. Dr. Rojo Aubrey has served as the clinical director and clinical supervisor at various local provider agencies, and has provided leadership and insight

to several clinical programs. His leadership and expertise have improved population, professional development, and system performance outcomes for various clinical programs. Although he no longer practices psychotherapy, Dr. Rojo Aubrey continues with his passion for helping students develop the knowledge and skills needed to become successful in the field of behavioral health.

Email Contact: thomas.aubrey@gccaz.edu

Dr. J. Eric Genry, PhD, is the Vice President of the Arizona Trauma Institute. He is a board-certified and internationally recognized leader in the study and treatment of traumatic stress and compassion fatigue. His doctorate is from Florida State University, where he studied with Professor Charles Figley—a pioneer of these two fields. In 1997, he codeveloped the Accelerated Recovery Program for Compassion Fatigue (ARP)—the world's only evidence-based treatment protocol for compassion fatigue. Dr. Gentry was original faculty, curriculum designer, and Associate Director of the Traumatology Institute at Florida State University. In 2001, he became the codirector and moved this institute to the University of South Florida, where it became the International Traumatology Institute. In 2010, he began the International Association of Trauma Professionals. He has trained tens of thousands of professionals to more effectively treat traumatic stress. In 2005, Hogrefe and Huber published *Trauma Practice: Tools for Stabilization and Recovery*—a critically acclaimed text on the treatment of traumatic stress for which Dr. Gentry is a coauthor. The third edition of this text was released in 2015. In 2016, he released his revolutionary *Forward-Facing Trauma Therapy* book. He is the author of numerous chapters, papers, and peer-reviewed journal articles in the areas of traumatic stress and compassion fatigue. Dr. Gentry is a licensed psychotherapist with over thirty-three years of clinical practice. He is the CEO and owner of Compassion Unlimited—a private psychotherapy, training, and consulting practice.

Email Contact: erigent@icloud.com

Transformative Care: A Trauma-Focused Approach to Caregiving is a groundbreaking book that defines a new paradigm for helping others in the 21st century. It is designed as an essential foundation for service providers to gain knowledge and skills for excelling in their role as a professional caregiver. This book goes far beyond simply defining and advocating for trauma-informed care (which has become an important new method for caregiving). Instead, it teaches the developing care provider the mastery and skillset needed to safely and effectively intervene, with a ***trauma-focused approach***, in the lives of those who are suffering from a painful past. Providers will learn how to facilitate healing and recovery in clients' and patients' lives, *without* overstepping the bounds of their professional scope of practice.

Readers will appreciate the honest and straightforward writing style of this book, one that's been written *by caregivers, for caregivers*. We invite you to join us on a journey of learning to become an instrument of transformation in the lives of those who need our help.

Get Certified! This book also contains the course content for the Certified Trauma Support Specialist (CTSS) Certification available through the Trauma Institute International. For more information, visit the Trauma Institute International's website at: **www.traumainstituteinternational.com**.